D0093985

The Definition of Death

The Definition of Death
Contemporary Controversies

EDITED BY
Stuart J. Youngner, M.D.
Robert M. Arnold, M.D.
and Renie Schapiro, M.P.H.

The Johns Hopkins University Press
Baltimore and London

© 1999 The Johns Hopkins University Press
All rights reserved. Published 1999
Printed in the United States of America on acid-free paper
9 8 7 6 5 4 3 2

The Johns Hopkins University Press
2715 North Charles Street
Baltimore, Maryland 21218-4363
www.jhu.press.edu

Library of Congress Cataloging-in-Publication Data
will be found at the end of this book.
A catalog record for this book is available from the British Library.

ISBN 0-8018-5985-9

To Rina and Julius Youngner.
Your love and support are always there.
—S.J.Y.

To my brother, Larry Arnold,
for his influence on my life.
—R.M.A.

To my parents,
for their undying gifts.
—R.S.

A young boy attending his first baseball game asked his father, "How can the umpires tell a ball from a strike?" The father suggested that after the game the boy pose the question to the three umpires.

When the boy asked the first umpire, he responded, "I call them as I see them." The second umpire answered, "I call them as they are." But the third umpire stepped back and stared at the boy. "Son," he said, "they ain't nothing till I call them!"

Contents

Acknowledgments

THERE ARE MANY persons without whom this project would not have been possible. First, we would like to thank the donors whose generous support of the Cleveland meeting in 1995 allowed the project to go forward. They include the University of Pittsburgh Medical Center; the Laerdal Foundation for Acute Medicine; University Hospitals of Cleveland; the Division of Organ Transplantation; the Fetzer Institute; the National Institutes of Health; Arter and Haden; Baxter Health Care Corporation; Case Western Reserve University; the Cleveland Foundation; the Greenwall Foundation; Hoffman-La Roche; Sandoz Pharmaceuticals; the United Network for Organ Sharing; Davis and Young Co., LPA; and Ruth Anna Carlson and Albert Leonetti.

The Planning Committee for the Cleveland Conference that helped give the project form and substance included Jeremiah Barondess, James Bernat, Richard Bonnie, Arthur Caplan, Rebecca Dresser, Joanne Lynn, and Fred Plum.

We also want to thank the scholars who participated in the Cleveland Conference and helped shape this volume by their insightful comments and suggestions. They include Martin Benjamin, Arthur Caplan, James Childress, David Cole, Michael DeVita, Rebecca Dresser, Karen Gervais, Grant Gillette, Else Sejer Larsen, Everett Medelsohn, Richard Rettig, John Robertson, James Walters, and William Winslade.

Robert Daroff, Chief of Staff at University Hospitals of Cleveland, gave his unconditional support and encouragement from beginning to end. Without him, the project would not have gotten off the ground. The success of this project also owes much to Kenneth Shine, Thomas Detre, Alan Meisel, Tom Murray, James McMonagle, and Allen Hull. Rick Whitbeck provided excellent administrative support for the Cleveland Conference. Barbara Juknialis always got us out of jams, and Jan Liber provided constant and graceful assistance throughout the project.

Introduction

THROUGHOUT HISTORY AND across cultures, the moment of death has held great fascination. The change in status from living person to corpse has not only clinical consequences but also profound psychological, legal, moral, religious, and economic implications. However, the advent of medical technology has raised a new set of troublesome questions about just when the transition between life and death occurs. Technology has made the determination of death both more difficult and more important: more difficult, because we can now stretch out the dying process; more important, because organ transplantation, concerns about the quality of life, and the need to conserve resources have challenged our reliance on the traditional cardiopulmonary criteria of death.

In the early 1980s, after the recommendation of a presidential commission, states adopted a new definition of death based on total and irreversible cessation of brain function. Thus, even when respiration and heartbeat were sustained by technology, a person could be declared dead if all brain functions were irretrievably lost.* Supporters of the new definition hailed it as medical and social progress and hoped it would help solve the problems of limiting futile treatment and of providing a new supply of organs to an ever-expanding waiting list of potential recipients. Opponents either questioned the conceptual foundation of whole-brain death or cautioned that adopting it would lead society down a slippery slope that increasingly disrespects life. Supporters and opponents alike recognized that only time and experience would reveal the full conse-

---

*This is referred to as *whole-brain death*. The term *brain death* has become a standard shorthand way of indicating that the death is determined by neurological rather than cardiopulmonary criteria. However, the term has caused confusion because it is sometimes used to describe the status of the brain as independent of the status of the person. Thus, we read in the newspaper, for example, that the patient is brain dead and death is imminent. Some argue that this usage is unfortunate because it has encouraged the erroneous notion that brain death is different from death. Others maintain that it is a reminder of the persistent ambiguity about the status of the brain-dead patient.

quences of this attempt to reconceptualize something as fundamental and sacrosanct as who is dead.

In many ways it is remarkable how well society has adapted to this new way of determining death. However, developments over the past decade have created uncertainties, not only about brain death but also about the proper application of the more traditional cardiopulmonary criteria. Some of these questions have arisen from clinical experience with the determination of death. Others result from unresolved conceptual confusion. In the early debates in the 1960s and 1970s, there was some disagreement over whether the whole brain or only some portion of it (either higher brain or brainstem) was required for a declaration of death. More recently, questions have also arisen about just what is meant by all brain functions.

Questions also have been brought to the fore by the increasing use of techniques to obtain organs from non-heart-beating cadavers (NHBCs). Several authors in this volume address this issue. NHBC protocols, adopted by many transplant centers and organ procurement organizations, provide for the removal of organs, with appropriate consent, from patients who are declared dead by traditional cardiopulmonary criteria rather than by the neurological criteria that have characterized organ procurement since the early 1970s and that continue to provide the overwhelming number of potential patients for organ retrieval. NHBCs fall into two general categories: (1) controlled death, in which ventilators are removed from ventilator-dependent patients in the operating room, and (2) uncontrolled death, in which catheters are immediately inserted to preserve organs of patients who either arrive dead in the emergency room or are unsuccessfully resuscitated there. Because of concern about damage that may occur to the organs as they remain in the patient's dead body, there is a premium on a quick pronouncement of death and rapid removal or preservation of organs. The controlled death NHBC protocol that has received the most scholarly attention (largely because the University of Pittsburgh engaged in a deliberately open process) is the one used at the University of Pittsburgh Medical Center (referred to as the *Pittsburgh protocol*). In this protocol, patients are taken to an operating room, where the ventilator is removed and, after a few minutes of asystole—the length of time being one of the controversies—the patient is declared dead and the organs are removed. Indeed, one of the controversies that surfaces in this volume is whether NHBC protocols, which rely on a cardiopulmonary criterion of death, ignore the neurological (whole brain) criteria, which may or may not be fulfilled at the time when organ retrieval begins. Finally, our changing moral and legal attitudes toward end-of-life decisions and an increasing recognition of cultural diversity in our society (e.g., many Orthodox Jews do not accept brain death) have also contributed to new thinking about brain-based criteria.

The essays in this volume reflect the deconstruction of what seemed to be a scientific, philosophical, and even public consensus about the definition and determination of death. This book brings together a group of internationally prominent scholars in the first comprehensive review of the clinical, scientific, sociocultural, ethical, and public policy implications of the determination of death. Expert in medicine, neuroscience, philosophy, anthropology, law, and religious studies, these scholars address a wide range of issues raised by our efforts to redefine death. Their analyses extend from the highly theoretical and technical aspects of defining death to very practical issues of medical practice and public policy in the United States. The book grew out of a conference held in Cleveland, Ohio, in November 1995, at which these and other scholars debated the issues.

Debates about the definition and determination of death have occurred almost solely among academics. By all appearances, the public has little understanding of or even interest in the issue. One might conclude that the quiet on the part of the public reflects acceptance. Alternatively, one could argue that the apparent indifference actually reflects a lack of awareness of the debate and its significance in their lives. What is probably true, based on the evidence we have, is that the public cares a great deal about the actual determination of death but conceptualizes or frames the issues in a very different manner from that of academic physicians, philosophers, lawyers, and social scientists. At the heart of public interest around death is not whether some pocket of cellular activity in a person who by all accounts is "gone" means that person is alive, but whether one can trust the medical profession to make determinations of death in the patient's interest, and not for some other purpose, such as increasing the supply of transplant organs.

The gap between the academic and the public awareness of the issues surrounding the definition and determination of death is like the electrical gap that exists between the ground and gathering storm clouds on a still summer evening. In the midst of a seemingly peaceful scene, a sudden discharge of energy can shoot a lightning bolt through the sky and disrupt the evening. This occurred in the spring of 1997, when stories in the *Cleveland Plain Dealer* and on the widely watched television show *60 Minutes* "warned" audiences that physicians were hastening death to obtain organs, in stories that were short on facts and long on inflammatory accusations. Only time will tell whether these reports result in a sustained loss of organ donation. Although they have not seemed to stimulate public interest in the controversies around the determination of death directly, such lightening bolts could injure fundamental public trust in the profession, and that in turn could affect how the public responds to the issues described in this book.

The book addresses the issues in the academic debate and considers their implications for public policy. Topics addressed include

—a historical review of the development of brain death, set in the context of earlier efforts to define and determine death;

—the current status of the clinical diagnosis for both neurological and cardiopulmonary death, including state-of-the-art technology and current standards;

—a philosophical critique of current definitions and criteria for death, including how much of the brain must be dead for a person to be dead, how we can logically justify choosing which brain functions are essential in distinguishing a living from a dead human being, and how we determine the irreversibility and time of death for both neurological and cardiopulmonary determinations of death;

—the empirical data regarding the American public's attitude toward and knowledge about the determination of death;

—a conceptual exploration of religious views regarding the definition of death;

—an examination of three medically advanced societies in which brain death has played out very differently from the United States— Japan, Germany, and Denmark—and how their experiences may inform U.S. public policy;

—a discussion of various possible public policy options regarding defining death. Should the current definition of death be further expanded, contracted, or simply left alone? In an increasingly pluralistic society, should we allow greater individual discretion about when death occurs? Should we take the even more radical course of uncoupling the determination of death from the various social behaviors (e.g., taking organs) that have heretofore been associated with it?

—an analysis of the interaction between philosophical argument, medical advances, and cultural beliefs in the development of public policy, including the degree to which the public (judges, legislators, the press, and the lay public) can and should understand the philosophical and scientific ambiguities about the determination of death, and of the problems we can anticipate in the future as our scientific understanding, clinical capabilities, health care system, and society evolve over the next three decades.

Each of the book's seven sections examines a different aspect of the problem of defining death. Each section is preceded by a brief introduction, written by the editors, that previews some of the main points of the chapters and suggests a larger context for some of the issues raised. Although each chapter or section can be read alone, the more extensive readers will recognize how themes cross chapter and section boundaries.

Contributors

ROBERT M. ARNOLD, M.D., Associate Professor and Head, Section of Palliative Care and Medical Ethics, Division of General Internal Medicine, Department of Medicine, and Director, Clinical Ethics Training Program, Center for Medical Ethics Education, University of Pittsburgh, Pittsburgh, Pennsylvania

JAMES L. BERNAT, M.D., Professor, Department of Medicine, Section of Neurology, Dartmouth Medical School, Hanover, New Hampshire

ALEXIA BLOCH, Ph.D., Graduate Research Assistant, Department of Anthropology, University of Pittsburgh, Pittsburgh, Pennsylvania

DAN W. BROCK, Ph.D., Charles C. Tillinghast Jr. University Professor of Philosophy and Biomedical Ethics and Director, Center for Biomedical Ethics, Brown University, Providence, Rhode Island

BARUCH A. BRODY, Ph.D., Leon Jaworski Professor of Biomedical Ethics and Director, Center for Medical Ethics and Health Policy, Baylor College of Medicine, Houston, Texas

ROBERT A. BURT, J.D., Alexander M. Bickel Professor of Law, Yale University, New Haven, Connecticut

COURTNEY S. CAMPBELL, M.A., Ph.D., Associate Professor, Department of Philosophy, Oregon State University, Corvallis, Oregon

ALEXANDER MORGAN CAPRON, LL.B., University Professor of Law and Medicine, Henry W. Bruce Professor of Law, and Co-director, Pacific Center for Health Policy and Ethics, University of Southern California, Los Angeles, California

R. ALTA CHARO, J.D., Professor of Law and Biomedical Ethics, University of Wisconsin, Madison, Wisconsin

RONALD CRANFORD, M.D., Professor, Department of Neurology, and Faculty Associate, Center for Bioethics, University of Minnesota, Minneapolis, Minnesota

H. TRISTRAM ENGELHARDT JR., Ph.D., M.D., Professor, Department of Medicine, Baylor College of Medicine; Professor, Department of Philosophy, Rice University; and Member, Center for Medical Ethics and Health Policy, Baylor College of Medicine, Houston, Texas

NORMAN FOST, M.D., M.P.H., Professor, Department of Pediatrics, and Director, Program in Medical Ethics, University of Wisconsin, Madison, Wisconsin

MARGARET LOCK, Ph.D., Professor, Departments of Social Studies of Medicine and of Anthropology, McGill University, Montreal, Quebec, Canada

JOANNE LYNN, M.D., Professor of Health Care Sciences and Director, Center to Improve Care of the Dying, George Washington University, Washington, D.C.

STEVEN MILES, M.D., Associate Professor, Center for Bioethics, University of Minnesota, Minneapolis, Minnesota

CHRIS PALLIS, D.M., Reader Emeritus in Neurology, Royal Postgraduate Medical School, University of London, London, England

MARTIN S. PERNICK, Ph.D., Professor, Department of History, and Associate Director, Program in Society and Medicine, University of Michigan, Ann Arbor, Michigan

FRED PLUM, M.D., University Professor and Chair, Department of Neurology, Cornell University Medical College, and Neurologist-in-Chief, The New York Hospital-Cornell Medical Center, New York, New York

BO ANDREASSEN RIX, M.D., M.A., Head, Department of Preventive Medicine, Frederiksborg County, Denmark

FRED ROSNER, M.D., Professor, Department of Medicine, Mount Sinai School of Medicine, New York, New York, and Director, Department of Medicine, Mount Sinai Services at Queens Hospital Center, Jamaica, New York

RENIE SCHAPIRO, M.P.H., Consultant to the Robert Wood Johnson Foundation and lecturer in public health, Yale University

BETTINA SCHÖNE-SEIFERT, M.D., M.A., Wissenschaftliche Mitarbeiterin am Ethik-Zentrum der Universität Zürich, Zurich, Switzerland

LAURA A. SIMINOFF, Ph.D., Associate Professor of Medicine and Bioethics, School of Medicine, Case Western Reserve University, Cleveland, Ohio

ROBERT M. VEATCH, Ph.D., Professor of Medical Ethics, Kennedy Institute of Ethics, Georgetown University, Washington, D.C.

STUART J. YOUNGNER, M.D., Professor of Medicine, Psychiatry, and Biomedical Ethics, Case Western Reserve University, and Director, Clinical Ethics Program, University Hospitals of Cleveland, Cleveland, Ohio

I

The Historical and Clinical Framework

PART I OF THIS BOOK lays the historical and clinical framework for the current discussion about death. In the first chapter, Martin Pernick takes the historian's view, grounding the effort to redefine death in a socio-cultural and developmental context. He reminds us that "the meaning of death is shaped by the interaction of social and professional changes in knowledge, power, and values" and cannot be understood separate from them. Pernick looks behind the scenes at the fateful Harvard ad hoc committee led by Henry Beecher in the late 1960s to illustrate how efforts to change the definition of death were consciously motivated to bypass troublesome moral problems. The ad hoc committee also reflected a growing (and, it could be argued, still growing) struggle between medical professionals and the public both to interpret broad social values and to control the decisions flowing from such interpretations. The themes of power and trust, elitism and populism run throughout Pernick's account. He demonstrates how public attitudes toward medical science can be simultaneously idolatrous and fearful and can shift from one to the other with tremendous implications for social behavior and policy. These discussions provide an important background for the debates about public policy later in the volume.

Fred Plum, in Chapter 2, provides a state-of-the-art review of clinical and technological means for making a diagnosis of brain death. He discusses the anatomical pathology of brain injury, which provides a useful insight into the dynamics of an unfolding catastrophic brain injury. He cautions about false-positive diagnosis and presents an important discussion of brain-damaged states that are sometimes clinically and conceptually confused with brain death.

Of more than passing significance is Plum's acknowledgment that two of the reasons for the acceptance of brain death when the concept was introduced in the late 1960s are no longer applicable. First, in contrast to the early cases of brain death, somatic survival is now possible for weeks and even months if aggressive critical care is pursued. Second, Plum concedes that not all brain function is lost in many patients diagnosed as brain dead. He anticipates the discussions in Part III (the clinical/philosophic interface) by retreating to the position long advocated by Christopher Pallis in England, that is, that loss of brainstem function alone is sufficient to make a diagnosis of death. Thus, by implication, Plum rejects the emphasis placed by the President's commission and virtually all state legislation on the loss of *all* brain functions. He also emphasizes the prognostic implications of brainstem death, rather than any conceptual arguments that might underlie it—"Once the brainstem functionally dies, there's no turning back," and "Neither Pallis nor I have been able to find by personal contact or in the professional medical literature a single example of a patient accurately diagnosed as being *brain stem dead* [emphasis ours] who subsequently recovered any vital brainstem function, much less any shred of arousal or consciousness."

When all is said and done, Plum emphasizes the reliability of a competent but low-tech clinical exam measuring the absence of brainstem function, but not necessarily all brain function. The reader will judge whether Plum's conclusions are a savvy compromise or the beginnings of a more widespread retreat from the notion of whole-brain death.

Brain Death in a Cultural Context

The Reconstruction of Death, 1967–1981

Martin S. Pernick, Ph.D.

NEWS ACCOUNTS OF THE world's first successful human heart transplant in 1967 made defining death seem as unprecedented as heart transplantation itself—a radically new set of issues produced by a radically new technology. That impression was wrong, in two ways. Controversies over the meaning of death long predated the 1960s, and they have never been simply products of technology. Both before and after heart transplantation, the meaning of death has been shaped by the interaction of social and professional changes in knowledge, power, and values.[1]

Ever since the mid-1700s, controversy and uncertainty about death have resulted in part from scientific discoveries, especially in two areas of basic physiological research, vivisection and suspended animation. But the meanings attributed to these scientific discoveries drew on changes in two other factors—physicians' perceptions of how best to solve specific clinical problems and public attitudes toward the medical profession.

In addition to such long-term continuities, this chapter shows that the period from about 1967 to 1981 also marked three major new developments. First, conceptual issues that physicians had categorized as pure science, abstract philosophy, or science fiction began to seem central to clinical practice. Second, decisions previously left to the discretion of individual practitioners began to be contested by other claimants to authority. And, third, the irreversible loss of the capacity for all brain functions won wide but not unchallenged acceptance as a means of diagnosing death.

In the late 1960s, the initial proponents of these changes were motivated by the effort to solve several practical problems, such as how to protect transplant surgery and when to withdraw futile treatments. Equally important, physicians hoped that brain-death criteria would help to defend their profession against newly revived populist mistrust. By 1981, however, the redefinition of death was repositioned, not as a defense of physicians against public criticism, but as a defense of the public against the invasive indignities of technological medicine. This change was vital to the success of brain-death legislation.

These new concerns about "death with dignity," however, did not replace older public fears of being abandoned too soon. Nor did they necessarily reduce the power of physicians to control the diagnosis of death. And the resulting legislation left many conceptual problems unresolved, although interest in these issues was once more relegated primarily to philosophers, physiologists, and mass culture.

After a brief sketch of the period 1900–1966, this chapter examines the years between 1967 and 1981, focusing on both the continuities and the changes. The goal is not to mine the past selectively for the roots of present concepts, nor to judge the past by its failure to fit modern conceptual categories, but to recreate the evolving meanings of death as understood in the context of each particular era.

Optimistic Uncertainties over Death, 1900–1966

Throughout this century, discoveries in two areas of physiology—the maintenance of living organs after their removal from the body and the resuscitation of organisms from various states of suspended animation—led to extensive debate about both the diagnosis and the meaning of death. In prior centuries, discoveries in these same two fields of research had provoked public and professional panic over the fear that living people were being buried alive. But in the early twentieth century, unprecedented public faith in medical science portrayed the discovery of new uncertainties not as dangers but opportunities, not as problems but as progress.

That the pieces of vivisected organisms could be kept alive separately had been demonstrated repeatedly since William Harvey in 1627 maintained the body of a decapitated rooster by inflating the lungs with a bellows. In the 1910s the perfusion techniques of Carl Ludwig and Sidney Ringer enabled Alexis Carrel to maintain isolated cultures of cells, tissues, organs (including the heart), and even preparations of entire organ systems. In the 1930s, Soviet and American scientists used these methods to preserve separate life in the heads and the bodies of decapitated dogs and apes, and in 1963 Maurice Albin and Robert J. White of Cleveland successfully maintained the isolated brains of rhesus monkeys.[2]

These experiments also proved crucial to the development of organ transplantation. In animals, kidney transplants were successful by 1920; human kidney transplants began in the late 1950s. Animal nervous tissue was transplanted several times between 1890 and 1917. In the 1940s and 1950s, head transplants were successful in dogs and apes;[3] in 1965, White and Albin reported transplants of isolated-brain preparations in a series of six dogs.[4]

Similarly, research on resuscitation, which began with the development of artificial respiration in the mid-1700s, also produced major advances in the first half of this century. Three generations of Russian and Soviet scientists from Bachmetieff in 1910 to Negovskii in the 1950s discovered that animals and people with no heart, lung, or brain activity could be revived after prolonged hypothermia, exsanguination, drug overdose, or other cause of suspended animation.[5]

Some of the same physiologists worked on both organ separation and suspended animation. In the 1930s the Soviet Institute of Experimental Physiology used a primitive mechanical heart-lung device both to maintain life in the severed heads of dogs and to revive whole dogs after 15 minutes of induced cardiac arrest. In the 1950s and 1960s, White and Albin used their research in hypothermia both to preserve dog brains for transplantation and to revive whole animals after prolonged cold-induced apparent death.[6]

Such discoveries led many scientists to propose new definitions of human life and death. For example, Thomas Edison and Harvard embryologist Charles Minot regarded individual life as a meaningless illusion and insisted that life meant only cellular life. In reply, many neurologists defined the integrative functions of the nervous system as constituting the life of an individual, distinct from the life of any other body parts.[7]

The Soviet researchers studying resuscitation insisted that their work reflected a specifically Marxist-materialist definition of life, in which death was not necessarily irreversible. They equated life with the interruptible motions of a machine, such as a clock. Thus, there could be two kinds of death—reversible (clinical) and irreversible (final). Death occurs when the body's machinery stops working; irreversible death is when the machinery is broken beyond repair. This view of death drew (without attribution) on concepts and metaphors dating back to those of the mid-eighteenth-century British pioneer in artificial respiration Dr. John Fothergill. Like the eighteenth-century materialists, their Soviet counterparts saw suspended animation as the curable form of death; resuscitation was literally resurrection. In his 1939 narration of a film documenting the Soviet experiments, British biologist J. B. S. Haldane declared without qualification about a dog in induced cardiopulmonary arrest, "The dog is dead . . . Ten minutes have elapsed since the animal died." The animal's subsequent "revival" thus demonstrated that death was not necessarily final.[8]

However, most Western researchers insisted that death was, by definition, always final and irreversible. In this view, suspended animation had to be simply inapparent life, because there was no such thing as reversible death. But if death was defined as permanent, there could be no permanent criteria for diagnosing it because physiologists kept discovering new ways of reversing previously irreversible changes. Short of physical disintegration, reversibility could only be determined by the success or failure of resuscitation. Thus, failure to respond to resuscitation became the key criterion for diagnosing death.

Adopting that criterion made it possible to continue defining death as irreversible. But it was useless for answering the key clinical question: When may physicians stop attempting resuscitation? And it left unanswerable the crucial conceptual questions about the nature of life during the interval in which no vital activity took place.[9]

A third source of debate over the meaning of death in the early twentieth century sprang from the growing controversy over euthanasia. Redefining death and allowing patients to die were both advocated as separate ways of resolving the same practical problem—deciding when to stop treating certain patients. As early as 1915, a prominent Chicago surgeon who publicly practiced eugenic euthanasia justified his actions by invoking a brain-based concept of life. He declared that a retarded infant's "tiny brain . . . was not a live thing—but a dead and fearsome ounce or two of jelly." He repeatedly insisted, "We live through our brains . . . Those who have no brains—their blank and awful existence cannot be called Life."[10]

The mass media avidly reported most of these developments, and, like the scientists, they speculated on the conceptual as well as the diagnostic implications. In the 1910s it was widely reported that suspended animation was "indistinguishable" from death. Media accounts often adopted the materialist equation of cardiac resuscitation with resurrection. Through the first half of this century, magazine articles with headlines like "What Is Death" reported that science had raised questions about the meaning of death and that physicians lacked both the diagnostic and the conceptual tools to answer them.

Although such claims had provoked panic in prior centuries, from about 1900 to the mid-1960s these uncertainties were presented to emphasize the fascinating mysteries of science rather than the terrors of the unknown. Mass media accounts raised hopes of immortality, rejuvenation, evolutionary supermen, resurrection, and even time travel and the elimination of racism, rather than the earlier panic over premature burial.[11]

But while physiologists and students of mass culture pondered the meaning of these discoveries at length, medical practitioners rarely participated in these discussions until about 1960.[12] Perhaps because of the media fascination with the speculative issues or because clinicians were unfamiliar with the physiological literature, the medical profession was slow to adopt discoveries ranging from hypothermia resuscitation to community-based cardiopulmonary resuscitation (CPR). Articles in the clinical literature on death continued to dismiss head transplants as impractical speculation and science fiction, even after physiologists had demonstrated such procedures on higher vertebrates.[13]

Clinicians gradually did begin to associate new discoveries in resuscitation with concrete clinical problems. In one early example, a 1959 French report described *coma dépasse,* a newly reported syndrome defined by the loss of all reflexes and all brain activity, in patients whose heart and lung functions could be maintained but whose consciousness never returned.[14]

The Institutional Chronology of Brain Death, 1966–1981

Beginning in the mid-1960s, a new sense of clinical urgency led to a novel series of committees and commissions on the definition of death. A Ciba Foundation symposium in London in 1966, the 1968 meetings of the World Medical Association in Sydney, Australia, the Second International Congress of the Transplantation Society, and the New York State commission on vital organ transplants, each drew upon and helped reinforce the belief that redefining death could help solve important practical problems.[15]

The most specific and best-publicized of these institutional efforts was the work of the Ad Hoc Committee of the Harvard Medical School to Examine the Definition of Brain Death, chaired by anesthesiologist Henry K. Beecher. Their 1968 report, published in the *Journal of the American Medical Association,* offered a set of criteria by which physicians could establish that a patient had suffered permanent loss of all brain functions, from consciousness to primitive brainstem reflexes, and proposed that these criteria be used by physicians as a new way of diagnosing death.[16]

In the decade after the Harvard report, judicial decisions and state legislation created a patchwork pattern of conflicting new and old methods for establishing that a person had died. To standardize this legal tangle, the newly created President's Commission for the Study of Ethical Problems in Medicine and Biomedical and Behavioral Research drafted a uniform model death law in 1981. Like the Harvard committee, this commission recommended that the permanent loss of all brain functions be accepted as a criterion for diagnosing death, but their statute also recognized the continued validity of heart-lung criteria for most cases. Over the next decade, their recommendations were adopted by most states, and they remain in effect across the nation today.[17]

The formulation and acceptance of *brain death* raises three key issues.

1. Why did clinicians suddenly become concerned about an issue long relegated to physiology and mass culture?
2. Why were whole-brain criteria for brain death adopted, instead of various proposed higher-brain alternatives?
3. Which competing interests got to decide these questions?

This chapter examines each of these questions in the context of first the late 1960s and then the early 1980s.

The Harvard Criteria and Late 1960s America

The Need for the Concept of Brain Death

Henry K. Beecher favored brain-based criteria for diagnosing death, not primarily to resolve conceptual uncertainties about the meaning of death, but to solve several practical problems he attributed to new technologies, particularly organ transplantation and respirators.[18] Transplant surgeons needed to remove kidneys, hearts, and other organs as quickly as possible without risking accusations of organ stealing or murder. But the precise role of transplantation in shaping the Harvard criteria remains very controversial. The Harvard report mentions transplants only briefly, in the introductory paragraph. Committee member and historian Everett Mendelsohn remembers transplants as having been a peripheral concern. His recollections are reinforced by the research of his former student, psychiatry professor Gary Belkin, who has carefully studied Beecher's papers.[19]

But other historians have drawn opposite conclusions from the same documents. David Rothman quotes the 1967 letter to Harvard Dean Robert Ebert in which Beecher first proposed creation of the committee: "The time has come for a further consideration of the definition of death. Every major hospital has patients stacked up waiting for suitable donor[s]." In response to an early draft of the committee report, Ebert warned Beecher to downplay such references to organ harvesting. "The connotation of this statement is unfortunate, for it suggests that you wish to redefine death in order to make viable organs more readily available." These examples suggest that Beecher felt more concern over transplants than was reflected in the committee's final report.[20]

To understand how transplantation influenced the Harvard criteria, one must distinguish several different concerns Beecher had about the new technology. He wanted not only to *promote* organ donation, but also to *protect* the profession against transplantation's critics. He hoped the Harvard criteria would not only increase the supply of organs but, more broadly, defend the entire medical profession against the public perception that transplant surgeons were organ-stealing killers.[21]

In addition, Beecher's repugnance at what he considered the futile waste of vital resources linked his concerns about transplantation and mechanical ventilation. He hoped to end the wasteful use of both respirators and transplantable organs by patients who could no longer benefit from them. The committee report also expressed great concern over the "burden" to patients, families, and society caused by maintaining those who had suffered "permanent loss of intellect."

In discussing respirators, Beecher clearly distinguished between redefining death and withdrawing treatment from the living. Yet his writings on brain death jumped back and forth from one topic to the other, not because he confused the two subjects, but because his concern was to solve the practical problem of when to terminate useless treatments. Whether the Harvard criteria were conceptualized as standards for defining death or as standards for withdrawing treatment from the living was less important to him than that the criteria gave physicians clear guidance on when to stop treatment. His criteria for terminating treatment could be justified on two very different conceptual bases. Beecher regarded that as a sign, not of conceptual confusion, but of the objective validity of the criteria.[22]

Several observers concluded that the Harvard criteria simply formalized and made public the ad hoc procedures many physicians had already been using to make private decisions about treatment termination. A 1968 *New York Times* editorial claimed that physicians had always made decisions about when to stop treatment and that they often used persistent loss of brain functions as an indicator that therapy should end. Likewise, a 1977 medical article recalled that, in the 1950s, resuscitation specialists used tests of brain function to select which patients not to attempt to revive.[23]

A third practical problem that played a little-noticed role in shaping Beecher's approach to death was human experimentation. Beecher was famous in the late 1960s not simply as a founder of academic anesthesiology but also as the author of a powerful exposé of medical abuses in human experimentation. He initially undertook his study of permanent coma as the chair of Harvard's Standing Committee on Human Studies. In the 1960s, many aspects of transplantation itself were still experimental, so regulating organ procurement was one part of regulating human experimentation. But Beecher also noted that permanently comatose bodies and their organs might be useful in many other kinds of experiments, such as testing new drugs. Beecher apparently hoped that experimenting on brain-dead bodies could reduce the need for live human guinea pigs and thereby avoid the ethical complications caused by using live human subjects.[24]

Beecher thus focused on the practical problems created by transplant and resuscitation technologies, while he largely ignored the more abstract conceptual uncertainties revealed by these same technologies. According to Mendelsohn, Beecher shunned abstractions during the committee's deliberations, insisting "I want to see it in the organs." The Harvard report never mentioned that the ability to isolate preparations of various "vital" organs had long since raised profound questions about the nature of personal and organism identity. Likewise, it completely ignored the long historical link between new resuscitation techniques and concern over the meaning of suspended animation. As an anesthesiologist, Beecher knew that a variety of conditions, from drug overdoses to extreme cold, could cause a reversible state that otherwise met his criteria for death. But the Harvard report said nothing about whether such exceptions implied the possibility of discovering other reversible deathlike states, nor did it mention uncertainty about the nature of life during such states. It simply listed two of the most common causes of suspended animation, cold and barbiturates, as exceptions to the proposed criteria, without any comment on their conceptual implications.[25]

Although the Harvard report mentioned both respirators and transplants as reasons for redefining death, all 17 *New York Times* articles on the issue from 1967 to 1970 and 9 of 14 such articles from 1971 to 1974 attributed the need to redefine death primarily to transplantation. The *Washington Post, Chicago Tribune,* and Associated Press followed suit. And, unlike Beecher, the press reported on the conceptual as well as the practical implications of both transplantation and brain death, especially in feature stories and opinion pieces.[26]

Whole Brain versus Higher Brain

The Harvard criteria specified that death required the termination of all functions of the whole brain—both conscious and reflexive activities. But even before the Harvard report, others understood *brain death* to mean primarily the permanent loss of consciousness. A 1966 article in *Time* magazine explained brain death as being "when the human spirit is gone." Volition, sensation, and thought seemed closer to defining the "human spirit" than did the primitive integrative reflexes included in the Harvard criteria. In 1971, Scottish neurologist J. B. Brierley, writing in the *Lancet,* urged that brain death be defined not by the loss of all brain functions, but solely by the permanent cessation of "those higher functions of the nervous system that demarcate man from the lower primates."[27] The ensuing controversy between advocates of whole-brain and higher-brain criteria for diagnosing brain death often reflected a much older conceptual contest over whether mental activity or bodily integration constituted the essence of human life.

Because the Harvard report advocated whole-brain *criteria,* those who favor whole-brain *definitions* have claimed that Beecher shared their concept that organic integration is the defining characteristic of life. But Beecher also frequently spoke as if he considered consciousness to be the crucial element. Thus, advocates of higher-brain definitions argue that Beecher really shared their equation of human life with personality or mental activity. In this view, Beecher used whole-brain criteria not because he held a whole-brain definition of life, but because no higher-brain criteria had yet been developed.[28]

However, both such claims distort Beecher's concerns. Beecher shifted back and forth between endorsing and rejecting consciousness as the conceptual foundation of his diagnostic criteria. For example, he concluded a 1970 lecture by declaring, "There is a need to move death to the site of the individual's consciousness, and if loss of consciousness is permanent, then to declare death." In the discussion period, however, when a priest asked him to clarify whether he meant to include cases of coma with "spontaneous respiration . . . but no consciousness," Beecher replied, "Oh, then he doesn't fit our criteria at all. We said no movements, no breathing."[29] Early in a 1967 lecture, he declared that "*our* basic concern is with the presence or absence of physiologic life," which he defined as meaning "when integrated tissue and organ functions cease . . . Although some have attempted to make a case for the concept of a corpse as one who is unconscious . . . from incurable brain damage, one can nevertheless orient the situation swiftly by a single wry question: 'Would you bury such a man whose heart was beating?'" Yet by the end of the same talk he seemed to endorse the view that death occurs "when consciousness is permanently lost."[30]

Beecher clearly understood that consciousness and physiological integration represented two different meanings of life and death. But his primary concern was not which competing theory of life won out, nor whether his own theoretical positions were consistent. What counted was solving such practical problems as protecting transplantation and ending useless treatments. In choosing between whole-brain and higher-brain death, as in choosing between redefining death and euthanasia, the pragmatic utility of the diagnostic criteria drove his interest in theoretical justifications, not the other way around. If two opposing concepts of death both were compatible with his criteria, Beecher saw that as objective confirmation of the criteria, not a troublesome conceptual confusion. Mendelsohn recalls the committee's conflation of criteria and definitions as having been "probably intentional" and the adoption of whole-brain criteria as a deliberately conservative effort to build a consensus among supporters of competing concepts.[31]

Who Decides? Professional Power

The unique significance of the heart and its transplantation played a major role in raising public and professional awareness of longstanding uncertainties in defining death. But the new concern over defining death after 1967 was not simply a response to new technology. Equally important was the resurgence of public criticism of the medical profession that also began in the late 1960s. From feminists to consumers' advocates to the nascent bioethics movement, critics attacked the domination of medicine by physicians and demanded autonomy for patients. Vietnam and Watergate fed growing mistrust of all institutions of established power, while environmentalism highlighted the hidden costs of all technologies. These changes brought a sudden end to a half-century of unprecedented popular enthusiasm for medical science and deference to physicians, in ways that profoundly influenced the debate over defining death.[32]

The Harvard committee urged the medical profession to adopt new criteria of death on their own. Committee member William Curran explained that, if the use of whole-brain criteria became the standard of medical practice, then the law would protect physicians who followed the criteria from any resulting malpractice charges. (Whether that would also protect against murder charges was much less certain.)[33]

Beecher's desire to keep the matter in medical hands reflected a widely shared medical mistrust of outsiders in general and his penchant for sarcastic attacks on lawyers and philosophers in particular. At a New York Academy of Sciences discussion of brain death in 1970, Beecher vented his frustration "that lawyers believe nothing should ever be done for the first time." Gary Belkin found that, in marginal comments on a paper by philosopher Robert Veatch, Beecher wrote that "these arguments, statements, etc. reveal how useless 'philosophy' of this kind is to intellectual life!" Beecher specifically exempted Curran from such criticism, but he clearly believed that sympathetic nonphysicians were on his committee to provide conceptual foundations for medically derived criteria and to sell medical decision making to their constituents—to preserve, not to challenge medical control.[34]

Many news accounts of the Harvard report accepted Beecher's view that defining death was a purely medical prerogative. As in their earlier reporting on antibiotics and polio vaccine, journalists generally portrayed heart transplants as another miracle of modern medicine. Redefining death was just one of the technical hurdles that physicians had to surmount to achieve this breakthrough.[35]

But even these enthusiastic initial reports also displayed a new suspicion and hostility toward medical authority. One letter to the *New York Times* protested Beecher's position that physicians alone could redefine death. "There is a desperate need for society to reassert its right to make policy in this field, and to subordinate the scientific community to a social consensus however unsophisticated that might be . . . There is a need to discipline the medical profession to understand that medical authoritarianism is as revolting as any other type of authoritarianism."[36] *Newsweek*'s 1967 article "When Are You Really Dead?" quoted an unnamed public health official: "I have a horrible vision of ghouls hovering over an accident victim with long knives unsheathed, waiting to take out his organs."[37]

Like their white counterparts in the late 1960s, most mainstream publications for African Americans strongly supported organ transplantation, while also expressing serious concerns. In the world's first successful heart transplant, one of the white donor's kidneys was transferred into a young "colored," or mixed race, recipient. In the second heart transplant, a white man received the heart of a "colored" stroke victim. Both operations took place in apartheid South Africa.

The mainstream black press, along with many northern white newspapers, hailed these events as a blow against the logic of racial segregation. In an editorial titled "No Place for Apartheid," the *New York Times* argued that such examples of surgical race-mixing provided a needed "opportunity to drive home the irrelevance of skin color."[38] An editorial in *Ebony* similarly applauded objective color-blind science for undermining racial separatism.[39] *Sepia* magazine's 1970 profile of black transplant surgeon Dr. Samuel Kountz emphasized that he, like Barnard, performed "interracial kidney transplants." "A kidney is just like a unit of blood—sometimes we don't even know who the donor is," Kountz declared.[40]

African-American publications also hailed heart transplantation as a metaphor for the possibility that racists might have a "change of heart," both in South Africa and elsewhere. The *Amsterdam News,* a Harlem community newspaper that rarely covered events outside New York and the American South, ran a pointed editorial: "In Capetown a doctor has transplanted a heart from one human being to another. Maybe he can give a new heart to the South African government too."[41] An editorial cartoon depicted two surgeons (one dark-skinned) labeled "brotherhood" replacing the heart of a white-haired, white-skinned patient tagged "world bigotry."[42] Syndicated black-press columnist Alfred Duckett wrote that segregationist governors George Wallace and Orville Faubus "have mean and evil hearts. Could these smart doctors cross such hearts and make them love instead of hate? That would be boss for South U.S.A. as well as South Africa."[43] Black publications also emphasized that black transplant surgeons and black recipients shared the mainstream culture's enthusiasm for medical research, but they demanded equal access to the resulting professional opportunities and life-saving benefits.[44]

But, even while they celebrated the first heart transplants, many of these articles also expressed strong misgivings. The editors of the *Amsterdam News* noted that using a colored heart to save a white man was "nothing new. For centuries South Africa has been using the black man's heart" to power the mines and factories of "this white-run industrial giant." The real change will come if and when "the African will possibly receive a white heart."[45]

In her "White-On-White" column, published directly opposite this editorial, Gertrude Wilson wrote:

> It was nice of the second patient to say that he "had no objection" to receiving a colored man's heart to keep him alive. Very broadminded of him, don't you think. It's too bad, though, that the colored man wasn't asked whether or not he "had any objection" to giving his heart to a white man to keep him alive . . . It gets right down to the heart of the apartheid laws . . . "No mixing of the races is allowed in any way shape or form—except for giving up your heart altogether to . . . pump the blood of a white man."

Wilson also drew sharp attention to the fact that both of the first heart recipients were Jews. "Well, all right, maybe it's just a coincidence. Maybe they have a big Jewish population in Capetown."[46]

Despite its generally upbeat assessment of transplantation, a March 1968 editorial in *Ebony* also provided the most explicit discussion of black concern. "Many black people today in both the United States and South

Africa fear hospitals because they believe that white doctors use black patients only for experimentation. Relatives of the hopelessly ill may refuse to give permission for transplantation because they believe that to do so will only cause the doctor to hurry a death in order to complete a transplant. It's a morbid thought but, nevertheless, it is one that will cross the minds of many black people."[47]

These commentators did not argue that brain death was an incorrect definition of death, and few besides Duckett mentioned the conceptual ambiguities. Rather, they feared that, however death was defined, white physicians would deliberately misdiagnose it in black patients to obtain organs for white recipients.

The tabloid press and low-budget movie industry also emphasized fear of organ stealing in their discussions of transplantation. Even in the technology-worshipping 1950s, a wave of horror movies about Franken-stein, mummies, and zombies had exploited the moral dangers of blur-ring the line between the dead and the undead. Moviemakers easily fit organ transplantation into this familiar genre, both before and after heart transplantation and brain death. Eleven feature films of the 1960s included organ transplants as a major theme. In every case, the organs for transplantation were procured by murder; none involved naturally dead or volunteer donors.[48]

Beecher worried that mass culture equated modern transplant sur-geons with nineteenth-century physicians who had robbed graves to ob-tain anatomical material. Indeed, he also saw some similarities. Both then and now, Beecher argued, the failure of the legal system to protect medical science from the uncomprehending masses threatened to im-pede medical progress. Beecher portrayed adoption of the Harvard cri-teria as essential for physicians to defend their profession against the rising tide of Luddite populism.[49]

Ironically, although Beecher saw himself as defending physicians, his approach was rejected by key segments of organized medicine. To some defenders of the medical profession, Beecher's public discussions of ethics seemed scientifically soft-minded and dangerously populist. At a 1968 hearing of the New York State Temporary Commission on Trans-plant of Vital Organs, surgeon Clarence Dennis responded to Beecher by implying that public involvement in medical ethics was unnecessary because "good science is good ethics."[50] Furthermore, Beecher did not always side with the technical elite within medicine. In part because most general practitioners and community hospitals lacked access to electro-encephalography (EEG), Beecher did not make the electroencephalogram one of the required tests for using the Harvard criteria, but merely indicated it could add confirming value.[51]

Most importantly, Beecher and the American Medical Association (AMA) disagreed over the best strategy for protecting professional power. While Beecher demanded united action by physicians to defend the profession's collective authority over death, the AMA until 1977 rejected all proposed standards of brain death as violating the professional discretion of the individual physician.[52]

From Promedical to Antimedical Defenses of Brain Death: The Report of the President's Commission, 1974–1981

The Need for the Definition of Brain Death

In the early 1970s, brain death stopped being explained as a way of protecting physicians against the public's fear of organ thieves and was instead heralded as a way of protecting the public against futile and callous medical interventions. This radical shift in the explanation of why brain death was necessary probably played a central role in the speed with which the model brain-death legislation proposed by the President's commission was enacted.

By the mid-1960s a few critics had begun to attack modern medicine for promoting complex invasive treatments that tortured the dying and prevented "death with dignity."[53] These charges formed part of a growing academic attack on the perceived cultural taboo against discussing death in public.[54] Initially, these criticisms were relatively muted, and they played little role in the 1968 Harvard report. As late as 1974, a *New York Times* article by future President's commission Executive Director Alexander Morgan Capron explained the need for brain death entirely in terms of transplantation examples, although he did mention that the issue was "not unique to transplant cases."[55]

But concern over the medicalization of dying rapidly expanded throughout the 1970s. From 1971 to 1974 the *New York Times* published at least 36 articles on "death with dignity," "thanatology," and termination of treatment; no such articles had been indexed under "death" in the preceding 3 years. These concerns sometimes reflected a new feminist attack on the allegedly masculine technocratic and compassionless approach to medicine.[56]

With the 1975–76 case of Karen Anne Quinlan, media attention to the issue exploded. Most news accounts carefully explained that Quinlan did not meet the criteria for brain death.[57] Yet they also reported an important parallel—both brain death and euthanasia were portrayed as attempts to stop physicians from using futile machinery that prolonged and intruded upon a good death.[58]

In 1981, the President's commission fully endorsed this shift. They attributed the need for brain death almost entirely to the respirator, and even commissioned an empirical study to show that transplantation was "much less" important than the need to "replace artificial support with more fitting and respectful behavior when a patient has become a dead body."[59] The plausibility of this claim was heightened by a long moratorium on heart transplants, caused by the difficulty of controlling organ rejection prior to the development of cyclosporine. Media coverage consistently repeated the commission's explanation that new criteria for death would protect the public from medical technology, rather than the other way around.[60]

Despite its remarkable success, this strategic repositioning of the issue did not completely coopt antiprofessional sentiment into support for brain-death criteria. Fears about being wrongly declared dead by hasty, uncaring, or organ-harvesting physicians still remained an important barrier to full public acceptance of both organ donation and brain death. Much to the dismay of the President's commission, an *ABC-Nightline* feature on their work included extensive coverage of a Connecticut nursing institution where patients received long-term respirator support based on the belief that no one could tell which comas were potentially reversible.[61] In a 1982 survey by Howard University surgeon Clive Callender and others, many African Americans expressed fear that blacks were being denied treatment so that white physicians could take their organs for sick white people.[62] The continuing legal battle over a 1992 case in which Penn State University physicians shut off the life-support system of a comatose (though not brain dead) black toddler despite vehement parental objections also probably exacerbated black suspicions about brain death.[63] The desire for death with dignity was added to, not substituted for, the deeply rooted fear of being abandoned too soon.[64]

The commission also only partly succeeded in its efforts to keep whole-brain death separate from the growing debates over abortion and euthanasia. They made sure their approach had support from the Catholic Church and the head of American Citizens United for Life. But the director of the powerful Bishops' Pro-Life Committee attacked their report as a step on the route to euthanasia.[65] Many newspapers linked the report with a coincidental Senate vote to limit abortion, while both pro-choice and pro-life forces debated whether the new criteria for determining death could help define the starting point of fetal life. Brain death continued to divide the orthodox Jewish community and the Japanese, among other ethnic and religious groups.[66]

Mass culture also retained its fascination with the conceptual uncertainties revealed by laboratory research in organ separation, suspended animation, and related fields that could be seen as blurring the lines between life and death. Journalism, films, and novels popularized such phenomena as cryonics (freezing the newly dead for future revival and cure),[67] bionics, cyborgs, robots, and artificial intelligence.[68]

The ability to revive ancient plant spores and to clone ancient DNA was featured in the 1990 book and 1994 movie *Jurassic Park*. The plot of the 1982 spy thriller *Fall Back* depended on the application to humans of White and Albin's 1965 brain transplant experiments and contained an acknowledgment citing their work.[69]

Medically induced suspended animation was the subject of the 1990 motion picture *Flatliners*.[70] In 1990, the *New York Times* reported hypothermia suspended animation simply as a new technical advance in surgery, without mentioning its relation to the concept of death.[71] But when CBS *60 Minutes* covered this story in 1995, the implications for the meaning of death were highlighted.[72]

Even though the mass media devoted considerable attention to the conceptual implications of physiological research on life and death, such abstractions remained subordinate to more practical and personal concerns. Defining death remained a sidebar to stories on heart transplants, Karen Quinlan, or abortion.[73] And, although bioethicists may consider the definition of death to be one of the most important events of the era, the news media did not always agree. The *Los Angeles Times* did not get around to reporting the President's commission report for almost 3 months.[74]

Whole Brain versus Higher Brain

Unlike the Harvard committee, the President's commission explicitly grounded its whole-brain criteria in a rejection of "higher-brain" definitions of death. They argued that higher-brain definitions were too radical a break with the past, that they were too subjective, and that no operational criteria yet existed for utilizing them.[75]

In response, many philosophers attacked what they saw as the conceptual flaws of the whole-brain definition, arguing instead for consciousness- or personality-based higher-brain alternatives. In general, whole-brain definitions appealed primarily to those who sought objective solutions for practical clinical problems, whereas higher-brain definitions attracted support from those who emphasized the need for value-based decisions and conceptual clarity.[76] The gulf between the two could be vast.[77]

However, these patterns may be due more to differences in professional cultures than to logically inherent differences in the competing concepts. Higher-brain definitions have been used to expand the professional role of philosophers, and consequently such definitions may have attracted more conceptually sophisticated advocates, but that does not mean that the whole-brain position is intrinsically incoherent. And many higher-brain advocates spent more time demonstrating the general need for values than they did defending the particular values they espoused. Few of the philosophers who supported higher-brain definitions considered to what extent their supreme valuation of mental functions might be a product of their particular professional culture, rather than a value shared to the same extent by other occupations and social classes.[78]

Still, since the passage of whole-brain legislation, interest in these conceptual issues has been much more evident among philosophers and physiologists and in mass culture than among clinicians. The issue has again been largely relegated to those groups who had pursued such questions in the decades prior to the 1960s.

Who Decides? The Ironic Role of Antielitism

Both Beecher and the AMA insisted that the criteria for declaring death were exclusively the province of the medical profession. They disagreed about whether individual physicians or the collective profession should have the final say, but both defended their strategy as the best way of keeping outsiders, especially lawyers, from participating in the process.

However, the legal profession consistently rejected the claim that physicians could unilaterally redefine death without the formal social approval provided by processes of law. Responding to Beecher, medical law expert Joseph Kelner insisted that "the stamp of community approval has to be placed by law." Capron reiterated the point, endorsing a 1974 declaration by California's deputy attorney general that brain death was "a matter for resolution by public bodies, and not merely by the medical profession."[79]

Initially, lawyers simply insisted on this procedural right to ratify medical authority. But in 1975 the American Bar Association (ABA) took sides on the substantive issues as well. In that year, ABA delegates endorsed "irreversible cessation of total brain function" as the legal standard of death.[80]

By 1977, 18 state legislatures had adopted a variety of differing statutes on brain death, many based on the ABA model. Perhaps recognizing that they had lost the procedural battle, the AMA that year abandoned its opposition to such legislative involvement. They accepted the original demand of lawyers for social ratification of medical authority, so long as such legislation increased rather than narrowed the substantive discretion permitted to individual physicians and the profession. If lawyers would agree to let physicians monopolize the choice and application of death criteria, physicians would allow their role and range of options to be formalized in law.[81]

This change in the AMA position formed the basis for the carefully crafted compromise negotiated by the President's commission. The commission's statute, approved by both professional organizations, left the choice between heart-lung and whole-brain criteria and the methods of applying them entirely up to the medical profession.[82]

Thus, despite its professed opposition to the medicalization of dying and its nonphysician leadership, the President's commission did not directly challenge the authority of physicians over death. Since 1968 nonphysicians have come to play a larger role in setting social policy toward death than they did for much of this century. But thus far these "outsiders" have generally accepted and formalized rather than restricted the power of physicians to decide who was dead.

The biggest change since 1968 has been that medical decisions are now made with more public awareness and legitimacy. Law and bioethics have publicly announced their acceptance of medical decision making, instead of physicians simply exercising it without the knowledge of outsiders. Such formalization of medical authority does not automatically either increase or decrease medical power. Rather, formal public acknowledgment of medical discretion both provides greater security for physicians to use their clinical judgment and creates procedures that someday could be used to limit such discretion.[83] The battle over brain death was neither a clear victory for "outsiders" over physicians nor a clear case of these outsiders being coopted by the medical profession.

And, while the short-term consequences can now be seen, their longer-term outcomes cannot yet be predicted.

New Criteria or New Definitions? The Polemical Uses of History

The distinction between the *criteria* used to diagnose death and the concepts used to *define* death is as central to the current epistemology of medicine as the distinction between autonomy and beneficence has been to current medical ethics. In both cases, however, the attempt to apply these 1970s distinctions retroactively to history, to make past ideas conform to present categories, has provoked bitter and largely sterile controversy.[84] The President's commission asserted that their criteria for whole-brain death did not require a new definition of death, yet Veatch and many other critics insisted that, in fact, they did. And, while I found many changes in the meaning of death from 1740 to 1960, some bioethicists argue that by their current standards these changes were only new criteria, not new definitions.[85]

Part of the difficulty in applying the distinction between definition and criteria is that even today the same physiological indicators are used as both criteria and definitions. A capacity like the ability to breathe, to integrate bodily functions, or to experience consciousness can be seen simply as a marker that indicates whether a more basic something else called *life* is still present. But the ability to perform these very same functions can also be considered not the indicator but the essence of life. Or these abilities may be regarded as necessary for life, without explicitly saying whether they are criteria or definitions. Thus, when someone identifies a particular capacity as vital, without explicitly stating whether it is the essence or merely a criterion of life, there is no unambiguous way to determine which conceptual role is being claimed.[86] This ambiguity is particularly common in the writings of problem-oriented clinicians like Beecher. Pragmatic physicians and lay people throughout history have written about what physiological functions to use in diagnosing death without distinguishing whether they saw those functions as the signs or the essence of life.

The current distinction between definitions and criteria was first clearly formulated only in 1977.[87] Thus, using it to categorize prior concepts inevitably distorts past concerns. Many past writers did distinguish between what they called the *tests* or *signs* of life and the *mean-*

ing of life. But that distinction cannot be fully equated with modern terms.

Furthermore, until the current century, the distinction between the signs of life and its meaning was itself controversial. For vitalists life meant the presence of an insubstantial essence such as spirit or soul, but materialists demanded that medical science reject such abstract "essences." For materialists, the signs of life *were* the essence of life, or at least the signs were all that objective medical science could ever know about the meaning.[88]

These problems of presentism are compounded by the polemical uses to which the distinction between definitions and criteria has often been put. The President's commission denied that their whole-brain criteria represented a new definition, in order to paint themselves as pragmatic moderates and to marginalize as radical dreamers those higher-brain advocates who demanded a new definition of death. Conversely, many supporters of higher-brain criteria proclaimed that their ideas did represent a new definition, as a means of asserting their superior intellectual rigor. Insisting that they have a new definition of death also served to create a sphere of special expertise for philosophers and relegated to physicians the supposedly purely technical task of devising and applying criteria.[89]

Both the Harvard committee and the President's commission recognized the value of comparing their work to the past, and Beecher's group even included historian Everett Mendelsohn as a member, yet both imposed current concepts on the past for polemical purposes. Mendelsohn did try to caution Beecher against forcing the past into modern categories. An early draft of the Harvard report included a passage taken from a November 1967 talk in which Beecher asserted that traditional heart-lung criteria had always served as indicators of the imminent death of the brain. In response, Mendelsohn correctly pointed out that physiologists long regarded the heart, not the brain, as the seat of the vital functions. But the final report left the draft passage intact. It simply added a statement that the heart was considered the "central organ," as if that fact somehow supported rather than undermined the claim that cardiac silence had been "the obvious criterion" that "the brain would die." Thus, the only section of the report to discuss history still distorted the past based on present-day polemical preconceptions, in words written by Beecher before the formation of the committee, over the objections of the committee's only professional historian.[90]

The current distinction between criteria and definitions has been extremely important for the past quarter century. But the effort to shoe-horn earlier ideas into this modern conceptual dichotomy violates the integrity of the past, in ways that preclude even asking the more important questions that need to be asked about how such categories have changed over time and why.

This chapter has argued that there were both important continuities and significant changes over time in the meaning of death. By highlighting the interaction of specific cultural and technological changes in producing past controversies, this history makes it easier to see the changeable elements—social and scientific—that make current definitions controversial and impermanent as well.

Death has long been a contingent and evolving concept, shaped by the intertwining of scientific, medical, social, and cultural changes. Though death is inevitable, its meaning has never been certain.

Notes

Research for this chapter was funded in part by a grant from the Burroughs Wellcome Fund.

1. Martin S. Pernick, "Back from the Grave: Recurring Controversies over Defining and Diagnosing Death in History," in Richard M. Zaner, ed., *Death: Beyond Whole Brain Criteria* (Dordrecht, Netherlands: Kluwer Academic Publishers, 1988), 17–74. The introduction and Section 1 below are based largely on 52–60 of that chapter.

2. B. J. Hendrick, "On the Trail of Immortality," *McClure's* 40 (January 1913): 304–17; J. Middleton, "Flesh That Is Immortal: Dr. Alexis Carrel's Experiments with Tissues of a Chicken," *World's Work* 28 (October 1914): 590–93; A. L. Chute and D. H. Smyth, "Metabolism of Isolated Perfused Cat's Brain," *Quarterly Journal of Experimental Physiology* 29 (1939): 379; Robert J. White, Maurice S. Albin, and Javier Verdura, "Isolation of the Monkey Brain: In Vitro Preparation and Maintenance," *Science* (September 13, 1963): 1060–61; personal conversation with Maurice Albin, May 11, 1995, Pittsburgh, Pa. See Robert J. White, "Experimental Transplantation of the Brain," in Felix Rapaport and Jean Dausset, eds., *Human Transplantation* (New York: Grune & Stratton, 1968), 692–709. One of the few studies of brain death to note such experiments was Delford L. Stickel, "The Brain Death Criterion of Human Death: An Analysis and Reflections on the 1977 New York Conference on Brain Death," *Ethics in Science & Medicine* 6 (1977): 179.

3. V. P. Demikhov, *Experimental Transplantation of Vital Organs* (New York: Consultants Bureau, 1962), 158. Soviet head transplants continued to be reported in the American press through the 1960s (see, e.g., *New York Times,* January 7, 1968,

51, and January 13, 1968, 17). Rosa Lynn Pinkus, "New Developments in Neuroscience: Historical and Ethical Issues in Neural Transplants," Office of Technology Assessment, Contract J3-4960.0, Final Report, 1989.

4. Robert J. White, Maurice Albin, and M. S. Locke, "Brain Transplantation: Prolonged Survival of Brain after Carotid-Jugular Interposition," *Science*, November 5, 1965, 779–81. Although the blood vessels were connected, no attempt to connect the nerves was reported. Personal conversation with Maurice Albin, Pittsburgh, Pa., May 11, 1995.

5. Pernick, "Back from the Grave," 54–55; "Between Life and Death," *Scientific American* 109 (1913): 362; V. A. Negovskii, *Resuscitation and Artificial Hypothermia* (New York: Consultants Bureau, 1962).

6. *Experiments in the Revival of Organisms,* motion picture (Voronezh Institute of Experimental Physiology, USSR, 1939). English version narrated by J. B. S. Haldane (Brandon Films, 1940). The film documents isolated maintenance of a dog's head and of a heart-lung preparation by S. S. Bryukhonenko. Copy from Indiana University Instructional Support Services science film archive. Personal letter, Maurice S. Albin to Martin Pernick, May 22, 1995, author's possession.

7. Since the nineteenth century, many physiologists have seen death as a process with no sharp dividing lines, while most clinicians and policymakers have demanded precisely such a single precise demarcation. Pernick, "Back from the Grave," 53–54. For Minot, see J. J. Farrell, *Inventing the American Way of Death* (Philadelphia: Temple University Press, 1980), 62. On neural integration versus consciousness, see W. U. Fox, *Dandy of Hopkins* (Baltimore: Williams & Wilkins, 1984), 219; W. Kaempffert, "What Is Clinical Death?" *Science Digest* 34 (August 1953): 76–77.

8. Negovskii, *Resuscitation,* 150–65. Negovskii's explanations of the political significance of his work closely tracked the shifting winds of Soviet ideology. By 1988, he attributed Soviet preeminence in this field not to Marxist materialism but to Socialist humanitarianism. Vladimir A. Negovsky, "Fifty Years of the Institute of General Reanimatology of the USSR Academy of Medical Sciences," *Critical Care Medicine* 16 (1988): 287, 290.

Experiments in Revival (motion picture). Haldane's father had done important work on the physiology of respiration, though he himself was known primarily as a geneticist. In his narration, Haldane specifically asked why these discoveries were all made in the Soviet Union. But the copy I examined does not provide an answer. Perhaps the film never included one. Or perhaps Haldane's answer was later censored as too pro-communist.

9. On the logical impossibility of developing experimental criteria for irreversibility, see D. Alan Shewmon, "The Probability of Inevitability: The Inherent Impossibility of Validating Criteria for Brain Death or 'Irreversibility' through Clinical Studies," *Statistics in Medicine* 6 (1987): 535–53. For eighteenth-century use of failure to respond to resuscitation as the criterion of death and the link to the debate over the meaning of suspended animation, see Pernick, "Back from

the Grave," 25–27. For the current view see F[rank] Gonzalez-Crussi, *Day of the Dead* (New York: Harcourt Brace, 1993), 138, in which successful resuscitation is the criterion proving that death did not occur, since what "defines death is precisely the irreversibility." Stickel, "Brain Death Criterion," 188.

As Veatch has noted, this criterion also makes it impossible to specify a time of death for a patient who has refused to permit resuscitation efforts. Robert M. Veatch, "The Impending Collapse of the Whole-Brain Definition of Death," *Hastings Center Report* 23 (July–August 1993): 20. For another attack on making irreversibility part of the definition of death, see David J. Cole, "The Reversibility of Death," *Journal of Medical Ethics* 18 (1992): 26–30.

10. Martin Pernick, *The Black Stork* (New York: Oxford University Press, 1996). Quotes from the *Chicago American*, November 29, 1915; *Chicago American*, November 26, 1915, 2; see also *Chicago American*, November 24, 1915, 2; *New York Medical Journal* 102 (1915): 1134; *Lancet* editor in *Current Opinion* 60 (January 1916): 43. Though some of his later cases involved microcephaly or anencephaly, these quotations refer to an infant whose brain was a normal size.

11. Pernick, "Back from the Grave," 55 and 63 n. 39 together list 12 typical examples. For the predicted end of racism, see R. C. W. Ettinger, "Can 'Deep Freeze' Conquer Death?" *Ebony* 21 (January 1966): 60–69. Quotation is from L. K. Hirshberg, "Between Life and Death," *Lippincott* 92 (1913): 651–52. Even Haiselden's radical actions and opinions were front-page news for years. Pernick, *The Black Stork*.

Also see the following educational motion pictures: *Experiments in the Revival of Organisms* (1939) and *Life Returns* (1934). The former documents the Soviet experiments in vivisection and suspended animation. The latter features surgeon Robert Cornish's experiments on reviving dogs clinically dead from anesthesia overdoses. It is available from Eddie Brandt films, Los Angeles.

On newspapers see Mita Giacomini, "A Change of Heart and a Change of Mind? Technology and the Redefinition of Death in 1968," *Social Science and Medicine* 44 (October 1997): 1472. I am grateful to Professor Giacomini for allowing me to see this work in manuscript.

12. Among the exceptions was surgeon George Washington Crile of the Cleveland Clinic.

13. At the Ciba symposium in 1966, brain transplants were dismissed as science fiction, although Albin and White had reported them in *Science* the year before. G. E. W. Wolstenholme and Maeve O'Conner, *Ethics in Medical Progress: With Specific Reference to Transplantation* (Boston: Little, Brown, 1966), 79. See also Giacomini, "Change of Heart," 1468.

Cardiopulmonary resuscitation pioneer Peter Safar noted that most of the techniques of modern CPR had been discovered by the early 1900s but were not implemented clinically because of clinicians' disinterest in laboratory experiments and their mistrust of lay involvement. Safar, "History of Cardiopulmonary-Cerebral Resuscitation," in W. Kaye and N. Bircher, eds., *Cardiopulmonary Resus-*

citation (New York: Churchill Livingstone, 1989), 1–53. Personal conversation with Peter Safar, May 11, 1995, Pittsburgh, Pa.

14. P. Mollaret and M. Goulon, "Le Coma Dépasse," *Revue Neurologique* 101, no. 1 (1959): 3–15.

15. *New York Times*, September 9, 1968, 3.

16. "A Definition of Irreversible Coma," *Journal of the American Medical Association* 205 (August 5, 1968): 337–40.

17. President's Commission for the Study of Ethical Problems in Medicine and Biomedical and Behavioral Research, *Defining Death: Medical, Legal and Ethical Issues in the Determination of Death* (Washington, D.C.: Government Printing Office, 1981).

18. The 1968 report lists these two technologies as the only reasons for a new definition. *Journal of the American Medical Association* 205 (August 5, 1968): 337.

Beecher's papers, including much material on the issue of brain death, are available at the Countway Library of Medicine, Holmes Hall, Harvard Medical School. See also David Rothman, *Strangers at the Bedside* (New York: Basic Books, 1991); Giacomini, "Change of Heart"; and Gary Belkin, Department of Psychiatry, Rhode Island Hospital, "Brain Death and the Historiography of Bioethics," unpublished manuscript, 1995. I am grateful to Dr. Belkin for sharing this paper with me.

19. Mendelsohn commented on the preliminary draft of this presentation, Cleveland, Ohio, November 2, 1995; Belkin, "Brain Death Historiography," 8, and personal correspondence, October 19, 1995.

20. Beecher to Ebert, October 30, 1967, and Ebert to Beecher, July 1, 1968, Beecher Papers, Box 6, Folder 17. In an early draft, Beecher explained that "the question before this committee" was to "advance the cause of organ transplantation" and to determine when "to turn off a respirator," April 11, 1968, Beecher Papers, Box 6, Folder 21. He predicted that brain death would generate "a vast supply of organs," Beecher to *New York Times*, January 22, 1968, Beecher Papers, Box 13, Folder 14a. Rothman, *Strangers*, 160–64; Giacomini, "Change of Heart"; M. L. Tina Stevens, "The Quinlan Case Revisited," *Journal of Health Politics, Policy and Law* 21 (summer 1996): 347–66, and "Redefining Death in America, 1968," *Caduceus* 11 (winter 1995): 207–19.

For murder prosecutions see *New York Times*, May 8, 1968, 23; February 24, 1974, sec. 4, 6; and May 27, 1972, 15. A few heart transplant surgeons did publicly express reservations about brain death, preferring to wait until the donor heart stopped beating before removing it. *New York Times*, September 9, 1968, 23.

21. Henry K. Beecher, "Ethical Problems Created by the Hopelessly Unconscious Patient," *New England Journal of Medicine* 278 (June 27, 1968): 1427.

22. Beecher, "Ethical Problems," 1425, 1428, 1430. In this regard, Beecher followed the 1958 precedent set by Pope Pius XII, who responded to a medical

request for guidance in when to stop treatment by discussing both the definition of death and the justifications for withholding heroic treatment from the
dying.

According to Everett Mendelsohn, the committee's main concern was for the
comatose patients and their families. Months before the creation of the Harvard
committee, Beecher proposed discussing brain death as part of an article to be
titled "The Right to Die." Beecher to Curran, June 14, 1967, Beecher Papers,
Box 11, Folder 17. However, the report expressed this concern solely in terms of
"burdens" and did not refer to issues of dignity, suffering, or autonomy.

23. *New York Times*, August 8, 1968, 32; Stickel, "Brain Death Criterion," 193.
These claims are supported by patient records from the period examined by
Belkin, "Brain Death Historiography." See also the use of brain criteria in kidney
transplant cases found by Giacomini, "Change of Heart," 1467, 1479.

Giacomini perceptively distinguishes those who used absence of brain waves
as a criterion of death from those who used presence of brain waves as a test for
continued life. The latter use was more common and had roots in earlier elec-
trodiagnostic efforts to prevent premature burial. See Pernick, "Back from the
Grave," 25.

24. Beecher, "Ethical Problems," 1430. The *New York Times* reported Beecher's early linkage between the definition of death and human experimentation,
December 10, 1967, 63. In September 1968, Beecher publicly repudiated such
experiments, but over a year later he continued to advocate them privately. *Man-
chester Guardian,* September 10, 1968, and Beecher to Mason G. Robertson, December 19, 1969, Beecher Papers, Box 6, Folder 38, and Box 13, Folder 14a.
David Dickson, "Human Experiment Roils French Medicine," *Science*, March 18,
1988, 1370; Henry K. Beecher, "Ethics and Clinical Research," *New England Journal of Medicine* 74 (1966): 1354–60; *Research and the Individual* (Boston: Little,
Brown, 1970).

25. Mendelsohn, comments, Cleveland, Ohio, November 22, 1995. Giacomini
also notes the lack of clinical concern with the conceptual implications of induced cardiac arrest during surgery in "Change of Heart," 1469.

26. *New York Times Index,* under "Death" and "Deaths." *Chicago Tribune,* August
5, 1968; *Washington Post*, August 5, 1968; Associated Press in *Ann Arbor News,*
August 5, 1968.

27. Pernick, "Back from the Grave," 58; "What is Life? When is Death?" *Time,*
May 27, 1966, 78; Leslie Ann Rado, "Communication, Social Organization and
the Redefinition of Death," Ph.D. diss., University of Pennsylvania, 1979, 99; J. B.
Brierley et al., "Neocortical Death after Cardiac Arrest," *Lancet,* September 11,
1971, 560–65. See also Vincent Collins, "Should We Let Them Die?" *Saturday
Evening Post,* May 26, 1962, 11–12.

28. Karen Grandstrand Gervais, *Redefining Death* (New Haven: Yale University
Press, 1986), 13.

29. Henry K. Beecher, "Definitions of 'Life' and 'Death' for Medical Science

and Practice," *Annals of the New York Academy of Sciences*, January 21, 1970, 474, 510.

30. "Ethical Problems Created by the Hopelessly Unconscious Patient," *New England Journal of Medicine*, June 27, 1968, 1426, 1429.

31. Mendelsohn, comments, Cleveland, Ohio, November 22, 1995; Stickel, "Brain Death Criterion," 178.

32. Rothman, *Strangers*, 148, 208; Martin Pernick, "Medical Professionalism," *Encyclopedia of Bioethics* (New York: Free Press, 1978), 3:1028–34.

33. *Journal of the American Medical Association*, August 5, 1968, 339.

34. Beecher, "Definitions of 'Life' and 'Death,'" 471–74, discussion on 509–10, quotation on 510; Henry K. Beecher, "After the 'Definition' of Irreversible Coma," *New England Journal of Medicine*, November 6, 1969, 1070; comments on Robert M. Veatch, "Remarks on Henry K. Beecher's Paper," Beecher Papers, Box 16, Folder 18; Belkin, "Brain Death Historiography."

35. See in particular *New York Times*, April 30, 1968, 51; May 19, 1968, 78; August 5, 1968, 35; August 10, 1968, 25; August 11, 1968, sec. 4, 12; September 9, 1968, 23; December 13, 1968, 17. For other examples, *Chicago Tribune*, August 5, 1968; *Washington Post*, August 5, 1968; Associated Press in *Ann Arbor News*, August 5, 1968.

36. *New York Times*, September 1, 1968, sec. 4, 11.

37. Pernick, "Back from the Grave," 57; "When Are You Really Dead?" *Newsweek*, December 18, 1967, 87.

38. *New York Times*, January 3, 1968, 32; January 7, 1968, sec. 4, 14. One of the few newspapers to cover the transracial component of the first transplant before its coverage of the second was the African-American *Chicago Defender*, December 16–22, 1967, 28.

39. "The Telltale Heart," *Ebony* 23 (March 1968): 118.

40. *Sepia* 19 (July 1970): 22–26, at 25. Such responses also echo earlier hopes that scientific uncertainties about death could be used to undermine racism. See *Ebony* 21 (January 1966): 60–69.

41. *Amsterdam News*, December 9, 1967, 16. The sentiment was repeated at the end of a second, more ambivalent editorial, *Amsterdam News*, January 13, 1968, 14.

42. *Amsterdam News*, January 13, 1968, 14.

43. *Chicago Defender*, January 13–19, 1968, 11.

44. *Ebony* 24 (May 1969): 82–84; *Sepia* 19 (July 1970): 22–26.

45. *Amsterdam News*, January 13, 1968, 14.

46. *Amsterdam News*, January 13, 1968, 15. The *New York Times* emphasized that the donor's mother had consented to the procedure, though it was not stated whether the issue of transracial transplantation had been raised (January 3, 1968, 32). Such concerns resonated with older stereotypes of Jews, especially Jewish physicians, as sucking or polluting the lifeblood of others. (South Africa did have a sizable urban Jewish population.)

47. *Ebony* 23 (March 1968): 118. For early charges that organ-stealing physicians used brain death as an excuse to kill blacks for their organs, see the Tucker case in Virginia and the Williams case in Wisconsin; *New York Times*, May 27, 1972, 15; *Milwaukee Journal*, February 4, 1971, 1.

48. *The Amazing Transplant* (1970), *The Blood Drinkers* (1966), *The Brain That Wouldn't Die** (1962), *Change of Mind** (1969), *Doctor Blood's Coffin* (1961), *Doctor of Doom** (1965), *Frankenstein Must Be Destroyed** (1970), *Hands of a Stranger* (1962), *The Head** (1965), *Jesse James Meets Frankenstein's Daughter** (1966), *Scream and Scream Again* (1970). Indexed in American Film Institute, *Catalogue of Motion Pictures: Feature Films 1961–1970* (New York: R. R. Bowker, 1976).

Six of the 11 films, marked with an asterisk above, involved brain transplants. They did not simply equate the brain with the essence of the individual. In almost all cases, the process of being embodied in a new setting produced a behavioral hybrid of the brain donor and recipient.

49. *New England Journal of Medicine*, June 27, 1968, 1427.

50. *New York Times*, December 13, 1968, 17.

51. Giacomini, "Change of Heart," 1476.

52. For the AMA's position see *New York Times*, December 5, 1973, 22, and December 4, 1974, 26. For the similar position of the 1968 World Medical Assembly, see *New York Times*, August 10, 1968, 25.

53. Giacomini "Change of Heart," 1470, quotes Harvard electroencephalographers using such language in 1963.

54. Barney Glaser and Anselm Strauss, *Awareness of Dying* (Chicago: Aldine, 1965); Glaser and Strauss, *A Time for Dying* (Chicago: Aldine, 1968); David Sudnow, *Passing On* (Englewood Cliffs, N.J.: Prentice-Hall, 1967); Elisabeth Kubler-Ross, *On Death and Dying* (New York: Macmillan, 1969); Philippe Aries, *Western Attitudes towards Death* (Baltimore: Johns Hopkins University Press, 1974); Jessica Mitford, *The American Way of Death* (New York: Simon & Schuster, 1963). Thanks to Charles Bosk for suggestions on the early sociological studies.

55. Alexander Capron, "To Decide What Dead Means," *New York Times*, February 24, 1974, sec. 4, 6.

56. In the eighteenth and nineteenth centuries, women were seen as especially likely to be misdiagnosed as dead, and women figured prominently in the campaign against premature burial. During both eras, women attacked the inadequacies of a mechanistic view of life, although the 1970s critique emphasized the fear of unduly prolonging, rather than prematurely ending, medical treatment. Mitford, *American Way of Death*.

57. On Quinlan see *New York Times*, September 25, 1975; October 1, 1975, 49; December 18, 1975, 30; May 2, 1976, 60.

58. *New York Times*, September 25, 1975; June 30, 1976, 48.

59. President's Commission, *Defining Death*, 23–24.

60. The *New York Times* published only three articles on defining death in 1981; none attributed the issue to transplantation. They published only one ar-

ticle on any aspect of transplantation that year. See also Rothman, *Strangers,* 166, for statistics on the decline of heart transplantation.

61. I had the privilege of watching this program with the commissioners and staff at Airlie House, where I was participating in the July 9, 1981, hearings on informed consent. There were audible groans during this segment of what was otherwise seen as an important boost for their work.

62. Clive Callender, James A. Bayton, Curtis Yeager, et al., "Attitudes among Blacks towards Donating Kidneys for Transplantation," *Journal of the National Medical Association* 74 (August 1982): 807–9.

63. *New York Times,* March 9, 1996, 6; *Harrisburg Patriot,* March 8, 1996, A1, A12.

64. Robert M. Arnold and Stuart J. Youngner, "The Dead Donor Rule: Should We Stretch It, Bend It, or Abandon It?" *Kennedy Institute of Ethics Journal* 3 (1993): 265; T[eo] Forcht Dagi, "The Obligation to Resuscitate," *Bulletin of the American College of Surgeons* 71 (November 1986): 8.

65. For right-to-life support see President's Commission, *Defining Death,* 11; for attack see *New York Times,* July 21, 1981, sec. 3, 2. For earlier attacks on brain death as euthanasia, see also *New York Times,* December 18, 1975, 30.

66. For example, see the paired stories in the *Washington Post,* July 10, 1981, and the combined story in the *Ann Arbor News,* July 10, 1981. On abortion see *New York Times* letters of Diane Ben-Ami, July 19, 1981, sec. 4, 20, and J. C. Willke, August 2, 1981, sec. 4, 20.

67. *New York Times,* May 27, 1967, 45; January 29, 1967, 58; August 2, 1968, 34.

68. *New York Times,* August 27, 1991, B5; Dorothy Nelkin and M. Susan Lindee, *The DNA Mystique* (New York: W. H. Freeman, 1995), 43.

69. Michael Crichton, *Jurassic Park* (New York: Knopf, 1990); *Jurassic Park* (Universal Pictures, 1993); Peter Niesewand, *Fall Back* (New York: Signet, 1982), 439. Thanks to Maurice Albin for providing a copy.

70. On *Flatliners* see James M. Walsh, *Films in Review* 41 (November/December 1990): 559–60. The term became so pervasively part of popular culture that it was used in the title of a dictionary of current slang. See Sid Lerner, *Trash Can, Fizzbos, and Flatliners: A Dictionary of Today's Words* (Boston: Houghton Mifflin, 1993). *Neomort* also achieved a degree of popular usage but had not been as widely accepted, according to Anne Soukhanov, *Word Watch* (New York: Henry Holt, 1995), 94–95. See also Robin Cook, *Coma* (Boston: Little, Brown, 1977).

71. *New York Times,* November 13, 1990, B5, B8.

72. Broadcast, April 2, 1995.

73. The pattern was set by *Newsweek.* Their story, "When Are You Really Dead?" ran as a sidebar to the main article on heart transplants, December 18, 1967, 87.

74. *Los Angeles Times,* September 25, 1981, sec. I-A, 3.

75. President's Commission, *Defining Death,* 38–41.

76. Daniel Wikler and Alan J. Weisbard, "Editorial: Appropriate Confusion over 'Brain Death'," *Journal of the American Medical Association*, April 21, 1989, 2246.

77. Beecher understood that defining death involved subjective value judgments, but he limited the committee to those aspects of the issue that he felt could produce objective consensus, precise standards, and pragmatic outcomes. Beecher could not fathom why Veatch insisted on discussing what Beecher considered insoluble value conflicts that would undermine agreement about the desired practical results. See Beecher Papers, marginal notes on Veatch typescript, Box 16, Folder 18; Beecher to Krister Stendahl, June 24, 1968, Beecher Papers, Box 6, Folder 30; and Beecher Papers, comments on remarks of Paul Ramsey, Box 16, Folder 16.

Veatch does not claim that higher-brain definitions are any *more* value-laden than any other concepts of death or than such other basic medical concepts as *disease* or *health*. Rather, he argues that all such concepts have unavoidable value-based components. Robert M. Veatch, *Death, Dying, and the Biological Revolution* (New Haven: Yale University Press, 1976); Veatch, *Value-Freedom in Science and Technology* (Missoula, Mont.: Scholar's Press, 1976). This is a position I have strongly supported in *The Black Stork* and elsewhere.

78. Botkin and Post, "Confusion"; Belkin, "Brain Death Historiography," 15–16 on Veatch. The tendency of academics to disproportionately value mental functions in decisions about euthanasia and eugenics can be documented from at least the 1910s. See Pernick, *The Black Stork*, Chap. 3; Botkin and Post, "Confusion," 131–32. Motion pictures rarely equated the brain with the individual; see note 48 above.

79. *New York Times*, August 11, 1968, sec. 4, 12; February 24, 1974, sec. 4, 6.

80. Stickel, "Brain Death Criterion," 184; *New York Times*, February 26, 1975, 44, slightly misquotes the ABA resolution. The resolution also did include a vague reference to the "usual and customary standards of medical practice."

Most statutes that recognize more than one set of death criteria assign the choice to the physician. However, in response to religious dissent, New Jersey allowed patients to choose among specified alternative criteria, a position endorsed by Veatch and other advocates of patient autonomy. Veatch, "Impending Collapse," 22.

81. In addition to Rothman, *Strangers*, see Stickel, "Brain Death Criterion," 182, 183, 190, 193; Rado, "Communication, Social Organization."

82. President's Commission, *Defining Death*, 1–2.

83. Belkin argues that, in the name of populist autonomy, Veatch constructed a new bioethics elite to replace medical authority; "Brain Death Historiography," 15–16. Some bioethicists may have used patient autonomy to mask their own drive for professional power. But those who believe that bioethics should monopolize the definition of death are contemptuous of Veatch for his insistence

that patients be allowed to choose between brain and heart-lung criteria. Professionalization is still a very divisive issue among bioethicists.

84. For efforts to force the past into the autonomy-beneficence straitjacket, see Jay Katz, *The Silent World of Doctor and Patient* (New York: Free Press, 1984), and, to a lesser extent, Ruth R. Faden and Tom L. Beauchamp, *A History and Theory of Informed Consent* (New York: Oxford University Press, 1986).

Many physicians in the nineteenth century would not have understood the modern distinction between autonomy and beneficence. They allowed considerable choice to some patients because they believed that choice was good for them. Understanding that past on its own terms in no way threatens support for autonomy today.

85. Veatch, "Impending Collapse"; Stickel, "Brain Death Criterion," 179; Gervais, *Redefining Death*, Chaps. 1–2; Gervais, "Review of *Death: Beyond Whole-Brain Criteria,*" *Bioethics* 3 (1989): 258.

86. Alexander Capron, "The Report of the President's Commission on the Uniform Determination of Death Act," in Zaner, *Death: Beyond Whole-Brain Criteria*, 159.

87. Stickel, "Brain Death Criterion," 178.

88. Pernick, "Back from the Grave," 25–27.

89. Gervais, *Redefining Death*, esp. 13; President's Commission, *Defining Death*, 41. See also Rothman, *Strangers*.

90. Mendelsohn to Beecher, June 5, 1968, Beecher Papers, Box 6, Folder 24; *New England Journal of Medicine*, June 27, 1968, 1426; *Journal of the American Medical Association*, August 5, 1968, 339. See also Giacomini, "Change of Heart," 1478. Mendelsohn's comments were quite deferential, and Beecher eventually did adopt Mendelsohn's view. See "The New Definition of Death, Some Opposing Views," typescript in Beecher Papers, Box 13, Folder 18.

Clinical Standards and Technological Confirmatory Tests in Diagnosing Brain Death

Fred Plum, M.D.

THE CONCEPT OF selective brain death, along with its medical, social, and philosophical implications, derives its origins from the success in the 1940s and early 1950s of critical care measures that first were applied to reduce the short- and long-term morbidity and mortality of acute poliomyelitis. That experience taught the imperative value of applying tracheostomy or endotracheal intubation to assure open airways. Ventilators gradually evolved from the oppressively claustrogenic iron lungs to the relatively simple bedside apparatus we use today. Aided by rapid developments in cardiopulmonary pharmacology and physiological monitoring, critical care technology moved first from the polio wards to the operating suite and then to the large variety of problem-specific intensive care units found in our tertiary care hospitals today.

The very efficiency of the new cardiopulmonary treatment measures then, as now, created unforeseen problems as well as therapeutic triumphs. By the mid-1950s, critical care technology was widely applied to treat severe brain damage such as that following head trauma, acute cardiopulmonary arrest, or other causes of pathological deep coma. It soon became apparent, however, that some of the more seriously damaged patients progressed insidiously from coma to a physiologically dissociated state characterized by well-functioning systemic organs but an irreversibly inactive brain. Three serious questions resulted: In life-supported patients with severe brain damage, what specific clinical and laboratory abnormalities unequivocally reflect the transition from a seriously impaired brain to a probably or certainly dead one? For how long and under what circumstances must such clinical or laboratory indicants persist for us to be absolutely sure of their implications? What ethical and legal considerations should apply to the discontinuation of artificial support in the presence of still-functioning fragments of the brain? Answers to the first two questions have become well established by experience but, as this book demonstrates, the last question remains a topic of active medical, philosophical, and ethical discussion.

Two early studies anticipated the road to current practice. Mollaret and Goulon in 1959 were the first to place on record the disconcerting appearance of previously comatose patients who had permanently lost all discernible evidence of brain activity but nevertheless maintained a heartbeat and a physiologically sufficient circulation for as long as one supplied cardiopulmonary support.[1] Subsequently, a Harvard committee in 1968 advanced the general understanding of the problem by explicitly identifying diagnostic criteria for "irreversible coma."[2] Three years later, Mohandas and Chou formulated the Minnesota Code for Brain Death, based largely on signs of absent brainstem functions (Table 2.1).[3] This almost exactly presaged that recommended in 1976 by the conference of the royal colleges in the United Kingdom.[4] In 1981, the *Journal of the American Medical Association* (*JAMA*) published guidelines for the diagnosis of brain death recommended by consultants to the President's Commission for the Study of Ethical Problems in Medicine and Biomedical and Behavioral Research (Table 2.2).[5] The commission recommended the adoption of the guidelines into the Uniform Determination of Death Act, which was developed in a collaboration among the American Bar Association, the American Medical Association, and the National Conference of Commissioners on Uniform State Laws.[6] In 1995, the American Academy of Neurology published its own consensus-derived practice guidelines for determining brain death, as had several other groups between 1981 and then.[7] An accompanying article by Wijdicks reviewed much of the neurological literature on the subject.[8]

Table 2.1. Minnesota Criteria for Brain Death

Known but irreparable intracranial lesion
Metabolic factors ruled out
No spontaneous movement
Apnea (4 min)
Absent brainstem reflexes: pupillary, corneal, ciliospinal, vestibular-ocular, ocu-
  locephalic, gag
All findings unchanged for 12 h

Source: Mohandas A, Chou SN. Brain death—a clinical and pathological study. *J Neurosurg* 1971; 35:211–18.

Table 2.2. Proposals for Diagnosing Brain Death Made by the President's Commission

An individual is dead who suffers:
  I. Irreversible cessation of circulatory and respiratory functions
 II. Irreversible cessation of all functions of the entire brain, including the
brainstem
    A. Deep coma
    B. Absence of all brain stem function, including the capacity to breathe
      spontaneously
III. Absence of confounding factors
    A. Cause of coma unequivocally established and sufficient
    B. Heavy sedation, body temp <32° C, severe neuromuscular blockade,
      shock ruled out
    C. Sufficient observation to confirm irreversibility
      1. No clinical change for 6 hours plus EEG silence or no cerebral per-
        fusion
      2. No clinical change for 12 hr
 IV. Consultation with an experienced physician to confirm the diagnosis

Note: These guidelines are rephrased from the 1981 proposal in *JAMA:* Guidelines for the determination of death. Report of the medical consultants on the diagnosis of death to the President's Commission for the Study of Ethical Problems in Medicine and Biomedical and Behavioral Research. *JAMA* 1981; 246:2184–86.

The Definition of Brain Death

As accepted by the President's commission in 1981, the diagnosis of brain death describes a condition in which "irreversible structural or specifically known damage has permanently destroyed all functional brain activity, including that of the brain stem." Two years later, Pallis restated

Table 2.3.   Diagnosis of Brain Death: The U.K. Code (1976)

1. Preconditions:
   Comatose patient, on a ventilator
   Positive diagnosis of cause of coma (irremediable structural brain damage)

2. Exclusions:
   Primary hypothermia (<35° C)
   Drugs
   Severe metabolic or endocrine disturbances

3. Tests (should be repeated, 1982):
   Absent brainstem reflexes
   Apnea (strictly defined)

Source: Pallis C. ABC of brain stem death. The arguments about the EEG. *Br Med J* 1983; 286:284–87.

and amplified the clinical criteria initiated by the Minnesota Code as well as the Conference of the Royal Colleges.[9] Termed in those reports *brainstem death* or *clinical death* (Table 2.3), the definition differed from that of the President's commission in two respects. It confined its scope to identifying without exception signs that unequivocally signify death of the brainstem but omitted the concept of brain death as affecting "all functions of the entire brain." Furthermore, it made no mention of technological procedures for diagnosis. As time has passed and the clinical indicants have become ever more strongly validated, institutions concerned with matters of brain death and transplantation have increasingly accepted the clinical guidelines of brain death enunciated by the Minnesota and U.K. codes (see, e.g., Ref. 7). Nevertheless, many transplantation protocols in the United States and in countries of Europe have retained an emphasis on the requirement for technological confirmation before proceeding with the logical removal of cardiopulmonary support implied in the declaration of brain death.

The reader may justifiably ask, "Why the brainstem, that's not where my consciousness comes from?" The reason is straightforward: The brainstem holds the critical nerve centers that make brain life possible. In the brainstem lie the structures that wake us up, the nervous centers that control the pupils inside our eyes, and all of the muscles that move our eyes. In the brainstem reside the sensors that allow us to hear, as well as those that give us the capacities to sense touch, taste, and a full mouth rather than an empty one. Through the brainstem descend all the neural wires that move our bodies and ascend the nerves that tell us what our bodies are feeling and even where our various parts are located in space. Without a brainstem we could neither chew, nor swallow, nor breathe. Without a brainstem I am no longer a person, I am no more than a hopeless collection of organs, incapable of human vitality. Almost always, patients who have been maintained by cardiopulmonary support for a few days beyond the diagnosis of brain death will be found to have brains that have turned into a fatty soup.

To the best of my knowledge, there is no clinical or technological evidence contradicting the conclusion that a nondrugged, nonfunctioning brainstem represents an absolute and not a probable indication that the entire brain shortly will die, usually within a day or so, but in rare cases after a few weeks. A meta-analysis of published accounts of over 1,900 persons who were diagnosed clinically as being brain dead but were continued on full life support until asystole supervened supports this conclusion.[10,11] Most of these individuals' bodies survived no more than a week, but in a few instances inexhaustible efforts to replace neurovegetative needs and neuroendocrine balance lengthened bodily survival to a matter of weeks or, rarely, even months (Table 2.4). Under

Table 2.4. Prolonged Visceral Survival after Brain Death

Patient (age)	Disease	Technological Findings	Duration (days)	Mode of Death	Reference
47 M	Acute posterior fossa hemorrhage	EEG 5–6 cps for 24 d	26	SCA	Ogata et al.[21]
23 F	Acute asystole	EEG isoelect, day 11	31	RD	Fabro[51]
36 M	Not described	No cerebral blood flow	36	?	Grenvik et al.[52]
27 F	Post fossa mass/ foramen magnum herniation	EEG isoelect, day 2	62	RD	Field et al.[53]
49 M	Acute CA	EEG isoelect	71	RD	Parisi et al.[54]
23 M	Acute SAH	EEG isoelect early	112	RD	Klein[55]
4 (?)	Meningitis	EEG isoelect	201	SCA	Rowland[56]

Note: Abbreviations used: EEG, electroencephalogram; SCA, spontaneous cardiac arrest; RD, respirator discontinued; CA, cardiac arrest; SAH, subarachnoid hemorrhage.

Table 2.5. Frequent Examples of Brain Damage Leading to Brain Death

I. Brain images abnormal and compatible
   A. Large mass lesions producing
      1. Side-to-side hemisphere shift plus herniation
      2. Arterial hemorrhage into ventricles
   B. Multiple, large, acute infarctions
   C. Severe traumatic-necrotic brain edema
   D. Cerebellar-pontine hemorrhages or infarcts compressing or destroying brainstem
II. Brain images negative or equivocal
   A. Acute cardiac arrest, CO poisoning, asphyxia
   B. Acute encephalitis
   C. Acute bacterial endocarditis, thrombotic purpura, etc.
   D. Cyanide or other fatal poison

these somewhat bizarre circumstances, when the brains were examined at autopsy they literally crumbled from autolytic necrosis.

The general principle of brain death has been upheld by statute or judicial opinion in each of the 50 states and has been at least partially adopted in most of the world's industrialized nations. Several considerations led to this acceptance. One was the widespread distribution of the recommendations of the President's commission. Another was the unfailing accuracy of the relatively straightforward clinical diagnosis of brain death when made by experienced physicians. Similar support came from postmortem examinations in patients who received cardiorespiratory support for a few days after brain death. Such brains invariably showed extensive neuropathological abnormalities precluding any possibility of restoring neurological activity.[12] In several instances, it took no more than a few days after brain death for the organ to undergo liquefaction necrosis extending rostrally from the foramen magnum to destroy most of the brainstem and sometimes much of the cerebrum as well.

Typical causes of preasystole brain death in adults are listed in Table 2.5. All of these conditions reflect structural injuries to the tissue. Most such injuries will be large enough to produce obvious abnormalities on computed tomographic (CT) or magnetic resonance imaging (MRI) scans, but some examples of anoxic-ischemic or hypoglycemic damage may leave only a microscopic trail of dead and dying neurons and support cells. The important point is that one must be extremely wary of diagnosing brain death unless the results of brain imaging or a well-documented, severe metabolic insult provide an acceptable cause. If not, deep areflexic coma should be regarded as the result of severe drug intoxication until proved otherwise.

The Diagnosis of Brain Death

Clinical Criteria

Clinical criteria for diagnosing brain death rest on three principal abnormalities: (1) severe coma of known cause, (2) absent brainstem reflexes, and (3) sustained apnea.

I. General conditions
   A. Known structural cause of absent brain function
      1. Known severe asphyxia, inflammation, or metabolic failure (e.g., Grade 4 hepatic coma or profound sustained hypoglycemia), or
      2. Physical findings or neuroimaged abnormalities compatible with producing death of the brain
   B. Confounding variables must be excluded. Reversible medical complications that may confuse clinical evaluation must be overcome or corrected. These include hypotensive shock as well as severe electrolyte, acid-base, or endocrine disturbances, such as those accompanying severe hypovolemia secondary to diabetes insipidus or moderate hypoglycemia.
   C. The presence of any anesthetics, muscle relaxants, or sedative drugs must be excluded or reduced to nonconfounding levels.
   D. Core body temperature should be $\geq 32°$ C.
II. Cardinal diagnostic findings
   A. No spontaneous or responsive cranial nerve activity can be identified after stimuli delivered anywhere in the body. No spinal activity can be elicited by stimuli delivered above the foramen magnum.
   B. Brainstem reflexes must be absent.
      1. Pupils must be:
         a) Unresponsive to bright light.
         b) Usually midposition (4–6 mm) or dilated (9 mm). Pinpoint

    pupils can accompany lethal pontine hemorrhages or infarcts.

  2. Oculocephalic reflexes to repetitive head turning must be absent. If so, the test must be followed by 50 ml of cold water irrigated against the tympanum on both sides. At least a 5-minute interval should separate the two irrigations, neither of which should induce eye movement.

  3. No corneal, jaw, pharyngeal, or laryngeal reflex or pain response involving cranial nerves can be elicited.

C. A failed apnea test is crucial and imperative. The apneic test is conducted only after all other signs of brainstem function have disappeared and should not be applied until all reasonable amounts of anesthetic or paralytic drugs have dissipated to non-confounding levels. Respiratory pH receptors in the lower brainstem have powerful survivor sensitivities that make them crucial sensors for any functional activities. Accordingly, the apneic test represents the ultimate physiological-clinical test to diagnose brain death. I know of no personal observation or well-documented report of a responsibly conducted, positive apnea test that has been reversed by subsequent recovery. Conversely, instances of omission of the apnea test have led to potentially unfortunate errors or premature assumptions of brain death.

    Some precautions are desirable during the apneic test. Unless carefully guarded against, anoxemia accompanied by cardiac arrhythmia, hypotension, or both can be induced by the test. Not surprisingly, this adversity disconcerts clinicians and ancillary staff, but it almost always can be prevented by preoxygenation followed by diffusion oxygenation during the test. Optimal procedure is as follows:

  1. Preoxygenate the patient by delivering 100 percent O_2 via the ventilator for several minutes before starting the test.

  2. After preoxygenation, draw baseline arterial blood gases to assure arterial oxygenation of >90–95 mm Hg and to determine the baseline $PaCO_2$. In the case of a low $PaCO_2$, it is inappropriate to "correct" the low value because that excessively lowers brain pH, somewhat confounding the test results. Then remove the ventilator and immediately deliver 4–6 L/min 100 percent O_2 into the endotracheal airway. Monitor cardiac rate and rhythm and observe carefully for any *respiratory* movement.

(Spinally generated, nonventilatory chest-body movement may occur but does not reflect brainstem function.) If either cardiac arrhythmia or breathing efforts appear, draw blood #2 and restart the ventilator. (Breathing efforts represent active brainstem function and a negative test.) Otherwise, maintain oxygenated apnea for 8 minutes, draw an arterial blood sample at the end, and restart the ventilator. An end-of-apnea $PaCO_2$ level of either >60 mm Hg or 20 mm Hg above the preapneic baseline indicates nonfunctioning of brainstem breathing centers and signifies brain death if accompanied by Findings A and B described above.

Confirmatory Tests

Electroencephalography

Electroencephalography is the most widely tested and utilized of the various confirmatory tests for brain death. It continues as such in many institutions in the United States and worldwide. Hughes reviewed early studies on the usefulness of EEG in confirming brain death.[13] Based on evaluations of the configurations and inter-rater interpretations of 1,665 EEGs, the American EEG Society confirmed the high association of an isoelectric EEG with brain death. Those interinstitutional analyses also confirmed earlier studies showing that isoelectric EEGs could reflect the completely reversible effects of deep, sedative-induced coma. Nevertheless, the possible occurrence of EEG silence accompanying functionally fully recoverable brain largely escaped attention at the time.

From its very initiation into the critical care environment, the problem of technical artifacts and physiological meaning has plagued the interpretation and biological significance of EEG in diagnosing brain death (Table 2.6). For example, as early as the second phase of the original American Collaborative Study on EEG in brain death,[14] 6 percent of 2,256 records were considered technically unsatisfactory for interpretation. Similar difficulties were encountered in other large series evaluating EEGs for isoelectric patterns. Inter-rater interpretations differed by 13–23 percent in three relatively large studies.[15–17]

Within the past few years, several investigators have found that a fraction of carefully evaluated patients with clinically dead brainstems have continued to generate cerebral electrical activity for a matter of hours to days after a clinical and, somewhat less often, an angiographic "con-

Table 2.6. Equivocal or Active EEGs in Clinical Brain Death

Source	EEG Activity
American Collab Study (1970)	6% of 2,256 unsatisfactory[14]
Subsequent studies (1977–90)	13–15% inter-rater conflicts[15–17]
Ashwal, Schneider (1975)	Present in 5 children brain dead for up to 12 days[18]
Grigg et al. (1987)	Present in 11/56 brain-dead patients,[19] children[2] + adults, max. 168 hr
Ferbert (1986)	2 adults, 48 hr[20]
Ogata (1988)	4 adults; 3 = 24 hr; 1 =24 d[21]

firmation" of brain death.[18–20] Ashwal and Schneider described 5 children (aged 1 to 30 months) with several different lethal illnesses, who retained low-voltage delta activity in EEG tracings up to 12 days after clinically diagnosed brain death.[18] All remained on life support until asystole supervened. One had minimal cerebral blood flow on a bolus isotopic blood flow study; the other 4 had no blood flow. Grigg et al. reported that, among 56 clinically brain-dead patients, 11 (including 2 children) retained detectable EEG activity for a mean of 36.6 hours and a maximum of 168 hours after diagnosis.[19] Cerebral blood flow, studied in 6 of these patients by nuclear perfusion or arteriographic techniques, showed no flow in 5 patients. Nine of the 11 had low-voltage theta or beta EEG activity throughout. Ferbert et al. reported a somewhat similar patient, clinically brain dead due to a large cerebellar-brainstem hemorrhage. The EEG maintained a steady alpha rhythm for more than 48 hours.[20] Furthermore, visual evoked responses could be obtained, and transcranial Dopplers identified a normal flow of the right middle cerebral artery. The same authors refer to a similar case recorded in the German literature. Ogata et al. described 4 patients diagnosed clinically as brainstem dead after cerebellopontine or primary pontine hemorrhage.[21] Three maintained "nonreactive alpha or slower activities" in EEGs for at least 24 subsequent hours; one, who was early decompressed via a ventricular drain, retained an active EEG for at least 24 days before cerebral isoelectricity and asystole terminated the macabre performance. At autopsy, only 1 of the 4 patients showed severe pathological changes outside the devastated brainstem.

These experiences and others cited by Pallis illustrate some of the biological inconsistencies encountered in applying EEG patterns to con-

Table 2.7. Sensitivity and Specificity of Immediately Utilized Confirmatory Tests for Brain Death

Test	n	Sensitivity (%)	Specificity (%)
EEG	1200+	±90	±90
SEPs	>100	100	±95
BAEP	43	100	94
Dig. Subtr Arteriogram	97	<96[a]	100
Transcranial Doppler	120	95	99
Extracranial Doppler	42	74	unacceptable
^{99}Tc-HMPAO	100	95[a]	100

[a]Immediate application after clinical diagnosis not reported.

firm brain death.[11] Possibly some of the reported low-voltage records were artifactual, resulting from using high-gain amplification in the electrically noisy environment of a critical care unit. Nevertheless, a number of the examples indicate that continuing cerebral electrical activity can proceed for at least many days, even after measurable blood flow to the brain has ceased. No such residually active EEGs in a patient clinically designated as brain dead was associated with any recovery, not even to a vegetative state.

Evoked Responses

As with EEGs, these tests suffer from a less than 100 percent specificity in diagnosis, with only brainstem auditory evoked potentials (BAEPs) enjoying a 100 percent sensitivity, provided that the acoustic nerve is intact (Table 2.7).

BRAINSTEM AUDITORY EVOKED POTENTIALS

BAEPs are short latency signals that monitor normal neural activity emanating from an activated, ipsilateral auditory nerve and relayed rostrally from the pons to the higher brainstem.[22,23] In the test, repetitive auditory stimuli normally ascend the brainstem and can be recorded from the scalp in the occipital area. BAEPs disappear in brainstem death except for the occasional appearance of an isolated Wave 1, transmitted from a still-functioning peripheral auditory nerve. The procedure requires large equipment, reducing its easy utilization in the critical care environment. A shortcoming of BAEPs is that auditory nerve damage or an electrode misplacement by an unskilled technician can sometimes prevent their appearance. When properly used, however, BAEPs can be valuable for evaluating patients in deep coma due to drug overdose because BAEPs maintain their presence during deep anesthesia. As a result, they potentially can distinguish severe pharmacological brainstem depression from brain death. Present medical practice seldom requires such verification now that barbiturates have been largely discarded as sedatives.

SOMATIC EVOKED POTENTIALS

Somatic evoked potentials (SEPs) have received greater attention than BAEPs in diagnosing brain death.[23] The most frequently employed approach consists of rapidly and repetitively stimulating a functioning sensory nerve, usually the median at the wrist, and recording averaged responses from electrodes placed successively: (1) over the brachial plexus at Erb's point, (2) in the midpoint of the back over the C2 vertebral spinous process, and (3) over the contralateral somatosensory scalp area. Independent, averaged potential peaks recorded at each of these points have been ascribed, respectively, to activity reaching the brachial plexus, the cervicomedullary junction (probably reflecting activity in the ascending dorsal column's sensory nuclei of the lower medulla), and the thalamus and the cerebral cortex. As with BAEPs, SEPs are not blocked by the presence of sedative or anesthetic drugs, although they slow down during hypothermia.

Absent SEPs at the cerebral cortical or thalamic level predict brain death with a high degree of probability. A small fraction of patients with absent cortical responses, however, may survive in a vegetative state.[24] Absent SEPs can be recorded in patients with intact cerebral functions who have suffered from high cervical-low medullary physiological transection. Irrespective of other injuries, no responsible report has described the preservation of SEPs in a patient who met clinical criteria for brain death. SEP procedures are time consuming and require expert technicians for proper application. The size of the SEP apparatus makes the procedures difficult to conduct in the intensive care setting.

MOTOR EVOKED RESPONSES

Motor evoked responses (MEVs) reverse the direction of SEPs. Single stimuli applied to the scalp over the cerebral motor cortex area normally evoke muscular twitching of the small muscles of the opposite hand. Preliminary testing suggests that MEVs may be difficult to elicit in some comatose patients prior to a positive apneic test,[25] a finding that may indicate no more than a failure of the stimulus to pass through damaged motor pathways located rostral to the lower brainstem. In no instance were MEVs identified after a positive apneic test. Presently MEVs cannot be regarded as defining or confirming the presence of brain death.

Arteriography

Mapping the geographic patterns of the brain's functioning arterial bed represents the major technological alternative to EEG in confirming brain death. Classic arteriograms, isotope studies, and Doppler sonograms have been applied to this task. All three procedures have disclosed at least fragments of remaining intracranial arterial perfusion in a small number of clinically brain-dead persons (Table 2.7). These remnants sometimes have been taken to indicate that parts of the brain still retain an independent function or a promise of recovering. We know of no evidence that supports this belief. The major question from the pathophysiological standpoint is why arterial flow should stop just because brain tissue is dead? To a large degree, the answer comes from understanding the pressure variables that build up when a brain dies within an inelastic skull.

Illnesses that selectively kill the brain can directly attack its neuroglial population or obstruct its major arteries. Either way, in the presence of large or diffuse injuries, the brain's vascular and supporting tissues each become progressively damaged as the process continues. Acute, primary death of neurons and supporting cells, such as that following severe anoxia or diffuse brain inflammation, leads to intra- and extracellular edema in the regions of injury. Rapidly expanding lesions, such as large infarcts, hematomas, and brain tumors, precipitate similar changes. The process is generated by a combination of inflammatory and immune reactions, the inevitable hydration of extravascular osmols that derive from the death of neurons and supporting cells, and, eventually, the local breakdown of the blood-brain barrier. Increased tissue bulk leads to increased local tissue pressure, which ultimately may squeeze critical capillary perfusion to the near-zero point. Once this occurs, more cells die and the potential sequence can merge into a positive feedback loop producing an ever-enlarging, self-sustaining, and progressive cycle of cell:

death → edema → increased tissue pressure → spreading ischemia →
cell death

A critical phenomenon that sooner or later guarantees the brain's eventual no-flow condition is the inelasticity of the adult skull. By limiting gross expansion of brain tissue due to repair efforts in the severely injured brain, the skull impedes venous drainage. This, in turn, further increases tissue pressure and accelerates the conversion of regional brain injury into ever-spreading, global infarction.

The limitations created by an inelastic skull help one to understand why arterial flow studies only sometimes show residual areas of blood flow in clinically brain-dead adults but often reveal such flow in young brain-dead children. A fact that reinforces the concept that the inelasticity of the skull contributes to the no-flow brain is that several adults who have had intracerebral decompression either by recent skull removal or by ventricular drainage have retained intracranial blood flow despite severe brain damage.[26] The relatively frequently found residual blood flow in the brains of clinically brain-dead children almost certainly can be attributed to the increased elasticity of their immature skulls.[27–29]

CLASSIC ARTERIOGRAPHY

In this initially most commonly used procedure, one injects contrast dye into the aortic arch and follows with digital subtraction of the skull to outline the intracranial arterial patterns. Under these circumstances, a total failure to identify cerebral perfusion has a 100 percent specificity for diagnosing brain death, but as many as 2–4 percent of studies reported in adults reveal at least some residual intracranial flow (Table 2.7). One reported patient with a rapidly enlarging lesion of the posterior fossa, presumably a hematoma, retained a total intracranial flow pattern but with a subtentorial circulation time of 10 seconds versus 4.5 seconds in the arteries of the carotid distribution.[30] Kosteljanetz et al. describe a 44-year-old man who became clinically brain dead after rupture of a basilar aneurysm producing extensive brainstem infarction.[31] Attenuated vertebrobasilar flow as well as above-normal supratentorial flow remained for at least 48 hours. Ventricular drainage was established on Day 1. Another study identified the presence of slowed arterial filling in 2 of 49 patients already pronounced brain dead by clinical and EEG criteria.[32] During recent years, I have received telephone calls from physicians disconcerted by finding continued cerebral (but not posterior fossa) arterial perfusion in patients brain dead for more than 12–24 hours. All patients had acute cerebellopontine hemorrhage or primary pontine infarction.

In clinical practice, arteriography has been a "last-word" test usually obtained 24 or more hours after brain death is suspected. This long delay may explain why so few examples of continued brain blood flow have been reported after brain death.

RADIOISOTOPE STUDIES

During the past 20 years, refined radioisotope techniques have facilitated the use and accuracy of tests of cerebral perfusion associated with brainstem death. Most compounds employed for present radionuclide scans use the lipid-soluble agent ^{99}Tc-HMPAO, which has the capacity to cross the blood-brain barrier rapidly and enter viable brain cells.[32] Used appropriately, ^{99}Tc-HMPAO marks both the flow distribution and, to a semiquantitative degree, the functional capacities of the brain. The relatively long half-life of the isotope (6.03 hours) and its slow disappearance from the tissue allow a more deliberate and less complicated approach than previous measures to image cerebral perfusion and possible functional areas. The technique can be facilitated by using a portable bedside gamma camera to monitor the pattern of blood flow in both anterior and posterior brain areas.

Scintigraphic studies of cerebral blood flow have confounded the clinical diagnosis of brain death more frequently than has classic arteriography. The explanation may lie in the fact that radioisotope scans can be obtained more easily and quickly than more cumbersome arteriograms; as a result, they are likely to be applied more immediately after clinical death is diagnosed. Unfortunately, the epiphenomenon of residual blood flow after brain death has sometimes delayed the diagnosis in such cases. In one hospital with a technologically based requirement for transplantation, for example, a ^{99}Tc-HMPAO scan performed 1.5 hours after clinically diagnosed brain death showed fragments of cerebral blood flow that led to a 24-hour delay in harvesting visceral organs for transplantation.[33] Among a total of 99 patients in other studies who received ^{99}Tc-HMPAO shortly after the clinical diagnosis of brain death, one patient showed complete cerebral perfusion and four possessed at least partial cerebral but not posterior fossa perfusion.[34–37]

TRANSCRANIAL DOPPLER ULTRASONOGRAPHY

Aasled et al. developed the noninvasive procedure of transcranial Doppler ultrasonography (TCD) to monitor critical aspects of intracranial blood flow in a variety of neurological disorders.[38] Methodologically, an "ultrasonic skull window" through the temporal bone permits insonation of the anterior, middle, and posterior cerebral arteries via probes that monitor their flow velocity and pattern. The vertebrobasilar arterial system can be insonated less consistently by surface probes placed over the base of the skull and aimed at the foramen magnum. Considerable skill and experience is necessary for placing the probes appropriately. Even well-trained operators find it difficult to obtain velocity measurements across the temporal bone in some 5 percent of patients. Among the 95 percent of patients who can be studied, flow patterns can identify endangered patterns of velocity as well as configurations that reflect absent perfusion of the major cerebral arteries insonated at the particular probe site. Normal TCD patterns usually identify high-velocity forward flow in the anterior circle of Willis throughout both cardiac systole and diastole. Impending loss of flow reveals itself by a lowered, absent, or reversed diastolic flow pattern.[39,40]

Detection of bilateral obstruction of cerebral arterial blood flow identifies potential or actual brain death. (Unilateral abnormalities of flow pattern can reflect the presence of an embolus or thrombus at the base of a selected cerebral artery.) Brief, short amplitude, abnormally sharp wave patterns (*spikes*) during systole alone (no diastolic flow present) or an oscillating to-and-fro flow pattern with forward flow during systole and backward flow during diastole identify irreversible loss of the circulation distal to the artery under examination. Absent evidence of blood flow activity at the base of the brain, however, must be regarded as a technical failure unless proved otherwise. Disappearance of all flow signals in the area of a previously active measurement identified by the same experienced technologist sometimes can be taken as circulatory absence. Even in this circumstance, however, one should be cautious about concluding brain death in the absence of clinical signs.

Several series have validated the sensitivity and specificity of TCD in confirming the clinical expression of brain death. The combined reports by Kirkham,[28] Hassler,[39] Ropper,[40] Petty,[41] and Feri[42] and their respective colleagues provide data on TCD activity in 120 postinfantile children (*n* = 23) and adults (*n* = 97) with clinically diagnosed brain death (Table 2.7). Eighty-four also had EEGs and 34 had arteriograms. In all instances, the latter tests seem to have preceded the ultimate TCD evaluation. Not all studies enumerated their failed attempts to insonate intracranial vessels (when described, 9–18 percent were indicated), and most of the studies omitted mention of vertebrobasilar artery flow velocities.

Within the above constraints, TCD confirmed an absence of blood flow in 114 of 120 cases of clinically diagnosed brain death, a sensitivity of 95 percent. In the 6 instances showing relatively good intracranial flow in the internal carotid–supplied arteries, either classic aortic arch or subtraction arteriograms confirmed residual blood flow in the same vessels. Only 1 patient, clinically dead from cardiopulmonary arrest, was reported as retaining completely normal TCD patterns of supratentorial arterial perfusion. No report indicated any clinical sign of brain life once the characteristic TCD brain-death flow patterns appeared.

Doppler flow patterns in extracranial (as opposed to intracranial) carotid and vertebral arteries (ECD) also have been evaluated in relation to clinical brain death. Their usefulness has turned out to be limited. In one recent study of 42 patients clinically diagnosed as being brain dead, ECD obtained typical no-circulation flow velocity patterns in only 31.[32] Nine additional patients showed a "suggestive" ECD pattern, hardly sufficient for diagnostic purposes. More importantly, Lewis et al. reported the case of a young man in whom ECD detected to-and-fro extracranial carotid artery flow 5 days after an episode of transient asystole.[43] Such a pattern, when identified by TCD, has thus far turned out always to identify brain death. This patient, however, reportedly recovered without neurological deficit.

Brain Death in Children

Criteria for this diagnosis have been established largely on the basis of Ashwal and Schneider's experience and accepted by the American Academy of Pediatrics and the Child Neurology Society.[44] The clinical guidelines are similar to those in adults (Table 2.8). They include known cause, nonremedial coma, absent brainstem reflexes including a standardized apnea test, and absence of severe hypothermia or intoxicating drugs. Recommended observation times from first diagnosis to removal of life support, as well as for laboratory verification, differ somewhat from those that apply to adults. Ashwal and Schneider's current view, based on additional patient observations, is that clinical examination alone is sufficient to diagnose brain death in most children (S. Ashwal, personal communication, 1995). No diagnostic errors have been reported when strict clinical guidelines were followed, but technological assistance is required for pretransplantation of organs.

A distressing report on inconsistencies in diagnosing brain death in children appeared recently.[45] One hopes that it does not reflect anything

Table 2.8. Diagnosis of Brain Death in Infants and Children

Diagnostic criteria are same as for adults.
Be sure that high sedative levels are absent.
Interval times between first and ultimate diagnosis:
   Preterm infants .... 72 hr
   Term to 2 mo .... 48 hr
   2–12 mo .... 24 hr
   >12 mo .... 12–24 hr
Either isoelectric EEG or CBF <3–4 ml/100 g/min

Source: Ashwal S, Schneider S. Brain death in infants and children. In: Berg BO (ed). *Neurologic Aspects of Pediatrics.* Stoneham, Mass.: Butterworth-Heinemann, 1992, 639–53.

more serious than an unwillingness to follow rigid standard practice. In a survey involving several reputable pediatric services, among 93 children who were declared brain dead, 5 apparently were diagnosed without a full clinical coma examination. Twenty-three had no apnea test, 82 had no repeat apnea exam, 3 had apneic tests shortly after barbiturates were stopped, and 4 of 30 infants less than 12 months old had no confirmatory tests of the clinical diagnosis. The findings suggest that hospitals would do well to conduct annual reviews of their criteria for brain death and of the accuracy of their fulfillment.

Spinal Movements in Brain Death

The spinal cord usually escapes the pathological impact of disorders that lead to brain death. As a result, a variety of reflex or spontaneous, complex spinal responses can affect as many as 75 percent of brain-dead patients.[46] These movements more often affect younger than older persons, and they occur more frequently when brain death has lasted for one or two days or more. Heytans et al. describe an example and reviewed the literature.[47]

The importance of spinally engendered movements in brain death lies not only in their existence but also in the neural complexity that their expression reflects. Spinal deep tendon reflexes commonly are preserved and often are hyperactive but never are spastic. Cutaneous abdominal as well as cremasteric reflexes often persist. Extensor plantar responses are uncommon, but brisk and uni- or bilateral leg reflex withdrawal can follow plantar stimuli. In contrast to brainstem reflexes, concurrent flexor-extensor posturing of the upper and lower extremities has not been reported. What do occur, however, are a variety of complicated, coordinated movements that possess the disquieting appearance of semipurposeful acts. Confirming the isolated spinal origin of these relatively coordinated activities, Ropper reports that short latency median nerve somatosensory evoked potentials appear at or below the cervical-medullary junction in such cases but that no responses can be elicited in more rostral structures.[48]

Neck flexion in brain-dead bodies with isolated spinal cords may induce a brief, brisk neck extension reflex. Neck flexion also may induce brief adduction of either or both shoulders accompanied by either flexion or extension movements of the forearms at the elbow. Neck flexion also may induce quick hip flexion. Occasionally, unilateral extension-pronation of an arm occurs. Sometimes the shoulders turn in and the back arches as a combined movement.

In some brain-dead patients even more complex body movements can occur, suggesting that the spinal cord holds within its ontogenetic organization the capacity to execute complex behavior in a semidirected way. Such movements can take several forms. One consists of rigidly raising one or both the flexed arms over the chest or neck, arching the back, and then deliberately returning the arms to rest. Others include independently raising one arm or the other, seemingly to reach a tracheotomy tube. Most startling of all is a complex act allegorically dubbed *Lazarus's sign*.[47] The phenomenon most often occurs during an apnea test or the terminal asphyxia of ventilatory removal. In it, the arms rise above the body and the body and head also may flex into a semisitting position for a matter of several seconds to minutes. The patient then flops back to the bed, flaccid, inert, and immobile. No movement of face or jaw accompanies the above motor activities, nor have we encountered examples of the postural coordination that occurs between the arms and legs in decerebrate patients.

The appearance of these many movements, both simple and well organized in motor pattern, can be disconcerting even to professionals. Further confirming their isolated spinal origin, however, we observed the phenomenon terminally in a patient whose autopsy a few hours later demonstrated liqufication necrosis of the lower brainstem down to the level of the foramen magnum. More important in clinical care is the disquieting effect such movements can have when witnessed by families.

Because of this, it seems wise to perform both apneic tests and the ultimate withdrawal of the ventilator in the absence of the family. If loved ones insist on witnessing the patient's final cardiac activity, they should be warned that spontaneous movements generated at the spinal level may be distressing to observe but in no way reflect the presence of residual brain function.

The Timing of the Withdrawal of Life Support

Natural death is not an event. It is a process in which different organs or parts of organs permanently lose their life-supporting properties at widely varying times and rates.[49] Death of the brain becomes inescapable when the organ irreversibly loses its capacity to maintain the vital integrative functions transacted by its autonomic-vegetative and consciousness-mediating centers. These centers lie in the brainstem and indispensably regulate what Claude Bernard (1865) called the *body's internal milieu*. They also contribute critically to a host of more complex integrated and cognitive neurological functions that express the body's relationships with the outer world. Accordingly, death of the brainstem dooms into silence whatever remnants of more rostral structures may continue to carry out. Neither Pallis nor I have been able to find by personal contact or in the professional medical literature a single example of a patient accurately diagnosed as being brainstem dead who subsequently recovered any vital brainstem function, much less any shred of arousal or consciousness.[11]

Most brain-dead patients are carried on life support until asystole supervenes within a few days of onset. Hung and Chen, for example, report that, of 73 such brain-dead patients, half experienced asystole by the third day but the bodies of 2 lived on until the 10th and 16th day.[50] Table 2.4 lists even longer intervals before either heart action spontaneously ceased or legal/family permission allowed discontinuation of ventilation. This can be taken as the dark side of advanced technological support systems. The medical costs are huge, the experience drains the emotional reserves of families and caregivers, and the longer cardiopulmonary support lasts the greater becomes the threat that the body's visceral organs will be unsuitable for safe and successful organ transplant.

Current U.S. practice of declaring brain death in many if not most cases remains heavily influenced by the 1981 recommendations of the President's commission that brain death must reflect the functional death of the "whole brain."[6] Lacking any strong data base to go on, some consultants felt uncertain that patients who fulfilled the criteria for brainstem death would never regain either autonomic functions or arousal. As a result, this country and most of Europe mandated a delay of several hours between the first and the ultimate clinical diagnosis of brain death. Furthermore, the commission encouraged technological affirmation of the ultimate step, especially when transplantation of still vital visceral organs was anticipated.

American medicine has now had 16 years to test these guidelines. Most who have strictly followed them during the interim have found them to be biologically overcomplicated, morally questionable, and practically undesirable. Recently, the New York State Health Commissioner convened 28 neurologists, critical care physicians, and experienced nurses to reconsider the state's regulations on brain death. Transplant surgeons were not included for ethical reasons. All conferees had participated frequently in diagnosing brain death on the basis of complete loss of brainstem function in the absence of confounding drugs. Also, however, every physician and critical care nurse at the meeting had experienced frustrating delays in withdrawing life-support procedures because of laboratory findings or fragments of cerebral electrical activity or a still partially open cerebral vascular bed. Also, all agreed that current requirements to confirm clinical diagnoses by potentially misleading technology create uncertainty for families, damage the morale of the critical care staff, increase institutional costs, and hamper the successful outcome of organ transplantation. Accordingly, based on available evidence, the convened experts recommended shortening the waiting period after the initial clinical diagnosis to 6 hours before proceeding with the final apneic test (Table 2.9). In exceptional cases, such as overwhelming, acute cerebral hemorrhages or direct, fatal injury to the brainstem (e.g., by physical trauma or gunshot), the time may be shortened to 2 hours, but brain death must be confirmed by technological procedures. The recommendations largely follow both the Minnesota and the British guidelines, except for shortening the ultimate waiting time in definitive cases.

Table 2.9. New York State Guidelines for Determination of Death by Irreversible Cessation of All Functions of the Entire Brain, Including the Brainstem (Age Greater than 1 Year)

Note: All 9 items must be answered YES to declare brain death.

	YES	NO
1. Have reasonable efforts been made to notify the patient's next-of-kin or other person closest to the individual that a determination of death based on cessation of brain function will soon be completed?	_____	_____
2. Is the cause of the coma known and sufficient to account for the irreversible loss of all brain function? *Note:* Coma of unknown cause (e.g., no evidence of brain trauma, stroke, hypoxic/hypotensive injury) requires a diligent search for the cause of coma before brain death determination. Similarly, the magnitude of the brain injury must be commensurate with irreversible cessation of all brain function.	_____	_____
3. Are CNS-depressant drugs, hypothermia ($<32°$ C) and hypotension (MAP <55 mm Hg) excluded as reversible causes of brain failure, and has any effect of neuromuscular blocking agents been excluded as contributing to the results of the neurological exam?	_____	_____

Note:

○ Specific levels of CNS depressants or neuromuscular blocking drugs are left to clinical judgment.

○ Brain death cannot be declared in the setting of hypothermia ($<32.2°$ C).

○ Shock, defined as a mean arterial blood pressure less than 55 mm Hg, prohibits the declaration of brain death. Pressors to support arterial blood pressure may be used (mean BP = [2 * BP diastolic + BP systolic]/3).

○ If levels of CNS depressants or neuromuscular blocking agents cannot be excluded as contributing to poor neurological status but cerebral angiography demonstrates there is no intracranial blood flow, then proceed to Item 4.

	YES	NO
4. Is all movement attributable to spinal cord function (i.e., there are no other spontaneous movements or motor responses)?	_____	_____

Continued on next page

Table 2.9—*Continued*

Note: All 9 items must be answered YES to declare brain death.

	YES	NO

Note: Posturing and shivering in the absence of neuromuscular blockade or learned movements in response to pain in any extremity or the head preclude the diagnosis of brain death. Deep tendon reflexes including stereotypic triple flexor responses in the lower extremities are compatible with brain death. These include spontaneous slow movements of an arm or leg. Bizarre movements of entirely spinal origin may sometimes occur in brain-dead patients. Also, coordinated movements can occur with shoulder elevation and adduction, back arching, and the appearance of intercostal muscle contraction without detectable tidal volumes. Finally, in a few patients, the "Lazarus sign" may develop when the ventilator is permanently disconnected; the head and torso may flex and for a few seconds rise from the bed with arms outstretched, then fall back and remain permanently flaccid in the supine position.

5. Absent cough and/or pharyngeal reflexes? _____ _____
6. Absent corneal and pupillary light responses? _____ _____
7. Absent caloric responses to iced water after visual examination of the tympanic membranes? _____ _____
8. Has an apnea test of a minimum five minutes duration showed no respiratory movements with a documented PCO_2 greater than 55 mm Hg with a pH of less than 7.40 or with a $PaCO_2$ that has risen more than 20 mm Hg above the level obtained immediately prior to the test. _____ _____

Note: Extreme caution should be exercised in the performance of the apnea test. The apnea test should be conducted only after all other evaluations are completed. An apnea test should be performed in such a manner as to minimize the risk of hypoxia or hypotension. Delivering a high concentration of oxygen to the airway (4 L/min) before and during the apnea test *reduces* the *risk* of hypoxic complications. If mean arterial blood pressure falls significantly during the performance of an apnea test, it should be discontinued with an arterial blood

	YES	NO

sample drawn to determine whether $PaCO_2$ has either risen above 55 mm Hg or increased by more than 20 mm Hg from the level immediately prior to the test. If so, this validates the clinical diagnosis of brain death.

9. Has one of the following four criteria (A, B, C, or D) been established?   _____ _____

    A.* Items 2 to 7 have been confirmed by two examinations separated by **at least six hours,** and Item 8, the apnea test, validates the clinical diagnosis of death.

    B. 1. Items 2 to 7 have been confirmed YES.   _____ _____
        2. An EEG shows electrocortical silence.
        3. A second exam **at least 2 hours** after the first confirms Items 2 to 7 as YES, and the apnea test validates the clinical diagnosis of death.

    C. 1. Items 2 to 7 have been confirmed as YES.   _____ _____
        2. No intracranial blood flow is evident.
        3. A second exam at least 2 hours after the first confirms Items 2 to 7 as YES, and the apnea test validates the clinical diagnosis of death.

    D. In the event that any of Items 2 to 7 cannot be   _____ _____ determined because the injury or condition prohibits evaluation (e.g., extensive facial injury precluding caloric testing), then the following criteria apply:
        1. ALL items which are assessable are YES.
        2. No intracranial blood flow is evident.
        3. A second exam **at least 2 hours** after the first confirms all assessable items as YES, and the apnea test validates the clinical diagnosis of death.

*In exceptional cases in which obvious traumatic-destructive damage has directly destroyed the lower brainstem, e.g., by obvious gunshot or similar physical mechanisms, brain death may be declared in two hours by clinical findings, the apneic test, and the presence of EEG silence or absent intracranial blood flow. Such procedures have generally been initiated in cases from which viable organs for transplantation may be obtained and either the family or the injured patient has given immediate or advance permission to take the organs for transplantation.

Source: Adapted from Truax BT, Munschauer FE. New York State Guidelines for Determination of Death (State University of New York at Buffalo).

Potential Misdiagnoses of Brain Death

Coma of Unknown Cause

Patients in deep coma who initially lack specific evidence of having either an intracranial structural lesion or a confirmed, potentially fatal metabolic illness must be considered to have drug-induced reversible coma until proved otherwise. Total flaccid paralysis, apnea, and even an isoelectric EEG can accompany reversible deep coma in patients with severe, self-induced drug poisoning. One must wait a day or so or obtain a negative blood toxic drug screen or cerebral blood flow measurement before making a certain diagnosis of brain death in such instances.

The Vegetative State

The *vegetative state* is a clinical condition lasting for at least several hours or days, in which the patient loses all recognizable evidence of self and surroundings, but sleep-wake cycles and other autonomic visceral functions remain. The term *persistent vegetative state* (PVS)[57] describes the behavior of a small number of survivors of severe brain trauma, asphyxia, or other causes who reawaken from coma within a few days or weeks but demonstrate thenceforth no detectable evidence of any cognitive awareness, that is, consciousness. Brief vegetative behavior can occur for a few days during the early recovery from moderately severe brain injury, but at that time is not incompatible with good cognitive recovery. The term *persistent vegetative state* has been arbitrarily applied to persons who remain vegetative for at least 1 month after initial brain injury. The diagnosis of PVS predicts a relatively poor prognosis, but not necessarily permanent vegetative unawareness. Permanent vegetative state is a probabilistic diagnosis anticipating the future. It requires a substantially longer time than the diagnosis of PVS and varies according to age and the nature of the brain damage.

Several authors have advanced the concept that the early vegetative state is tantamount to a state of chronic "cerebral death."[58] This cannot be accepted because a substantial fraction of patients who remain vegetative immediately after trauma or illness undergo fairly rapid subsequent recovery, and a few even become independent. It is true that adults who remain in the PVS 1 month after asphyxial coma have less than a 5 percent likelihood of making a subsequent good cognitive outcome and only a 15 percent probability of regaining any consciousness at all. By contrast, however, relatively young persons who appear vegetative at 1 month after traumatic brain injury have about a 25 percent chance of making a good recovery, with about half the overall group regaining at least some degree of cognition.[59] After 6 months, however, even those with traumatic injury retain less than a 5 percent chance of becoming independent, with perhaps another 10 percent remaining dependent but regaining some capacity for interpersonal interactions. Very few persons older than 40 years do as well. To epitomize, the likelihood that patients in a vegetative state will never regain consciousness is probabilistic, not absolute. The accurate diagnosis of brain death, by contrast, is absolute.

The Locked-in State

The *locked-in state* describes a condition caused by several different, reactively uncommon neurological disorders that sometimes resemble acute brain death to the untrained eye. The most likely disorder to be misdiagnosed consists of a reversible, acute cranial-body polyneuropathy that rapidly involves motor nerves extending from the oculomotor nerves down to those innervating the toes; the result can block all body movement.[60–63] Severe cases of this rare condition can paralyze the pupillary constrictors as well. Related in pathogenesis to the more common, immunologically related Guillain-Barré types of polyneuropathy, cranial-body neuropathy characteristically comes on rapidly after a banal respiratory or gastrointestinal illness. Within a matter of hours to a day or so, progressive paralysis spreads over the entire body and head. Breathing and swallowing functions tend to disappear at about the same time and require intubation and ventilatory substitution. The diagnosis has sometimes been confused with basilar artery insufficiency or encephalitis, but a careful analysis of the history and examination belies such interpretations. Once paralysis sets in, only the history, the electrophysiologically and electrically tested absence of peripheral motor nerve conduction, and the continued presence of a slow alpha and relatively normal wake-sleep EEG pattern reassure care givers that the totally de-efferented body contains a normally thinking brain. For as yet unexplained reasons, some such patients lose alpha blocking on the EEG and subsequently cannot recall the period of the acute illness.[60,61] In the absence of severe acute complications, however, most recover completely.

Several other causes of severe motor paralysis also may produce syndromes that at least partially resemble brain death but do not fulfill current guidelines.[64] These include acute ischemic strokes or hemorrhages that affect lower pontine and upper medullary structures, thereby leaving patients with quadriparesis, respiratory insufficiency, and sufficient damage to lower cranial nerve function to inhibit or prevent any means of verbal or gestural communication. Slightly more rostrally placed infarctions or myelinolytic lesions that destroy the descending corticospinal motor pathways as they course through the base of the pons spare slightly more function. They paralyze the extremities and lower cranial nerves but spare the oculomotor nerves as well as lower brainstem areas that initiate automatic breathing. Consciousness often is retained, both acutely and especially chronically. Many persons with either medullary or basis pontis lesions develop the ability to communicate by laboriously learning codes transmitted by eye movements. Clinical and ethical problems of long-term management abound.

Iatrogenic Problems

Professional caregivers in the past occasionally made errors in prematurely diagnosing brain death. The problem reflected carelessness more often than ignorance. Presently, premature, inappropriate declarations of brain death occur much less often but have not vanished. A more important problem in nonmetropolitan areas of the state of New York has been that general physicians have been reluctant to diagnose brain death and arrange transfer for organ transplantation because many extant protocols require technological confirmation or the consulting participation of a specialist. The New York State Health Department presently is making efforts to overcome such hesitation by establishing a check-off protocol of the necessary steps and providing direct instruction by experienced physicians to family practitioners.

The Value of Using a Nonfunctioning Brainstem as Diagnostic of Brain Death

The physiological practicalities of functional brain death do not necessarily imply the immediate, simultaneous death of the organ's many minifunctions.[49] Only the areas critical to survival and communication (i.e., brainstem functions) are tested in most standard clinical protocols. This fact has created ethical problems for some persons, especially nonphysiologists. The issues at hand were recently reviewed and thoughtfully discussed by Halevy and Brody.[65]

Pallis expresses the practical British view that brain death equates with death of the brainstem because the stem regulates nearly all of the body's vegetative-anatomical functions and activates the normal conscious state.[11] Indeed, the clinical criteria for brain death as applied in most of the industrial world are based entirely on the critical examination of brainstem function. Furthermore, as this chapter has emphasized, the accurate clinical diagnosis of brainstem death has always identified irreversible, lethal injury irrespective of the presence of spared functional remnants detected by electroencephalographic or brain arterial perfusion studies.

The argument in favor of the brainstem criteria has to be advanced biologically, not semantically. The brainstem is the ontogenetic predecessor of the thalamus and the cerebrum, as well as being the machine in humans that drives those more rostral structures during their conscious, functioning life. As the persistent vegetative state indicates, brainstem life without cerebral cognitive function is biologically possible so long as the body's external needs are met by care givers. All evidence indicates, however, that the cerebrum cannot survive for more than days or, rarely, weeks once the brainstem and hypothalamus no longer remain to serve its every autonomic, endocrine, and nutritional need. Once the brainstem functionally dies, there's no turning back—the brain will never regain its humanity. Nor can we expect medicine or society to bear the costs once the brain surrenders its vitality.

Continuing expensive treatment for a brain-dead body is a medical travesty that represents a deplorable consumption of the limited medical and social resources of the community. Moreover, the continued preservation of a body unable in any way to support its internal or external needs creates a situation that can be emotionally devastating for both loved ones and care givers. Unless physicians are as firm about diagnosing brain death as cardiac death, families inevitably will sustain impossible hopes, deplete their emotional and financial reserves, and prolong their grief until the unavoidable final event occurs.

The Opportunity for One Final Gift to Humanity

Surgical and accompanying immunologic skill has vastly improved the capacity to sustain the physiological integrity of visceral organs for transplantation. When the brain dies but bodily organs temporarily survive, the sooner the transfer can be carried out, the better is the chance for functional survival. The practical value is evident, but the principle has received too little publicly as a humanistic act. Advance wishes by persons (or their families) to have their bodily organs removed and donated so that others may live represent the last direct gift to humanity that any of us can make.

References

I am indebted to the Annie Laurie Aitken Charitable Trust for assistance in the studies leading to this summary review.

1. Mollaret P, Goulon M. Le coma depasse. *Rev Neurol* 1959;101:3–15; Morison RS. Death: Process or event? *Science* 1971;173:694–98.

2. Report of the Ad Hoc Committee of the Harvard Medical School. A definition of irreversible coma. *JAMA* 1968;205:337–40.

3. Mohandas A, Chou SN. Brain death—a clinical and pathological study. *J Neurosurg* 1971;35:211–18.

4. Conference of Royal Medical Colleges and Their Faculties in the UK. Diagnosis of brain death. *Br Med J* 1976;2:1187–88.

5. Guidelines for the determination of death. Report of the medical consultants on the diagnosis of death to the President's Commission for the Study of Ethical Problems in Medicine and Biomedical and Behavioral Research. *JAMA* 1981;246:2184–86.

6. President's Commission for the Study of Ethical Problems in Medicine and Biomedical and Behavioral Research. *Defining Death: A Report on the Medical, Legal and Ethical Issues in the Determination of Death.* Washington, D.C.: Government Printing Office, 1981.

7. American Academy of Neurology. Practice parameters for determining brain death in adults (summary statement). *Neurology* 1995;45:1012–14.

8. Wijdicks EFM. Determining brain death in adults. *Neurology* 1995;45:1003–11.

9. Pallis C. ABC of brain stem death: The arguments about the EEG. *Br Med J* 1983;286:284–87.

10. Plum F, Posner JB. *The Diagnosis of Stupor and Coma.* 3d ed., revised. Philadelphia: FA Davis, 1983, 320.

11. Pallis C. Brainstem death. In: Braakman R (ed). *Handbook of Clinical Neurology,* 13(57): *Head Injury.* New York: Elsevier Science Publishers, 1990, 483.

12. Walker AE. Pathology of brain death. *Ann NY Acad Sci* 1978;315:272–80.

13. Hughes JR. Limitations of the EEG in coma and brain death. *Ann NY Acad Sci* 1978;315:121–36.

14. Silverman D, Masland RL, Saunders MG, Schwab RS. Irreversible coma associated with electrocerebral silence. *Neurology* 1970;20:525–33.

15. Walker AE, and collaborators. An appraisal of the criteria of cerebral death. *JAMA* 1977;237:982–86.

16. Bennett DR. The EEG in determination of brain death. *Ann NY Acad Sci* 1978;315:110–20.

17. Buchner H, Schuchardt V. Reliability of the electroencephalogram in the diagnosis of brain death. *Eur Neurol* 1990;30:138–45.

18. Ashwal S, Schneider S. Failure of electroencephalography to diagnose brain death in comatose children. *Ann Neurol* 1979;6:512–17.

19. Grigg MM, Kelly MA, Celesia GG, Ghobrial MW, Ross ER. Electroencephalographic activity after brain death. *Arch Neurol* 1987;44:948–54.

20. Ferbert A, Buchner H, Ringelstein EB, Hacke W. Isolated brain stem death: Case report with demonstration of preserved visual evoked potential (VEPs). *Electroencephalogr Clin Neurophysiol* 1986;65:157–60.

21. Ogata J, Imakita M, Yutani C, Miyamoto S, Kikuchi H. Primary brain stem death: A clinico-pathological study. *J Neurol Neurosurg Psychiatry* 1988;51:646–50.

22. Goldie WD, Chappa KH, Young RR, Brooks EB. Brain stem auditory and short latency somatosensory evoked potential in brain death. *Neurology* 1981;31: 248–56.

23. Chatrian GE. Electrophysiologic evaluation of brain death. In: MJ Aminoff (ed). *Electrodiagnosis in Clinical Neurology*. New York: Churchill Livingstone, 1992, 737–94.

24. Houlden DA, Li C, Schwartz ML, Katic M. Median nerve somatosensory evoked potentials and the Glasgow coma scale as predictors of outcomes in comatose patients with head injuries. *Neurosurgery* 1990;27:701–7.

25. Firsching S, Wilhelms S, Csescei G. Pyramidal tract function during onset of brain death. *Electroencephalogr Clin Neurophysiol* 1992;84:321–24.

26. Alvarez LA, Lipton RB, Hirschfeld A, Salamon O, Lantos G. Brain death determination by angiography in the setting of a skull defect. *Arch Neurol* 1988; 45:225–27.

27. McMenamin JB, Volpe JJ. Doppler ultrasonography in the determination of neonatal brain death. *Ann Neurol* 1983;14:302–7.

28. Kirkham FJ, Levin SD, Padayachee TS, Kyme MC. Transcranial pulsed Doppler ultrasound findings in brain stem death. *J Neurol Neurosurg Psychiatry* 1987;50:1504–13.

29. Medlock MD, Hanigan WC, Cruse RP. Dissociation of cerebral blood flow, glucose metabolism and electrical activity in pediatric brain death. *J Neurosurg* 1993;79:752–55.

30. Greitz T, Gordon E, Kolmodin G, Widen L. Aortocranial and carotid angiography in determination of brain death. *Neuroradiology* 1973;5:13–19.

31. Kosteljanetz M, Ohrstrom JK, Skodt S, Teglbjaerg PS. Clinical brain death with preserved cerebral arterial circulation. *Acta Neurol Scand* 1988;78:418–21.

32. Nau R, Prange HW, Klingelhofer J, et al. Results of four technical investigations in fifty clinically brain dead patients. *Intensive Care Med* 1992;18:82–88.

33. Laurin NR, Driedger AA, Hurwitz GA, Mattar AG, et al. Cerebral perfusion imaging with technetium-99m HM-PAO in brain death and severe central nervous system injury. *J Nucl Med* 1989;30:1627–35.

34. Larar GN, Nagel JS. Technetium-99m-HMPAO cerebral perfusion scintigraphy: Considerations for timely brain death declaration. *J Nucl Med* 1992;33:2209–13.

35. Schlake HP, Bottger IG, Grotemeyer KH, Husstedt IW, Brandau W, Schober O. Determination of cerebral perfusion by means of planar brain scintigraphy and ⁹⁹ᵐTc-HMPAO in brain death, persistent vegetative state and severe coma. *Intensive Care Med* 1992;18:76–81.

36. De la Riva A, Gonzalez FM, Llamas-Elvira JM, Latre JM, et al. Diagnosis of brain death: Superiority of perfusion studies with ⁹⁹Tcᵐ-HMPAO over conventional radionuclide cerebral angiography. *Br J Radiol* 1992;65:289–94.

37. Schauwecker DS. Tc-99m HMPAO brain survival study reveals flow to the cerebrum but none to the cerebellum. *Clin Nucl Med* 1992;17:984–85.

38. Aasled R, Markwalder TM, Nornes H. Noninvasive transcranial Doppler ultrasound recording of flow velocity in basal cerebral arteries. *J Neurosurg* 1982;57:769–74.

39. Hassler W, Steinmetz H, Gawlowski J. Transcranial Doppler ultrasonography in raised intracranial pressure and in intracranial circulatory arrest. *J Neurosurg* 1988;68:745–51.

40. Ropper AH, Kehne SM, Wechsler L. Transcranial Doppler in brain death. *Neurology* 1987;37:1733–35.

41. Petty GW, Mohr JP, Pedley TA, et al. The role of transcranial Doppler in confirming brain death: Sensitivity, specificity and suggestions for performance and interpretation. *Neurology* 1990;40:300–303.

42. Feri M, Ralli L, Felici M, Vanni D, et al. Transcranial Doppler and brain death diagnosis. *Crit Care Med* 1994;22:1120–26.

43. Lewis RR, Beasley MG, Gosling RG, Padayachee TS, et al. Investigation of brain death with Doppler shift ultrasound. *J R Soc Med* 1983;76:308.

44. Ashwal S, Schneider S. Brain death in infants and children. In: Berg BO (ed). *Neurologic Aspects of Pediatrics.* Stoneham, Mass.: Butterworth-Heinemann, 1992, 639–53.

45. Megia RE, Pollack MM. Variability in brain death determination practices in children. *JAMA* 1995;274:550–53.

46. Ivan LP. Spinal reflexes in cerebral death. *Neurology* 1973;23:650–52.

47. Heytens L, Verlooy J, Gheuens J, Bossaert L. Lazarus sign and extensor posturing in a brain dead patient. *J Neurosurg* 1989;71:449–51.

48. Ropper AH. Unusual spontaneous movements in brain dead patients. *Neurology* 1984;34:1089–92.

49. Morison RS. Death: Process or event? *Science* 1971;173:694–98.

50. Hung TP, Chen ST. Prognosis of deeply comatose patients on ventilators. *J Neurol Neurosurg Psychiatry* 1995;58:75–80.

51. Fabro F. Letter to editor. *N Engl J Med* 1982;306:1361.

52. Grenvik A, Powner DJ, Snyder JV, et al. Cessation of therapy in terminal illness and brain death. *Crit Care Med* 1978;6:284–91.

53. Field DR, Gates EA, Creasy RK, et al. Maternal brain death during pregnancy: Medical and ethical issues. *JAMA* 1988;260:816–22.

54. Parisi JE, Kim RC, Collins GH, Hilfinger MF. Brain death with prolonged somatic survival. *N Engl J Med* 1982;306:14–16.

55. Klein RL. Letter to editor. *N Engl J Med* 1982;306:1362.

56. Rowland TW, Donnelly JH, Jackson AH, et al. Brain death in the pediatric intensive care unit: A clinical definition. *Am J Dis Child* 1983;137:547–50.

57. Jennett B, Plum F. Persistent vegetative state after brain damage: A syndrome in search of a name. *Lancet* 1972;1:734–37.

58. Truog RD, Fackler JC. Rethinking brain death. *Crit Care Med* 1992;20: 1705–13.

59. The Multi-Society Task Force on PVS. Medical aspects of the persistent vegetative state. *N Engl J Med* 1994;330:1499–1508, 1572–79.

60. Carroll WM, Mastaglia FL. "Locked-in coma" in postinfective polyneuropathy. *Arch Neurol* 1979;36:46–47.

61. Kotsoris H, Schleifer L, Menken M, Plum F. Total locked-in state resembling brain death in polyneuropathy. *Ann Neurol* 1984;16:150.

62. Drury I, Westmoreland BF, Sharbrough FW. Fulminant demyelinating polyradiculopathy resembling brain death. *Electroencephalogr Clin Neurophysiol* 1987;67:42–43.

63. Marti-Masso JF, Suarez J, Lopez de Munain A, Carrera N. Clinical signs of brain death simulated by Guillain-Barré syndrome. *J Neurol Sci* 1993;120:115–17.

64. Plum F, Posner JB. *Diagnosis of Stupor and Coma.* Philadelphia: FA Davis, 1966, 93.

65. Halevy A, Brody B. Brain death: Reconciling definitions, criteria and tests. *Ann Intern Med* 1993;119:519–25.

II

The Interface between Philosophy and the Clinic

As MARTIN PERNICK points out in Chapter 1, controversy has surrounded the determination of death throughout history. The chapters in this part demonstrate how quickly issues that were once uncontroversial, because they were either unimportant or unrecognized, can suddenly become the object of bitter debate.

To be sure, controversy surrounded brain death from the beginning. Some persons rejected it as an unacceptable devaluation of human life for crass utilitarian reasons. Others criticized its philosophical underpinnings, arguing that the notion of higher-brain death—that is, the loss of consciousness and cognition—was a more coherent concept. But, as brain death won the day through widespread legal recognition, professional endorsement, and public acceptance and as critics (liberal and conservative) were marginalized, inherent flaws in the formulation of brain death remained undiscovered or were ignored as unimportant by supporters and critics alike.

From the start, the criterion for whole-brain death was functional rather than anatomic. What mattered was the loss of identified functions of the brain, not activity in individual cells or clusters of cells. Further, in narratives on this new definition of death, theorists on the President's commission and elsewhere contended that only integrative function mattered. But these theorists, such as James Bernat, who writes here, did not specify a hierarchy among the integrated functions. And the law simply ignored any distinction between functions, implying that all brain functions must be lost for a person to be declared dead. Loss of *all* brain functions is what was sold to the American public.

In 1993 Baruch Brody and his colleague Amir Halevy documented that many patients diagnosed as brain dead retain not only some brain functions, but truly integrative function as well. In Chapter 3 Baruch Brody presents the dilemma and offers a radical analysis and solution. Death, he says, is a fuzzy set; there is no clear border between life and death. Rather than fruitlessly trying to resolve the seeming contradiction between whole-brain criteria and definition (as Bernat and Pallis attempt to do), he suggests uncoupling the determination of death from the various legal and social consequences usually associated with it, such as burial, unilateral treatment termination, and removal of organs. Norman Fost makes a similar proposal in Chapter 9. Bernat and Pallis disagree. Each seeks to maintain the status quo, Bernat by further modifying the criteria of death and Pallis by sticking to the notion of brainstem death.

Bernat has steadily modified his 1981 position. For example, while consciousness was not initially in his list of integrative functions, he has subsequently added it. In Chapter 4 he makes a further modification by distinguishing between relevant and irrelevant integrative functions in order to reject Brody's contention that persisting neurohormonal function (the production of argenine vasopressin) is, indeed, an important integrative function. Bernat argues that this neurohormonal function is not "critical" in the sense that it is less essential than other integrative functions to the continued life and health of the organism and that it is not "clinical" in that it is "not detectable on ordinary bedside neurological examination." Time will tell whether Bernat's introduction of the modifiers *critical* and *clinical* does the philosophic work of resolving the apparent contradiction between whole-brain criteria and definition.

In Chapter 5 Pallis takes a simpler tack. The functions identified by Brody are not functions of the brainstem. They do not have to be ignored or rationalized. They are simply irrelevant. Pallis gives a conceptual justification for his brainstem criterion—that it is embedded in a coherent sociohistorical matrix that recognizes both loss of consciousness and loss of the ability to breathe spontaneously as the functions that distinguish a dead from a living human being.

Joanne Lynn and Ronald Cranford, in Chapter 6, raise other "perplexing" issues, long ignored (or "quiet," as they say) because they had no real practical consequences: the time of death, the appropriate standard of proof that death criteria have been fulfilled, and the attendant question of what is meant by *irreversibility*. All definitions and criteria of death and, indeed, all death statutes stipulate that the loss of function, neurological or cardiovascular, must be "irreversible." Lynn and Cranford point out with relentless logic that there are four important times relating to a declaration of death: when the function is lost, when it is found to be lost, when the loss is irreversible, and, finally, when the loss is known to be irreversible. They also point out that statutory definitions of death give two criteria (cardiorespiratory and neurological) that stand independently.

As Lynn and Cranford point out, forcing clarity on these complicated and potentially divisive issues would not have been useful two decades ago because no practical consequences hung in the balance until the advent and public discussion of non-heart-beating cadaver organ procurement protocols in the early 1990s. NHBC protocols force the issue by attempting to push the declaration of death back as far as possible in the Lynn/Cranford time line. In doing so they raise inescapable choices about the precision with which we know the loss or function is irreversible and what we mean by irreversible in the first place—that is, does it mean that we cannot reverse the loss or choose not to reverse it?

The chapters in these sections raise important but as yet unanswered questions about public perception and policy. *Irreversible* loss of *all* brain functions was an essential part of the package that facilitated the American public's acceptance of a new, neurologically based definition of death. How can (or should) the public be told that (1) the line between life and death may be "fuzzy" even to physicians; (2) only some brain functions are important while others can be ignored; (3) the notion of whole-brain death should be abandoned in favor of brainstem death; or (4) while there is no real scholarly consensus about how to set the time of death, it is being defined to facilitate the maximum procurement of organs for transplantation?

3

How Much of the Brain Must Be Dead?

Baruch A. Brody, Ph.D.

THE PROPONENTS OF THE standard criterion of brain death (death occurs at that point in time when there is an irreversible cessation of functioning of the entire brain) encounter difficulties in reconciling it with the definition (irreversible loss of integrative functioning) and the clinical tests (no stem reflexes, no respiratory efforts, no responsiveness) normally associated with that criterion. The solution to this problem is neither to defend the standard criterion by modifying the tests or the definition nor to look for another criterion based on another definition and to employ other tests that confirm the satisfaction of that criterion. Rather, one should recognize that (1) criteria of death postulate a particular point as an answer to a series of questions, (2) death is a process rather than an event that occurs at a particular point in time, and (3) the answers to these different questions are to be found at different points in the process, so that no one point can be picked as the moment of death. Rather than seeking a point in the process to serve as the criterion of death and as an answer to these questions, one should choose different points in the process as appropriate answers to the different questions.

Halevy and I made these arguments in a 1993 paper.[1] This chapter expands on that position. In the first section, "Restating the Problem,"

I briefly review our evidence of the difficulties faced in reconciling the tests, the criterion, and the underlying definition. Under "Possible Responses," I amplify our criticisms of several suggestions that have been made in response to these difficulties, including the suggestion that advances in neurology might provide better tests that would resolve the difficulties. In the final section, "The Halevy-Brody Response," I explain our theory and use it to evaluate the current debate about procuring organs from anencephalics.

First, however, I want to make it clear that part of the intellectual background to our 1993 paper is the acceptance of the fundamental insight of fuzzy logic, namely, that the world does not easily divide itself into sets and their complements. Death and its complementary property life determine mutually exclusive but not jointly exhaustive sets. Although no organism can fully belong to both sets, organisms can be in many conditions (the very conditions that have created the debates about death) during which they do not fully belong to either. That is why you cannot find the answers to the questions by finding the right moment in the process to serve as the moment for belonging to the set of the dead. Death is a fuzzy set.

Restating the Problem

To understand the difficulties Halevy and I raised, one needs to remember that the whole-brain criterion of death, with its associated clinical tests, is put forward on the basis of a definition that provides its rationale. According to the definition, the organism is alive only when its functioning is integrated. Given that both the cortex and the stem play central roles in the integration of the functioning of the organism, the organism dies only when all of these integrative functions of all of the parts of the brain irreversibly cease. This is the criterion of death. The clinical tests (such as those for responsiveness/voluntary movements and apnea) test for the presence of these integrative functions.

Both the cortical criterion of death and the cardiorespiratory criterion of death are also based upon definitions that provide their rationales. According to the cortical definition, life requires the functioning of a person. Given that the cortex is the physiological location for functions (such as consciousness, thought, and feeling) that are essential for the existence of a person, death occurs when the cortex irreversibly loses the capacity for those functions. According to the cardiorespiratory definition, the organism is alive only when the vital "bodily fluids"—air and blood—continue to flow through the organism. Given that this flow requires respiration and circulation, the organism dies when those two functions cease.

For each of these definitions, there are, of course, problems either with the definition or with the relation between the definition and its associated criterion. Parts of the body other than the brain help integrate the organism's functioning, so why does the first definition lead to the criterion of the cessation of the integrative functions of only the brain? Is it sufficient for death, as the second definition maintains, that the person has stopped functioning, or must other functions also cease before death has occurred? If the flow of the "vital fluids" is maintained artificially, is the organism still alive according to the third definition, especially if the organism is conscious and capable of responding and moving spontaneously? I shall return to aspects of these problems below. What I want to note for now is that adherents of these three competing criteria have recognized the importance of there being justifying definitions for the criteria; without such a definition, all that you have is an arbitrarily chosen criterion. This point is central for understanding the difficulties raised in our paper.

Halevy and I called attention to the fact that there are organisms who satisfy all of the standard clinical tests for whole-brain death but who have not lost all of the integrative functions of the brain. The most important example is neurohormonal regulation. The presence of this residual neurohormonal regulation in a significant percentage of organisms who satisfy the usual tests for brain death and whose respiration and circulation are being maintained artificially (usually to allow for the possibility of organ donation) is well documented. Most crucially, this regulation is just as much and as important an example of the integrative functioning of the brain as is the brain's control of respiration or of responsive movements. Given the definition behind the whole-brain criterion, this functioning of the brain should have to cease before the criterion is really met. As the usual tests do not ensure this, they are inadequate as tests for the satisfaction of the criterion *given the definition that supposedly justifies that criterion.*

In the article in the *Annals of Internal Medicine,* Halevy and I also call attention to two other functions of the brain that do not necessarily cease when the normal clinical tests are met: (1) continued functioning of the auditory pathways as evidenced by brainstem evoked potentials and (2) continued cortical functioning as evidenced by EEG readings. I would today put less emphasis on them. To begin with, the latter is present only in very special cases and the extent of the former is not clearly known. Second, and more important, while they constitute brain functions, it is not clear that either integrates the functioning of the entire organism. If not, then both should be irrelevant to the death of the organism. According to the definition that supposedly justifies the whole-brain criterion, only the integrative functioning of the brain must irreversibly cease before the organism dies, so these functions may not count.

Halevy and I emphasized these other two functions to illustrate another problem. Patients who meet the normal clinical tests for brain death may not satisfy the criterion used by the President's commission and embodied in the law, the "irreversible cessation of all functions of the brain." These examples are very relevant to illustrate the dissonance between the clinical tests and that legal criterion. The point I am making here is that they may not be relevant to illustrating the dissonance between the clinical tests and the whole-brain criterion justified by the associated definition, a criterion that refers only to the cessation of *integrative* functions.

In short, our difficulty may be stated as follows: (1) the true whole-brain criterion of death is that the organism dies when all of the integrative functioning of the entire brain ceases; (2) when the normal clinical tests are met, at least one form of integrative functioning of the brain, neurohormonal regulation, has often not ceased, and there may be other forms of integrative functioning that have not ceased; (3) there is, therefore, an incongruity between the normal clinical tests and the whole-brain criterion as understood in light of the definition that justifies it.

Possible Responses

Given the above argument, one can identify a series of possible responses: (1) The incongruity between tests and criterion exists, but we should not worry about it because it occurs in only a few cases or because it makes no difference, as current practice works well. (2) These residual functions are either not integrative functioning or not integrative functioning of the right type, so there is really no incongruity between tests and criterion. (3) There is an incongruity between tests and criterion which cannot be ignored, and we should resolve it by improving the tests employed through advances in neurology. (4) There is an incongruity between the clinical tests and the criterion which cannot be ignored, and we should resolve it by adopting some other criterion based on some other justifying definition. (5) The incongruity is indicative of a fundamental problem that is best resolved by giving up on the search for a single criterion of death that answers all of the questions that a criterion of death is traditionally understood as answering. This last response is the conclusion Halevy and I adopted.

Should we worry about the incongruity, since it occurs in only a few cases? The claim that it occurs in only a few cases is mistaken. If, of course, organisms are declared dead on the basis of the usual tests and removed from life support, neurohormonal regulation (and many other functions of the organism) will soon cease. But that may show only that taking dependent living organisms off life support soon produces death. The crucial question about the extent of the incongruity is how often these functions are still occurring when the usual tests are first met and before the organism is taken off life support. The data cited in our 1993 paper show that this occurs in a significant percentage of cases.

Should we worry about the incongruity even if it occurs in many cases, since the use of the current tests works well? It all depends upon what you mean by "the tests work well." They certainly have enabled the organ procurement programs to harvest a significant number of additional organs by declaring death on the basis of the tests without waiting for neurohormonal regulation to cease. They also have enabled physicians to discontinue life support in many cases where the families insisted on doing everything so long as death had not occurred. The need to respect that family preference stops when death is pronounced on the basis of the current tests, even when neurohormonal regulation has not ceased. But does that mean that the tests have worked well? Not if the organisms in question still are alive, as they are according to the current criterion when regulation has not yet ceased. If they are still alive, the use of the current tests has in many cases resulted in killings to harvest organs and in discontinuing life support by misleading families about when death has occurred. It is hard to understand why that should be described as working well. I suggest below that the claim that the current tests work well can be reconstructed to make some sense once one drops, as Halevy and I have advocated, the search for a criterion of death. But until one does so, the incongruity means that the current tests are not working well.

Are the residual functions integrative functions or integrative functions of the right type? Bernat has suggested that they are not:

However, in some cases, a critical number of neurons have been destroyed but a few continue to function in isolation. For example, some unequivocally whole-brain-dead patients continue to manifest rudimentary but recordable electroencephalographic activity or hypothalamic neuroendocrine activity sufficient to prevent diabetes insipidus. Because these isolated nests of independently operating neurons no longer contribute critically to the functions of the organism as a whole, their continued activity remains consistent with the whole-brain criterion of death.[2] (569)

I am not convinced by this objection. Although it is true that the residual cortical activity is separated from the functioning of the organism as a whole and is in that sense an isolated nest of operating neurons, this is just not true of the neurohormonal regulation that, by definition, is integrated with the functioning of the rest of the organism. Another residual functioning that Bernat does not mention, intact auditory pathways, is harder to classify, although it is certainly not a clear-cut example of purely isolated nests of operating neurons. That is why I said above that, for the purposes of this chapter, the residual neurohormonal functioning deserves the most attention. It is without any doubt residual integrative functioning of the very sort that is supposed to mean that the patient is still alive, according to the justifying definition that lies behind the whole-brain criterion of death. This last point also serves as a criticism of Pallis's recent response to our argument:

What is the *philosophical* significance, for instance, of a given TSH level detected a specified number of hours after a clinical diagnosis of brain death? . . . A "concept" which "dares not speak its name" in fact often lurks behind most such "challenges." It is that death on neurological grounds should mean but one thing: the irreversible loss of function of the totality of the intracranial contents . . . This is advanced without specification of the functions, the loss of which would demarcate the living from the dead. This approach hardly warrants being described as a "philosophical" concept of death.[3] (21)

The relevant functions are, of course, the brain's integrative functions, and the level of thyroid-stimulating hormone (TSH) is evidence that some of them are still intact. None of this requires, of course, that all of the intracranial contents should have stopped functioning.

I confess that I am surprised by Dr. Bernat's response. After all, his

1981 paper with Culver and Gert is a landmark paper precisely because it clarified for the first time the justifying definition of continued integrative functioning ("functioning of the organism as a whole") as lying behind the whole-brain criterion.[4] In that paper, the first example of the functioning of the organism as a whole is neuroendocrine control (390). Why, then, does Bernat now describe it as a purely isolated nest of operating neurons?

Isn't the obvious response to modify the clinical tests so that the criterion of the irreversible cessation of the integrative functioning of the entire brain is satisfied when the new set of tests is met? Couldn't we test for neurohormonal regulation and (if we were concerned about it as integrative functioning) for intact auditory and visual pathways? In fact, the use of such tests has been suggested by various authors.[5,6] There is, however, a major problem, which Halevy and I noted, with this suggestion. Data from the transplant community,[7] which has studied this question to determine whether hormone replacement should be part of the management of potential donors, suggest that hormonal levels due to residual neurohormonal functioning may remain intact for more than 72 hours. These are some of the best data available. They include patients where angiography indicated a complete cessation of intracranial blood flow, indicating the presence of a dual blood supply.

Consequently, the adoption of these new tests would mean a serious challenge to the transplant community in maintaining both the viability of organs and the willingness of families to donate. There could be a significant loss of organs. Moreover, putting aside the transplantation setting, maintaining organisms on life support until the new tests are met, when the families insist that everything be done until death occurs, can be very expensive, so we should not rush to add additional tests.

There is a crucial difference between the criticism of this response and the criticism of the other responses. The problem with the first three responses is that they fail on intellectual grounds. The justification for the brain-death criterion means that the functions which remain and are the source of the dissonance cannot be disregarded if one wants to maintain intellectual honesty. The problem with the fourth response is that it fails on practical grounds. We want to be able to harvest organs and to disconnect life support unilaterally long before the suggested new tests are satisfied. Some might suggest that this is irrelevant. If we want theoretical soundness, we must pay the practical prices. One of the merits of the proposal Halevy and I put forward is that it offers the opportunity to be both theoretically sound and practical. I will return to this point below.

Perhaps the best response is to modify the criterion of death and the justifying definition. Three versions of this response are found in the literature: (1) Adopt as the criterion of death the permanent cessation of respiratory activity or the permanent cessation of cardiac as well as respiratory activity (the two options most advocated in the debate in the Orthodox Jewish community about brain death and organ transplantation).[8] (2) Adopt as the criterion of death the permanent cessation of respiratory activity and of consciousness (Pallis's brainstem criterion).[3] (3) Adopt as the criterion of death the permanent cessation of consciousness (the higher-brain criterion).

There is more to be said about each of these suggestions than is possible in this chapter, so I will confine myself to just a few observations. (1) The adoption of the view that death requires the irreversible cessation of both cardiac and respiratory functioning may mean a significant and expensive prolongation of the dying process as well as the end of organ transplantation as we know it. A strong futility policy might avoid the former, while a modification of the Pittsburgh protocol might preserve some transplantation.[9] Unless we have powerful intellectual reasons for preserving that criterion, other than adherence to the traditional definition, it is a poor suggestion on practical grounds. (2) Neither a purely respiratory criterion nor a combined respiratory/consciousness criterion lends itself to a justifying definition. The former criterion involves only one of the traditional vital "bodily fluids," and it is hard to see why one is to be preferred to the other. The latter criterion comes from two very different definitions, and it is hard to see why the two criteria should be combined. Pallis points out quite correctly that they are "embedded in coherent historical and cultural matrices" (21). However, the fact that each is embedded in a coherent matrix does not ensure that their combination is embedded in a coherent matrix. (3) The suggestion that we adopt a higher-brain criterion for the death of the person, based upon the definition that the person dies when the cognitive and affective functioning required to be a person ceases, makes a lot of sense when discussing the death of the person. But are we only looking for an account of the death of the person? Perhaps we really want an account that encompasses the death of the full organism? We certainly seem to want that type of account before burial or cremation.

The Halevy-Brody Response

Our response to the incongruity begins by recognizing that the death of the organism is a process rather than an event. Consider the organism that suffers damage to its brain so that it is no longer conscious and can no longer engage in responsive or voluntary movements. At some later stage, it loses the capacity to breathe on its own so that its respiration must be supported artificially. At a later stage, its capacity to regulate hormonal levels stops. Somewhere during this time period, its auditory pathways stop functioning. Finally, its heart stops beating. Is it really meaningful to suppose that the organism died at some specific point in this process? Isn't it more reasonable to say that the search for a criterion of death (a specific moment) made sense when these points were always close in time to each other because medicine lacked the capacity to protect some of the functions when the others had stopped, but no longer makes sense today when medicine can, and sometimes has good reasons to, keep some of the functions going for longer periods? Isn't it more reasonable to say that the organism was fully alive before the chain of events began, is fully dead by the end of the chain of events, and is neither during the process. Fuzzy logic enables us to say that in a precise fashion.

But don't we have to identify a specific point of time at which the organism died? Aren't there important questions which need to be answered and can only be answered by identifying the precise point in the process at which the organism died? These questions include when life support can unilaterally (without patient or surrogate concurrence) be withdrawn, when organs can be harvested, and when the organism can be buried or cremated. Perhaps not. While traditionally it has been thought that the way to answer these questions is to find that precise moment of death, perhaps that is the mistake. Perhaps these questions need to be examined and answered each on its own, with the answer to one question (some point in the process) not necessarily being the answer to the other questions. That is the heart of Halevy's and my proposal.

In our paper, we suggested that life support could in these cases be unilaterally withdrawn when the organism no longer composes a person because the cortex no longer functions. We emphasized that allowing for this unilateral withdrawal would constitute an appropriate stewardship of social resources. Elsewhere, I have argued that even those moral and religious traditions that place great emphasis on the value of the life of human organisms can accept such appeals to stewardship.[10] Notice, by the way, that such an argument would not apply to those *rare* cases where the resources of the patient or family paid for the full costs of the continued care.

In our paper, Halevy and I suggested that organs could be harvested at that stage in the process after the loss of cortical functioning when the organism can no longer breathe on its own. This, of course, corresponds to current practice. We defended it, however, not by adopting some criterion of death justified by some definition of death. Instead, we argued for it on the grounds that it preserves the proper balance between trying to maximize the supply of organs to save lives and trying to preserve public support for organ transplantation by not harvesting organs in cases that would be socially unacceptable.

This approach offers, I believe, a basis for evaluating AMA approval—later withdrawn—of harvesting organs from still-breathing anencephalics,[11] allowing for a reasoned consideration of their proposal while rejecting their justification of it. The AMA continues to accept the current criterion of death, with its implication that such anencephalics are still alive. They also recognize that harvesting organs means, on their own assumptions, killing the anencephalic organism, although they avoid using that word, preferring to talk instead about "sacrificing" it. To justify their conclusion, they argue that anencephalics, who have never and who never will experience consciousness, can be killed because they have no interest in being alive and there are no compelling social interests in preserving their life. This argument succeeds only if one is willing to change deontological constraints ("thou shall not kill living human organisms") into teleological rules ("killing human organisms is wrong when their interests or social interests are harmed"). The implications of this are very disturbing.

I respectfully suggest that the Council on Ethical and Judicial Affairs adopted this change without even arguing for it because the council, following much of the recent bioethical literature, does not understand deontological constraints. Things would be very different if they argued that anencephalics are in that class of in-between organisms that are neither fully alive nor fully dead. Then, they might argue that the deontological constraints do not apply to them and that we should settle the question by balancing the benefits of additional organs (needed, e.g., by other newborns with hypoplastic left hearts) against the risks to public acceptance of organ procurement if the public does not see anencephalics as being in this in-between category. That, I submit, could be the basis for a reasoned discussion of the AMA proposal, one following the framework presented in our paper.

There is, however, one further complication that must, I now believe, be taken into account. In our article and in the analysis just presented, the assumption is that the deontological constraint against killing human organisms applies only to those who are fully alive; once the organism is in the in-between range, we need only consider the policy trade-off. But is that assumption necessarily true? What happens to deontological constraints in a world of fuzzy sets? This additional issue will require a reasoned discussion, although the contours of the discussion are at the moment quite unclear.

What about burying or cremating the organism? Here, we suggested, maximum leeway could be given to respecting family sentiments by waiting for asystole, which usually occurs soon after all support ends. We can adopt that approach, saying that, on the basis of the traditional definition, the organism is fully dead only at that point, because that does not require us to wait for asystole before withdrawing life support unilaterally or harvesting organs.

In conclusion, then, our response answers the three questions in ways that are both theoretically defensible and practically useful. It is able to do so only because it does not answer them by adopting a consonant definition, criterion, and test of death. The dissonance we identified makes that impossible in a world that also needs to harvest organs and control health care expenditures. It is able to do so, instead, because it recognizes the implications of the fact that death is a process in a world governed by fuzzy logic.

References

1. Halevy A, Brody B. Brain death: Reconciling definitions, criteria, and tests. *Ann Intern Med* 1993;119:519–25.

2. Bernat JL. Brain death occurs only with destruction of the cerebral hemispheres and the brain stem. *Arch Neurol* 1992;49:569–70.

3. Pallis C. Further thoughts on brainstem death. *Anaesth Intensive Care* 1995; 23:20–23.

4. Bernat JL, Culver CM, Gert B. On the criterion and definition of death. *Ann Intern Med* 1981;94:389–94.

5. Barelli A, Della Corte F, Calimici R, et al. Do brainstem auditory evoked potentials detect the actual cessation of cerebral functions in brain dead patients? *Crit Care Med* 1990;18:332–33.

6. Imberti R, Filisetti P, Preseglio I, et al. Confirmation of brain death utilizing tyrotropin-releasing hormone stimulation test. *Neurosurgery* 1990;27:167.

7. Gramm HJ, Meinhold H, Bichel U, et al. Acute endocrine failure after brain death. *Transplantation* 1992;54:851–57.

8. Bleich JD. *Time of Death in Jewish Law.* New York: Z Berman, 1991.

9. Arnold RM, Youngner SJ. The dead donor rule: Should we stretch it, bend it, or abandon it? *Kennedy Inst Ethics J* 1993;2:263–78.

10. Brody BA. The economics of the law of rodef. *Svara* 1990;1:67–69.

11. Council on Ethical and Judicial Affairs. The use of anencephalic neonates as organ donors. *JAMA* 1995;273:1614–18.

4

Refinements in the Definition and Criterion of Death

James L. Bernat, M.D.

DESPITE THE GENERAL acceptance of the concept of brain death in the Western world, the subject of the definition and criterion of death continues to provoke important scholarly debate. As I have summarized recently, those accepting the validity of declaring human death based on neurological grounds generally can be divided into the "whole-brain," "higher-brain," and "brainstem" theorists.[1] Most scholars have accepted the desirability of analyzing the concept of death by first agreeing on its definition, then formulating a general, measurable criterion to show that the definition has been fulfilled by being both necessary and sufficient for death, and finally developing a series of medical tests to prove that the criterion of death has been satisfied.[2]

As Bernard Gert, Charles Culver, and I explained more than 15 years ago, several assumptions underlie our analysis. First, *death* is a nontechnical word that is used widely and correctly. Any attempt to define death formally must capture this ordinary nontechnical meaning. Second, death is fundamentally a biological concept, so that all and only living organisms can die. Death has important social, psychological, religious, cultural, anthropological, and spiritual dimensions, but it is ultimately a biological event concluding the life of every organism. Third, death is irreversible. Accounts of people allegedly returning from the dead are simply instances of returning from dying. Finally, we presume that a living organism can be distinguished from a dead one with reliability and that the time an organism dies can be stated with some degree of accuracy, at least in retrospect.[3]

Amir Halevy and Baruch Brody have argued that agreement on a single criterion of human death may not be possible because death is not an event but an ineluctable process during which no single point can be chosen to demarcate the moment of death.[4] Brody expands on that analysis in this volume. This position was first propounded by Robert Morison in a famous debate with Leon Kass in 1971.[5] In Chapter 3 Brody cites the fashionable field of "fuzzy logic" as the rigorous philosophical defense that death is a process and that there can be no unified criterion of death. According to this concept, because death and life are mutually exclusive but not jointly exhaustive sets, death represents a fuzzy set, and thus no single criterion of death possibly can be found.

Indeed, while some types of dying make death more closely resemble a process, other types of death more closely resemble an event. Clearly, it takes a finite time for the physiological functions vital for life to cease and for physicians to determine that the cessation of vital functions is irreversible. In some chronic conditions, a person's transition from dying to death may appear nearly seamless. And now that the determination of human death using neurological tests (brain death) has become accepted medical practice, a physician's determination of a patient's death may itself take as long as 24 hours. In this regard, I agree that death can be viewed as a process.

Conversely, in instances of sudden death from trauma or cardiopulmonary arrest, the depiction of death as an event seems to be more accurate. Here the irreversible cessation of vital functions may be reduced in duration to no longer than a few moments. Additionally, there are important pragmatic reasons for us to prefer considering death as a determinable event: social reasons, such as burial practices, life insurance awards, and the reading of wills, and medical reasons, such as organ transplantation and the unconsented withdrawal of intensive therapies.

Everyone agrees that two boundary processes occur at the end of life: the process of dying that occurs before death and the process of bodily disintegration (putrefaction) that occurs after death. On balance, I believe that it is most coherent to consider death as the event that separates the process of dying from the process of bodily disintegration. Although in some chronic conditions, the event of death follows a gradual process of dying, I believe it is socially desirable and biologically plausible to ask physicians to identify an event of death, although the precise timing of that event may not be determinable beyond a small range and, in some cases, may be determinable only in retrospect.

The determination of death using whole-brain tests is consistent with a concept of death as the event that separates the processes of dying and bodily disintegration. In the brain-dead patient, apnea produces cardiac standstill within a few minutes and the process of bodily disintegration follows unless the dead patient's ventilation (and, hence, circulation) is supported artificially. In this circumstance, the brain-dead patient does not display the process of progressive bodily disintegration in the same way as the patient declared dead by cardiopulmonary tests. In brain death, the brain undergoes a process of putrefaction and autolysis, but the remainder of the body does not disintegrate until systemic circulation ceases.

Refinements and Their Reasons

The presence of cases in which death more closely resembles a process has stimulated rejection of the event formulation and questioned the very possibility of finding a unitary criterion of death. Nevertheless, I disagree with Halevy and Brody on both of their conclusions: (1) that the problems they have identified with my account and those of other theorists on brain death represent fatal flaws for producing a coherent concept linking the definition, criterion, and tests of death and (2) that the current accounts attempting to identify a single criterion of death should be discarded in place of their recommended series of pragmatic steps based on states of brain functioning. Here I will show that (1) refinements in my account of death satisfactorily answer the criticisms they raise; (2) there is no necessity, therefore, to invoke their radical solution; and (3) their account raises thorny problems that are best left untouched.

To summarize briefly my current account,[6] death is defined best as the permanent cessation of the critical functions of the organism as a whole. The best criterion of death is the permanent cessation of the clinical functions of the whole brain. The best tests for death are those published by the medical consultants to the President's commission and explained in technical detail by the American Academy of Neurology: for the patient not maintained on a ventilator, the prolonged loss of respiration or circulation or both functions; for the patient maintained on a ventilator, the prolonged cessation of measurable clinical functions of the whole brain.[7]

Brody points out correctly that my account has evolved over the past 15 years. Indeed, I have refined somewhat both our originally proposed definition and criterion of death in response to examples cited by critics that represent valid exceptions to my account. For example, in 1981 Charles Culver, Bernard Gert, and I cited the neuroendocrine control of fluid and electrolyte balance as one instance of a function of the organism as a whole.[8] Subsequently, it was shown clearly that many patients declared brain dead using accepted tests for brain death exhibited continued hypothalamic secretion of antidiuretic hormone (ADH) sufficient to prevent diabetes insipidus.[9] I agree with Brody that this retained activity of the secretory hypothalamus probably represents more than the mere functioning of an isolated nest of neurons, although in some cases the posterior pituitary gland alone may secrete enough ADH to prevent diabetes insipidus, at least temporarily. Nevertheless, I concede that this example shows that not *all* functions of the organism as a whole must be lost in brain death.

In response to this example, I have refined our earlier account of the definition of death. Death should be defined as the permanent cessation of the *critical* functions of the organism as a whole. Obviously, there are a large number of activities of the organism as a whole. They comprise a hierarchy of functions of varying levels of criticality to the life and health of the organism. *Criticality* refers to the extent to which a given function of the organism as a whole is necessary for the continued health and life of the organism.

Awareness, breathing, and circulatory control are more critical to life than is the secretion of ADH. Assuming an adequate water intake, patients can survive for long periods without ADH. A patient who fulfills the tests for whole-brain death and therefore has permanently lost awareness, the capacity to breathe, and the capacity to maintain circulatory control still should be considered dead by our account despite the possibility that some hypothalamic neurons continue to secrete ADH. Although appropriate ADH secretion is an example of a function of the organism as a whole, it is not an example of a critical function.

Julius Korein has provided a rigorous basis for regarding the brain as the critical system governing the functioning of the organism as a whole using arguments from thermodynamics theory.[10] When the brain is destroyed, the critical system is destroyed and the organism no longer can survive in a state of minimal entropy production. With destruction of the organism's critical system, inevitable spontaneous fluctuations will irreversibly further degrade the organism and increase entropy until all systems no longer retain the capacity to operate. The beginning of this process is the loss of certain functions of the brain that subserve the critical functioning of the organism as a whole.

In response to the claim that not *all* functions of the brain are absent in clinically determined brain death, I have refined our earlier criterion of death, which had been "the permanent cessation of all functions of the whole brain." I have refined this criterion of death to become "the permanent cessation of the *clinical* functions of the entire brain." This criterion had been accepted by the President's commission and used in the Uniform Determination of Death Act.[11] Subsequently, it was shown that EEG activity recordable from the scalp surface persisted in some patients unequivocally determined to be brain dead by accepted tests.[12] This rudimentary EEG activity neither responds to sensory stimuli nor appears to represent coherent brain functioning. Rather, it represents isolated nests of neurons whose random and purposeless cellular electrical activity can be recorded technologically but whose functioning is utterly divorced from that of the organism as a whole.

Christopher Pallis has correctly observed that the bedside tests for brain death performed by physicians do not routinely assess the functions of large portions of the brain, such as the occipital lobes, basal ganglia, and thalamus. He accurately pointed out that the usual bedside determination of whole-brain death in actuality focuses on an assessment of brainstem functions.[13]

Although the adjective *clinical* in my refined criterion was absent from my earlier account, clearly it was the clinical functions of the brain that I and the President's commission had in mind when we used the term *functions*. The President's commission clarified their account by making the important distinction between what they called "systemic, integrated functioning" and "physiologic activity."[14] My term *clinical functions* refers to what the President's commission called "systemic, integrated functioning." My term *clinical functions* includes physical signs of brain functions that are detectable on ordinary bedside neurological examination but excludes the meaningless cellular activities of isolated nests of surviving neurons, as well as those brain activities that cannot be measured at the bedside, phenomena that the President's commission called mere "physiologic activity."

Should ADH secretion be classified as a clinical function? If it is, then there is an inconsistency between the definition and criterion of death, as Brody correctly observes. I believe that ADH secretion should not be classified as a clinical function because its presence or absence is not assessed or detected on a usual clinical examination and requires a laboratory test for diagnosis. Flagrant diabetes insipidus often can be suspected when a patient is observed to produce an inappropriately large urine output, but the diagnosis of diabetes insipidus cannot be made without at least measuring the urine specific gravity.

The determination of death using neurological or cardiovascular tests is a clinical determination based on a physician's ordinary physical examination. Although laboratory testing (e.g., EEG, evoked potentials, monitoring of intracranial blood flow) may be useful to confirm death in selected cases, death determination is and should remain a clinical procedure.

Critics may point out that apnea testing as currently practiced involves a high-technology procedure and therefore seems to violate the rule that death determination is solely a clinical evaluation. Ordinary apnea testing, however, requires simply observing an unventilated patient or disconnecting a ventilated patient from the ventilator and observing for the prolonged absence of breathing. The technological component has been added to prevent concomitant hypoxemia and other potential dangers, thereby to protect the patient during the test. But the technological portion is not necessary to prove apnea or to determine death.

Brody's final criticism centers on the alleged preservation of the functioning of brainstem auditory pathways as evidenced by retained brainstem auditory evoked potentials when other clinical tests for brain death have been satisfied. He supports this claim by citing a single report of two cases of alleged brain death with partially retained brainstem auditory evoked potentials.[15] I am respectfully skeptical of the validity of this report on two grounds: (1) It contradicts hundreds of other reported observations that consistently show that all brainstem auditory evoked potentials are absent in brain death.[16] (2) It contradicts the unified pathophysiology and pathology of brain death that is accepted widely by knowledgeable scientists and scholars.

Refinements Surpassing the Alternatives

The seeming incompatibility of the definition and criterion of death has led some scholars to conclude that no unitary criterion of death ever can be identified. Brody has reached this conclusion and suggests that, rather than attempting to reach consensus on our ability to identify the moment of death, each question about a patient's life support should be considered on its own merits. For example, he suggests the adoption of a rule that physicians could withdraw a patient's life support without family consent in those instances in which the organism no longer composed a person. This is a pragmatic and generally reasonable approach to the vexing problem of what to do with the tragic patient in a persistent vegetative state who remains alive but has lost personhood.

Brody recognizes that PVS patients are not dead, and he does not confound the distinction between death and loss of personhood, as has been done by several scholars who support a higher-brain formulation of death.[17] Death is a biological concept, and only biological organisms can die. Personhood is a psychosocial and spiritual concept, and personhood cannot die except in a metaphorical sense. When we say that a person died, we are referring to the organism that was the person. Charles Culver, Bernard Gert, and I argued that the decision to withdraw life support from a patient in a persistent vegetative state (who remains alive but arguably has lost personhood) is an important question, but one that should not be obscured by purposely blurring the important distinction between death and the loss of personhood.[18]

Brody's rule has a provocative exception. I was startled to read in Brody's defense of preemptively withdrawing life-sustaining treatment in PVS cases that his rule would not necessarily apply to patients whose families wished life-sustaining treatment to be continued and were able to pay for it. Thus, according to this scheme, those PVS patients who could afford medical treatment would live and those who could not would die. This highly questionable moral position is an example of the type of difficulty that results from favoring a series of pragmatic rules rather than attempting to agree on a definition and criterion of death. Certainly, it is reasonable to consider allowing some patients in PVS to die by withdrawal of life-sustaining treatment, based on factors such as the patient's prior wishes and the physician's responsibility for stewardship of society's resources. But, as I think Brody would agree, such an action must be acknowledged to represent allowing a living person to die. Although of markedly diminished capacity, the PVS patient is alive.[19]

Brody recommends awaiting asystole before burying or cremating the PVS patient from whom life-sustaining treatment has been stopped. But why should this wait be necessary? Because of, Brody adds, the desirability of "respecting family sentiments." What Brody does not point out is that family sentiments oppose burying or cremating a spontaneously breathing and heart-beating PVS patient because it is obvious to families and to everyone else that spontaneously breathing and moving PVS patients are not dead. And, as the well-publicized, tragic case of Nancy Cruzan demonstrated, the "short" interval between stopping hydration and nutrition and the development of asystole in such patients can last as long as 2 weeks.[20]

Brody touches on the vexing deontological problems inherent in his proposal. As he accurately observes, the clear deontological rule prohibiting the killing of living human beings would have to be modified when fuzzy logic shows that some people, such as anencephalic infants, fall in an ambiguous state between life and death. Brody is fully aware of the serious moral implications of this change. Formerly clear deontological constraints themselves become fuzzy in a world of fuzzy sets.

Identifying the definition and criterion of death is an elusive task. It requires a reasoned philosophical and biological analysis to determine the critical functions of the organism as a whole and a careful scientific study to determine the precise neuroanatomical and neurophysiological correlation of these functions. Our ability to measure these functions accurately undoubtedly will increase with future advances in technology. These technological advances should permit us to identify with greater specificity and measure with greater exactitude that set of neurons in the brainstem, diencephalon, and cerebral hemispheres that subserves the critical functions of the organism as a whole.[21] I believe that such an attempt to generate consensus on the philosophical and biological question of the definition and criterion of death has a far greater chance to succeed than does an attempt to develop a social consensus on a series of ad hoc, pragmatic rules denying that there is an identifiable moment of death.

References

1. Bernat JL. How much of the brain must die in brain death? *J Clin Ethics* 1992;3:21-26.

2. This analysis was developed in Capron AM, Kass LR. A statutory definition of the standards of determining human death: An appraisal and a proposal. *Univ Penn Law Rev* 1972;121:87-118; Bernat JL, Culver CM, Gert B. On the definition and criterion of death. *Ann Intern Med* 1981;94:389-94.

3. Bernat JL, Culver CM, Gert B. On the definition and criterion of death. *Ann Intern Med* 1981;94:389-90.

4. Halevy A, Brody B. Brain death: Reconciling definitions, criteria, and tests. *Ann Intern Med* 1993;119:519-25. Linda Emanuel agrees with this position. Emanuel LL. Reexamining death: The asymptotic model and a bounded zone definition. *Hastings Cent Rep* 1995;25(4):27-35.

5. Morison RS. Death: Process or event? *Science* 1971;173:694-98; Kass LR. Death as an event: A commentary on Robert Morison. *Science* 1971;173:698-702.

6. The most recent detailed formulation of my position can be found in Bernat JL. A defense of the whole-brain concept of death. *Hastings Cent Rep* 1998; 28(2):14-23. See also Bernat JL. *Ethical Issues in Neurology.* Boston: Butterworth-Heinemann, 1994, 113-43.

7. President's Commission for the Study of Ethical Problems in Medicine and Biomedical and Behavioral Research. *Defining Death: Medical, Ethical, and Legal Issues in the Determination of Death.* Washington, DC: Government Printing Office, 1981, Appendix F: Guidelines for the Determination of Death. The commission's battery of tests has been modified recently by an expert panel. See also Quality Standards Subcommittee of the American Academy of Neurology. Practice parameters for determining brain death in adults. *Neurology* 1995;45:1012-14.

8. See Bernat JL, Culver CM, Gert B. On the definition and criterion of death. *Ann Intern Med* 1981;94:390.

9. I have reviewed the relevant ADH data in brain-dead patients in Bernat JL. How much of the brain must die in brain death? *J Clin Ethics* 1992;3:25.

10. Korein J. The problem of brain death: Development and history. *Ann NY Acad Sci* 1978;315:19-38.

11. Charles Culver, Bernard Gert, and I criticized the President's commission for choosing a bifurcated criterion of death for the Uniform Determination of Death Act but not for the wording of the neurological portion of the statute. See Bernat JL, Culver CM, Gert B. Defining death in theory and practice. *Hastings Cent Rep* 1982;12(1):5-9.

12. I have reviewed the relevant EEG data in brain-dead patients in Bernat JL. How much of the brain must die in brain death? *J Clin Ethics* 1992;3:25.

13. Pallis C. *ABC of Brainstem Death.* London: *British Medical Journal* Publishers, 1983.

14. President's Commission, *Defining Death*, 33.

15. Barelli A, Della Corte F, Calimici R, et al. Do brain stem auditory evoked potentials detect the actual cessation of cerebral functions in brain dead patients? *Crit Care Med* 1990;18:322-23.

16. The data showing absent brainstem evoked potentials in brain death were reviewed in Wijdicks EFM. Determining brain death in adults. *Neurology* 1995;45:1003-11.

17. For example, see Veatch RM. Brain death and slippery slopes. *J Clin Ethics* 1992;3:181-87.

18. Bernat JL, Culver CM, Gert B. On the definition and criterion of death. *Ann Intern Med* 1981;94:391.

19. For the medical characteristics and legal status of patients in persistent vegetative states, see Multisociety Task Force on PVS. Medical aspects of the persistent vegetative state. *N Engl J Med* 1994;330:1499-1508,1572-79.

20. Annas GJ. The long dying of Nancy Cruzan. *Law Med Health Care* 1991; 19:52-59.

21. See Bernat JL. How much of the brain must die in brain death? *J Clin Ethics* 1992;3:26.

5

On the Brainstem Criterion
of Death

Chris Pallis, D.M.

ALTHOUGH THERE ARE active proponents of higher-brain formulations of death, most physicians still espouse the whole-brain criterion when seeking to diagnose death on the basis of the patient's neurological status. There has been recent controversy concerning the adequacy of the whole-brain criterion, and it is to this matter that I address my comments.

Basically, the criticisms have been of two types. Some critics have stressed the persistence of various endocrinological or electrical functions in patients otherwise fulfilling current clinical requirements of whole-brain death. They argue that, if the secretion of pituitary hormones or any kind of electrical activity generated within the skull persists (for however short a time), the "whole of the brain" cannot be dead. Most such critics avoid defining death, thereby eschewing the need to relate the persisting function (which is the source of their concern) to persisting life of the "organism as a whole."

Other critics of the whole-brain criterion start from much wider premises. They argue that criteria and tests for death cannot be discussed in a philosophical vacuum. They correctly point out that, unless one starts with a *definition of death*, it will be difficult—if not impossible—meaningfully to discuss the relevance of any particular *criterion of death* and, *a fortiori,* to discuss the merit of *tests* (designed to establish whether the said criterion had been met or not).

These difficulties were comprehensively addressed by Halevy and Brody in 1993,[1] and Brody addresses them in Chapter 3 of this volume. Here I seek to point out how the concept of brainstem death is impervious to the first kind of challenge, while fully compatible with—and in fact enhancing the value of—the second. The notion of brainstem death avoids the cultural problems involved in claiming that vegetative patients (who meet the higher-brain criterion of death, but who are still breathing spontaneously) are dead. It simultaneously avoids the valid indictment that some patients said to meet the whole-brain criterion of death may, for a while, retain "life" in some neuronal aggregates above the level of the brainstem.

I start by stating where I agree and where I disagree with Professor Brody and others who share his concern about the "whole of the brain" not being dead in patients alleged to be suffering from whole-brain death.

1. *I agree that death is a process and not an event.* I have been arguing this thesis for the last 15 years.[2–7] Even a "classical death," at home and remote from all the paraphernalia of intensive care technology, does not result in an immediate loss of function in all body parts. After irreversible asystole mini-electrocardiographic activity can for a while be recorded from within the cardiac cavities.[8] The pupils remain for up to 2 hours responsive to miotics.[9] Skin, bone, and arterial grafts remain viable, even if harvested a whole day after irreversible asystole.

But in this process there may be dramatic points of no return. The events occurring after human decapitation illustrate the point rather dramatically. The heart continues to beat after severance of the head from the body.[10] That is anatomical decapitation. Brain death has been described as "physiological decapitation."[11] The subject of our deliberations is, in a sense, an exploration of the limits of this analogy.

2. *I agree with Professor Brody that "many patients who meet the standard clinical tests of brain death still maintain some brain functioning and therefore do not satisfy the whole-brain criterion of death."*[1] But then, as I will show, I am not arguing for a whole-brain criterion of death. Let those who are advocating such a criterion deal with the problems their stance entails! One of these problems will be to respond to papers with titles such as "Electroencephalographic Activity after Brain Death"[12]—or to cope with others headed "Paradoxical Contributions of EEG during Protracted Dy-

ing."[13] Contributions of this kind rapidly become quixotic to the point of incoherence.

3. *I agree with—and much admire—Professor Brody's ruthlessly logical description of the "six possible responses" to an untidy array of awkward facts.* I also confess that I am offering what Professor Brody calls "another criterion of death": the *brainstem* criterion as opposed to the *higher-brain* criterion and to the *whole-brain* criterion.[1] I disagree, however, that advocacy of the brainstem criterion is some kind of retreat from the whole-brain criterion or some kind of attempt at tidying up a reality cluttered with too many discordant facts. The concept of brainstem death was, after all, being advocated in the United Kingdom in 1976 and 1979 (i.e., before the 1981 report of the President's commission).[7]

Professor Brody is wrong when he suggests that the concept of brainstem death is primarily a prognostic one (in that it implies that asystole is inevitable and "would occur within days"). That brainstem death currently carries such a catastrophic cardiac prognosis is true.[2,4,7] And it is also true that this had to be stressed at one stage, in the United Kingdom, in the course of heated public controversy on brain death.[5] But in my writings and talks on the subject, I have always emphasized that, in my opinion, the brainstem dead were dead (because irreversibly unconscious and irreversibly apneic) *irrespective of their cardiac prognosis.*[2,4,7] I have also pointed out that, with the anticipated advent of the artificial heart (and with the established advent of pharmacological techniques capable of maintaining "prolonged somatic survival"), the fact that "the brain dead were already dead" would assume an increasing and very practical significance.

I have consistently argued that the real conceptual challenge facing us today is the need to accept the fundamental notion that "brainstem death [is] death in its own right" and that this notion has a tenable philosophical basis. I have protested at repeated references, by our less well-informed journalists, to the "switching off of life-support machines," pointing out that, in cases where repeated tests for brainstem death had proved positive, the ventilators were clearly already ventilating cadavers and that cadavers have no prognosis, at least in this world.[5,7]

4. *I agree with Professor Brody that it is meaningless to discuss tests for death without what he calls a "justifying" definition of death.* For many years I have been arguing that what physicians do—or do not do—in intensive care units should be logically derived from explicitly formulated philosophical premises.[2,4,7] This has not always gone down well with colleagues in the United Kingdom who boast of their pragmatism.

I strongly *disagree* with Professor Brody, however, when he asserts that the criterion of brainstem death lacks a "justifying definition." I suggested in 1983 that death occurred when a pathological event (whether cardiologic or primarily intracranial) produced both irreversible loss of the capacity for consciousness and irreversible loss of the capacity to breathe and that this should be considered a valid definition of death.[2] The suggestion has quite recently received an official imprimatur.[14]

Professor Brody dismisses the brainstem criterion (and the concept of death from which it is derived), stating that the "criterion comes from two very different definitions, and it is hard to see why the two criteria should be combined. Pallis points out quite correctly that they are 'embedded in coherent historical and cultural matrices.' However, the fact that each is embedded in a coherent matrix does not ensure that their combination is embedded in a coherent matrix." I beg to differ. The single matrix in which my definition is embedded is a sociological one, namely Judeo-Christian culture. Inasmuch as Western civilization retains any moral or ethical standards, they are still influenced by the culture in question. It is important, in my opinion, that, even if we today express our views in modern physiological and secular terms, we recognize their cultural roots. The "loss of the capacity for consciousness" is much the same as the "departure of the conscious soul from the body," just as the "loss of the capacity to breathe" is much the same as the "loss of the breath of life."

That granted, we can go further: we can, respectively, find the requisite anatomical bases for these occurrences (1) in the bilateral destruction of the paramedian tegmental parts of the mesencephalon and rostral pons and (2) in the destruction of the so-called respiratory center of the lower medulla. For those interested in philology, I have described the widespread identity, in various languages, of terms denoting *soul* and *breath*.[4] I think it is legitimate to look at words—and ideas—in relation to the company they keep.

5. *I disagree with Professor Brody on important neuroanatomical and clinical points.* In his critique of the whole-brain concept, Professor Brody writes that "many patients meeting all of the standard clinical tests for brain death still have some cortical, midbrain or stem functioning."[1] This may be true as far as the cortex and diencephalon are concerned (as attested by residual EEG and hormonal activity), but it certainly is not true in relation to the brainstem. The evidence given by Professor Brody warrants closer inspection. The attempt to invalidate the brainstem criterion

on this basis just does not stand up to critical evaluation. Let us look at the three cases Professor Brody quotes to buttress his argument.[15,16]

Professor Brody writes, quite explicitly, that "brainstem function, as shown by evoked potentials, can continue despite a patient's meeting the standard clinical tests for brain death."[1] He then goes on to assert that "brainstem evoked potentials . . . assess the functional integrity of the auditory and visual pathways from the receptors through the stem to the cortex." The trouble with this is that the *pathway (between retina and visual cortex) at no place involves the brainstem.* Ferbert's patient,[15] clinically diagnosed as brain dead but having preserved visual evoked responses, may constitute a problem to those subscribing to the whole-brain criterion. The case, however, is irrelevant to those concerned primarily with brainstem function.

The auditory pathway does, however, traverse the brainstem. Did the two Barelli cases,[16] cited as evidence by Professor Brody, really meet "the standard clinical tests for brain death?"[1] A critical feature of the standard tests is the exclusion of exogenous intoxication as a factor possibly contributing to the patient's neurological status. The first patient referred to by Barelli and his colleagues was a 28-year-old woman hospitalized for "severe acute colchicine poisoning" who sustained a cardiorespiratory arrest. Twelve hours later "all brain death criteria became evident." The brainstem auditory evoked responses persisted, however, for "a few minutes."

Benjamin Franklin, who suffered from gout, is said to have introduced colchicine into the United States. It is a drug capable of depressing the respiratory center, and acute colchicine poisoning causes an ascending paralysis of the central nervous system.[17] I doubt that the patient in question would have been diagnosed as brain dead in the United States. In the United Kingdom this case would not have met the preconditions for a diagnosis of brainstem death.

Barelli's second patient was a 60-year-old woman who developed a cardiorespiratory arrest of unspecified etiology. On the fourth day "all brain death criteria had occurred." Brainstem auditory evoked responses are said to have persisted, monaurally, for another 72 hours. There are no details as to the primary diagnosis or concerning outcome.

It is on this rickety tripod (two irrelevant and one grossly underdocumented case) that Professor Brody bases his clinical evidence of persisting brainstem function in whole-brain death. *Parturiunt montes, nascetur ridiculus mus!*[18]

6. *On variable "accounts of death."* Professor Brody advocates an "al-

ternative approach that does not acknowledge any sharp dichotomy between life and death and incorporates the proposition that the questions of when care can be unilaterally discontinued, when organs can be harvested, and when a patient is ready for the services of an undertaker should be answered independent of any single account of death."[1]

Something very similar was argued over 15 years ago by Alistair Browne, another philosopher.[19] Browne wrote that, "even granting that important legal, moral and medical consequences flow from the determination of death, and that it is undesirable to be left in limbo on these matters, it still does not follow that we ought to precise the definition of death. There remains the alternative of leaving the definition of death in its present indeterminate state, and going on to specify what can be appropriately done to whom, when." Browne then makes a number of suggestions, concluding: "I do not want to insist that these particular rules ought to be adopted; my point is only that we can remove any uncertainty in practical affairs without fiddling with the definition of death." I responded to Browne's article,[3] arguing that "the only real alternative to an overall philosophical concept of death [is] a set of arbitrarily assembled rules of conduct . . . Who would issue such rules?" I asked, "and on what basis?" History, I pointed out, tended to show that, when prescribed observances and practices had no roots in generally accepted conceptual frameworks, they faced one of two fates: they were either abandoned (and sooner rather than later), or they were sustained by the threat of sanction. Were I addressing this issue today, I would add that the main beneficiaries of such an arrangement in the United States would undoubtedly be U.S. lawyers!

Professor Brody's suggestions about what we could do with patients in a vegetative state (stop feeding and hydrating them), with patients in whom the standard clinical tests for whole-brain death have been satisfied (harvest their organs), and with patients in irreversible asystole (summon the undertaker) are appealing, but mainly, I think, because of their spurious simplicity. To place the vegetative state at the head of an implied *sequence* of events which proceeds from higher-brain death via whole-brain death to final cardiac asystole is tidying up reality just a little too much. Persistently vegetative patients seldom follow a clinical evolution of this kind. Professor Brody's statement is not, in my view, a philosophical justification for different concepts of death (based on the undoubtedly correct perception that "death is a process"). It is rather a recognition of the primacy—in the real world—of the logistics of practical patient care: one just does not want transplant coordinators in wards for the demented elderly or morticians in intensive care units and operating theaters (if for no better reason than that their presence might clutter up access and startle both relatives and nursing staff). We have problems enough as it is.

Stuart Youngner and his colleagues have commented, in a sensitive and observant manner, on the current states of "knowledge and concepts among health professionals" in the United States when questioned about brain death and organ retrieval.[20] The disarray was impressive. I would ask Professor Brody: "Are you seriously envisaging compounding the chaos by questioning the need for a uniform definition of death? It is not reassuring for people to hear physicians tell them that there are several kinds of death (as distinct from several ways of dying). It has been said that 'we shape both ourselves and our societies by the accumulated effects of particular choices' (what we do, we become). Please keep this in mind."

References

1. Halevy A, Brody B. Brain death: Reconciling definitions, criteria, and tests. *Ann Intern Med* 1993;119:519–25.

2. Pallis C. *The ABC of Brainstem Death*. London: *British Medical Journal* Publishers, 1983.

3. Pallis C. Whole brain death reconsidered: Physiological facts and philosophy. *J Med Ethics* 1983;9:32–37.

4. Pallis C. Brainstem death: The evolution of a concept. In: Morris PJ (ed). *Kidney Transplantation: Principles and Practice*. Philadelphia: WB Saunders, 1988, 123–50.

5. Pallis C. Death. In *Encyclopaedia Britannica*. Chicago: Encyclopedia Britannica, 1986.

6. Pallis C. Brainstem death. *Med Leg J* 1987;55:84–107.

7. Pallis C. Brainstem death. In: Vinken PJ, Bruyn GW (eds). *Handbook of Clinical Neurology*. Amsterdam: Elsevier, 1990, 57:441–96.

8. McMichael J. History of atrial fibrillation. *Br Heart J* 1982;48:193–97.

9. Paillas JE. Les critères de la mort du donneur dans les transplantations d'organe. *Marseille Med* 1970;107:369–80.

10. Dujardin-Beaumetz E. Note historique et physiologique sur le supplice de la guillotine. *Bull Soc Med Leg France* 1870;5(2):49–74.

11. Rosner F, Tendler MD. Definition of death in Judaism. *J Halacha* 1989;17:14–31.

12. Grigg MA, Kelly NA, Celesia GC, et al. Electroencephalographic activity after brain death. *Arch Neurol* 1987;44:948–54.

13. Spudis EV, Perry JK, Link S, et al. Paradoxical contributions of EEG during protracted dying. *Arch Neurol* 1984;41:153–56.

14. Working Party Report. Criteria for the diagnosis of brainstem death. *J R Coll Physicians Lond* 1995;29:381–82.

15. Ferbert A, Buchner H, Ringelstein EB, et al. Isolated brainstem death. *Electroencephalogr Clin Neurophysiol* 1986;65:157–60.

16. Barelli A, della Corte F, Calimici R, et al. Do brainstem auditory evoked potentials detect the actual cessation of cerebral functions in brain dead patients? *Crit Care Med* 1990;18:322–23.

17. Goodman LS, Gilman AG. *The Pharmacological Basis of Therapeutics.* 7th ed. New York: Macmillan, 1985, 709.

18. "The mountains are in labour—an absurd mouse will be born" (i.e., much ado about . . . very little). Horace. De Arte Poetica, 139.

19. Browne A. Whole-brain death reconsidered. *J Med Ethics* 1983;9:28–31.

20. Youngner SJ, Landefeld CS, Coulton CJ, et al. "Brain death" and organ retrieval: A cross-sectional survey of knowledge and concepts among health professionals. *JAMA* 1989;261:2205–10.

6

The Persisting Perplexities in the Determination of Death

Joanne Lynn, M.D., and Ronald Cranford, M.D.

CONTROVERSY OVER HOW TO determine death seems likely to be part of the human condition. Consider the chagrin of the Romans discovering that Jesus was not dead, despite having been crucified and entombed! However, for most of our history the issue was of relatively minor importance, signaling at most how long one must wait between apparent death and burial. This changed with the advent of two developments in medicine: first, treatments that could sustain respiration and circulation despite the patient having lost all brain functions, and second, the transplantation of useful organs from newly dead bodies.

For most of our history, when a person's breathing stopped, death followed very quickly (even appearing to be simultaneous). Iron lungs and anesthesia bellows, in the first half of this century, demonstrated that death from respiratory arrest alone could often be averted. This forced us to be clear that it was the cessation of heartbeat that really signaled death.

By the end of the 1960s, cardiopulmonary resuscitation and cardiopulmonary bypass machines had forced a reexamination of precisely what could be meant by the "cessation of heartbeat." It could not just be the stilling of the heart, for that could be supplanted temporarily by bypass and could be ended with reinitiation of effective heartbeat. Again, clarity came about in the refinement of the conception of death to mean the cessation of effective circulation. Thus, even if the circulation is maintained by artificial means, without a heartbeat, the person is alive. However, even if the heart beats for a while but is ineffective in maintaining circulation (as might happen, e.g., if the heart were removed or if the great vessels were disrupted), then the patient is dead.

This understanding was shaken again by the advent of patients who had circulation restored after a cardiac arrest but who had no brain function thereafter. These bodies could be maintained in intensive care for days, but had no prospects of self-initiated breathing and certainly no prospects for any volitional action. After some public and professional dispute and discourse, our society has agreed to classify such patients as dead and to define death to include the permanent cessation of neurological function.

This has been a more difficult step than the clarification of cardiovascular criteria, since the direct assessment of neurological function has not been a prominent part of the traditional determination of death (beyond the check of the pupils made famous in dozens of Western movies). Furthermore, the patient whose neurological function has ceased does not "look dead," unlike the correct intuitions induced by those sustained with respirators and bypass machines (and not dead) and those afflicted with loss of circulation (and thus dead). Nevertheless, at least in America and Europe, persons who have forever lost all neurological function are classified as dead, and continued treatment to sustain circulation in a dead body is held to be warranted only to allow for transplantation or for the needs of family.

Appropriate care of the patient could probably have been achieved with a public policy of stopping treatment and then pronouncing death on the basis of circulatory arrest. However, one pressure to declare this condition to be death was the interest in securing the dead person's organs for transplant (initially the kidneys, later the liver and the heart, and now others as well). Transplantation offered the many suffering from renal failure the hope of substantial improvement, but few had suitable family donors and cadaver donors were useful for only a very short time after the cessation of circulation. Taking kidneys from those who were dead but who had circulation sustained (the *brain dead*) largely bypassed these problems.

By the time the President's Commission for the Study of Ethical Problems in Medicine and Biomedical and Behavioral Research issued its report in 1981,[1] death was widely understood as being the irreversible cessation of the life of the person, which could be known by finding either that circulation had irreversibly ceased or that all neurological functions had irreversibly ceased.[2] The commission was never quite clear as to whether the two criteria stood independently or whether the circulatory criteria were adequate precisely because they always indicated the irreversible loss of neurological functions. At that time, nothing turned on this issue and it seemed unlikely that forcing clarity would be useful. Most likely, citizens were reassured by having the traditional criteria visibly present and would have resisted making larger changes in their traditional views.

Likewise, the commission's report did not deal carefully with two persisting but largely quiet controversies. First, the commission was silent on *when* a person is dead, whether declared to be dead using circulatory or neurological criteria. Second, the commission was silent on the appropriate standard of proof for criteria concerning death, whether the set of criteria that were promulgated by the commission's work or those proposed in the future. Although one could always make law school exam cases in which these matters were conceivably important, there were no real situations in which their resolution mattered, and it seemed more important to build upon the growing consensus than to divert attention to issues that made little, if any, difference.

This has, however, changed. The recent practices of taking organs for transplant very quickly after planned circulatory arrest and especially of restoring circulation after declaring death on circulatory grounds have required renewed attention to the fine structure of the declaration of death. All three of the issues left unaddressed by the commission have become important in this new context: (1) whether death is really always neurological or whether it is really a binary concept including also circulatory cessation, (2) when in the sequence of events around dying a person is dead, and (3) what standard of proof will be required to accept a set of criteria and practices for the determination of death. In this chapter, we will present an analysis of the issues in these three areas.

The Time of Death

Whether one is using criteria of circulatory or neurological function, each patient has four potential points in time that are of importance in determining that death has occurred (Table 6.1).[3] The latest point (termed here Time 4) is when the critical function has been lost and has

Table 6.1. Possible Times of Death

	Time 1	Time 2	Time 3	Time 4
Circulatory	Circulation stopped	Circulation examined and known to have stopped	Cessation becomes irreversible	Cessation known to be irreversible
Neurological	Onset of coma with apnea	Neurological exam shows functions to have stopped	Cessation becomes irreversible	Time or further exam shows cessation to be irreversible
Reason to use	The "real" end of a person's life, but often hard to know precisely and always retrospective	Fairly reliable and not very manipulatable, but timing reflects behavior of physicians	Virtually impossible to know precisely, if not identical to Time 1 or 2	Quite reliable but also quite manipulatable

Note: It is Time 4 when death can be known to have occurred in all cases, although it might then be said to have occurred at any of the prior times.

been determined to have been lost irreversibly. This is the first point in time at which the patient can be known to have died, and the first time when the physician (or anyone else) can pronounce death. In effect, there really is a Time 5, when death is pronounced, which is always after Time 4, though it most often follows immediately.

The earliest time (Time 1) is when the patient actually loses the critical function, even though the loss may not be documented by a physician then and certainly cannot be known to be irreversible. For circulatory criteria, for example, Time 1 is when the person is known to have drowned, even though no examination was possible until the body was recovered some hours later. For neurological criteria, for example, Time 1 is when the person became comatose and lost brainstem functions during a cardiopulmonary resuscitation attempt, although the degree of irreversible neurological loss could not be known until many hours had passed. In addition, two intermediate times (Time 2 and Time 3) always occur. Time 2 is usually apparent when the patient is first examined and found to have lost the critical function that later is found to be an irreversible loss. Time 3 is often inapparent: when the patient's loss actually becomes irreversible, even though that fact is not known until Time 4. Although all other times must follow the sequence given or occur simultaneously, Time 2 and Time 3 can reverse their order, if irreversibility of loss occurs before the loss itself is measured.

The person who collapses (Time 1) and is found to have no heartbeat (Time 2) might receive efforts at resuscitation for hours before it can be known that circulation cannot be restored (Time 4). Time 3, the actual start of irreversibility, occurs at some unknown time during the resuscitation efforts. Likewise, the person who has taken an overdose and is found and resuscitated for circulation but who has no neurological recovery will have a Time 1 when neurological function actually ceased, a Time 2 when its cessation is first documented,[4] a Time 3 when it actually became irreversible, and a Time 4 when its irreversibility is established.[5] With a drug overdose, Time 1 and Time 2 can be separated by some minutes (before discovery), but Time 2 and Time 4 can be separated by days (before drugs are metabolized sufficiently to apply clinical criteria).

The reason to air these descriptive issues now is that the time we choose to use as the time of death has important policy implications. No research data have been collected about how these times are used in declaring death. Clearly, however, different physicians and different regions have been recording different possible times of death, usually unreflectively, mostly because it has not made any difference. In medical care until recently, all cadaver organ donation and all rituals of mourning (including burial or cremation) occurred after Time 4. Only in the exceedingly rare case in which an inheritance or insurance issue turned upon the exact time of death did it matter which time was recorded, and judges could do as well as policymakers in deciding such cases.

However, now some transplant teams hope to harvest transplantable organs at the earliest possible time after death.[6,7] Some have therefore instituted plans that press the determination of death to be as efficient as possible by, for example, restoring circulation after a few minutes of cessation of spontaneous circulation and proceeding with organ retrieval with artificially sustained circulation.[8]

The presentation of the sequence of times above illuminates why this practice reflects a faulty understanding of the determination of death under current criteria, whether the physician is using circulatory or neurological criteria. In either case, the physician must establish that the relevant function has ceased and that this cessation is irreversible. If the physician is using neurological criteria, documenting the irreversibility takes some time and testing, during which the circulation must be sustained artificially (at least by artificial ventilation). The organs are sustained in the dead body during this time and the declaration of death proceeds in the usual way, with harvesting of organs thereafter.

However, if the physician is using circulatory criteria, the patient cannot be declared dead until the cessation of circulation is known to be irreversible. If treatment reverses the cessation of circulation, then the circulatory criteria are not met and the physician must use neurological criteria. Unless the physician allows cessation of circulation to become irreversible or establishes that death has occurred using neurological criteria, the patient, quite simply, is not known to be dead by either of the criteria now in use. Under these protocols, Time 4 has not occurred for either set of criteria, and one cannot know that death has occurred until Time 4. Claiming that the patient has died and then reversing the circulatory arrest would manifest confused thinking and misapplication of the criteria.

As to which time should be taken to be the time of death, we have no strong view. Conceptually, the time at which the person actually died is Time 1, when the critical function ceased which eventually proved to have been irreversible. However, that time is often difficult to establish, and it is awkward for the physician to pronounce death on Wednesday and for the family to begin mourning then, only to have the death certificate say that the patient who they all prayed for had actually been dead since the previous Sunday. Time 3 is almost never known unless it corresponds with Time 1 or 2, so using it would often be speculative. Times 2 and 4 are more reliably determined and are more in concert with societal expectations, but they are manipulatable and, since they are established by the happenstance of the timing of examinations, they do not reflect something important that happened within the patient at that time. Certainly, one of the desirable features of a policy for determining death is that it yields a time of death that relates to the patient's physiology rather than the behaviors of other persons and the functioning of the care system (e.g., how quickly patients are found or when examinations are scheduled). Only Time 1 meets this need. However, Time 1 is almost certainly not the time that physicians try to record as the time of death now, so using it would also be the most substantial policy change, and it is often rather difficult to determine with the customary appearance of precision.

One problem with trying to resolve the narrow issue of which time to construe as the time of death is that discussion of it is likely to have the adverse effect of increasing public discomfort with the practices of the determination of death and therefore with organ transplantation, even though there is properly no connection. Leaders in the field will have to take this into consideration as they define their agenda for the near future. It may well be best to be clear about the criteria and their application and to continue the ambiguity about which time to use as the official time of death.

The Certainty of Death

No statement based on past experience can ever be entirely certain. Divine intervention in the course of Jesus' apparent death was hardly predictable from statistics! In general, uncertainty can be reduced by having a larger number of observations and a well-supported general theory that organizes causes and effects in a way that enhances the reliability of inferences. That acknowledged, how certain are we about current determinations of death, whether based upon published guidelines or as applied in actual practice? The answers are actually rather unsettling.

To know how long one must wait after the cessation of circulation, for example, one must know (1) how long a body can go without circulation and have it sometimes spontaneously resume; (2) how long a body can go without circulation and have it possible to restart with re-suscitation (or the equivalent, by substituting with artificial means), and (3) since Time (2) is longer than Time (1), whether we will accept a decision not to try to resuscitate (or to supply circulation artificially) as allowing use of the earlier time.

The published data do not authoritatively tell us how long after ces-sation of circulation spontaneous resumption of circulation might occur. General wisdom would hold that it is exceedingly unlikely after a minute at normal body temperature and unheard of after two. However, data relevant to estimating a rate over time could arise only in monitored settings and would require review of long, naturally occurring periods of loss of circulation which did not lead to resuscitation attempts. This would seem most likely to happen in Holter monitor situations where no CPR is instituted. However, to our knowledge there are no reports of records of this sort, and no estimates of the likely denominators that would allow extrapolation into very small rates. Thus, we have only an-ecdotes, expert opinion, and general experience upon which to rely. In such circumstances, those who would make policy would be well advised to stay on the conservative side of expert opinion, rather than to press for the shortest possible delay.

There is a little more information on how long a body can be apneic and asystolic and still have a resuscitation start the heart. DeVita's review of the available information reports small numbers and unusual cases. Nevertheless, his cases are troubling. He includes case reports of cessa-tion of circulation at normal body temperature which were ended with successful resuscitation after 15 minutes or more.[9] There are reports of much longer periods in hypothermic persons, especially children.[10,11] The rates of success after as few as 3 minutes go down dramatically, but successes with full or partial neurological recovery still occur. One could not call a person dead until one had exceeded the time span known to be consistent with recovery of circulation.

However, should one have to wait longer than the longest known case? If we construct a statistical model using all data ever available, it will never have a rate of zero—it will always have some progressively declin-ing rate of expected successful resuscitation. How low should the ex-pected rate be at the threshold of declaring death?[12] This is quite difficult to say. At some point, as the proverb would say, events are in the hands of God. Surely, expected rates of less than one in a million qualify as miraculous. Whatever statistical rate seems adequate will be buttressed by reasonable theoretical underpinnings for the irreversibility of the circulatory problem. Nevertheless, the reasonable rate to accept for potential error will certainly require delay of at least 10 minutes during efforts at resuscitation, depending upon response. When the body is making some response to resuscitation efforts, the delay before death can be determined will be much longer. Such complex criteria have not been published.

Since there is ordinarily a delay of only a few minutes for lifeless patients for whom there will be no effort at resuscitation and the delay will be much longer when resuscitation is to be tried, how long one must wait might well depend upon the plan of care. In either case, Time 1 above is the same, and Times 2 and 3 might or might not change, but Time 4 is certainly delayed by efforts at resuscitation. This illustrates one example of how the latter times depend upon decisions and conditions of persons other than the patient. What delay is held to be required before a patient can be declared dead then depends upon whether decisions about the course of care can be included in the practice guidelines.

If the plan of care is not allowed to affect the determination, then everyone must wait for this longer period (or the waiting period can start after efforts at resuscitation or supplementation have ceased). Either approach is likely to reduce the usefulness of transplantable organs. If the plan not to use any resuscitation or circulation is to be included in the protocol for determining death, confusion is likely and clear criteria are needed.

In no case can one declare death from irreversible loss of circulation after a suitable period and then provide an artificial circulation. Neurological criteria must be used to determine death in such cases, as there obviously has been no irreversible cessation of circulation.

As to the accuracy of criteria now in use, the purely statistical likelihood of error is surprisingly substantial. How can one know whether a particular set of guidelines for the determination of death is accurate? What is the gold standard? A person determined to be dead must not later have return of any circulatory or neurological function. However, our definitions have a certain self-enforcing quality—once a person is declared dead, we undertake activities, such as withdrawal of ventilator and removal of vital organs, which ensure that any errors are not found or at least that persons who were very near death but not quite dead would soon be made dead by any criteria.

To test whether the criteria and tests are adequate, we would have to give some population of patients maximal support, watching for any return of function before incontrovertible evidence of death. For circulatory function, some rather diffuse data would seem to confirm the estimates above, though imperfectly. However, for neurological criteria, probably less than one thousand patients have been followed carefully and with maximal support after a determination of death was made by neurological criteria. The problem is that we cannot be certain that the rate is zero even if 0/1,000 patients recover neurological function despite maximal support after death is diagnosed by neurological criteria. Statisticians tell us that, after studying 1,000 patients, we can be only 95 percent certain that the error rate is less than 0.3 percent.[13] Practically, this means that we can be pretty sure that no more than 3 of the 1,000 patients we say are dead using neurological criteria will regain some neurological function. The public might justifiably be outraged to learn that this is the rate that the medical profession can actually defend.

This rate, however, is buttressed by both a large number of persons who had less than maximal life support and who died without any neurological recovery (or with autopsy evidence of complete brain destruction) and by a comprehensive model that helps us to understand how the brain dies. When a brain is injured, the tissues swell. When the injuries are severe and extensive and the skull is intact, the swelling is enough to make intracranial pressure rise above the blood pressure and thereby to cut off circulation. This ensures that any brain tissue that escaped the first injury will be lost to the ensuing pressure injury. This sequence greatly buttresses the statistical base for assuring certainty.

Nevertheless, we have been inattentive to the fact that many persons determined to be dead by neurological criteria do not develop diabetes insipidus,[14,15] retaining enough hypothalamic function to generate vasopressin. Preservation of hypothalamic function in brain death occurs more often in anoxic-ischemic injuries than in traumatic injuries. The reason for this difference is probably because the increased intracranial pressure in anoxic-ischemic injuries may not be sufficient to eliminate blood flow to the brain and might allow preservation of some relatively anatomically protected or anoxia-resistant cells.[16,17] Perhaps the residual blood flow is more likely in the hypothalamus and those cells are more resistant. These possibilities have not been researched, and their implications for our understanding of declaring death by neurological criteria have not been considered.

In addition, the determination of death is more problematic when this sequence of brain injury from intracranial pressure is not likely to occur. These cases include young children, whose sutures between skull bones have not closed, and persons with extensive skull injuries. The problem of how to determine their death has been left to increased observation time and additional testing (the nature of which is largely left to the judgment of the treating physician).[18] Very few such patients have been reported with follow-up observation for recovery of function or with careful brain examination at autopsy.

Despite the warnings above, for persons with (1) intact skulls, (2) substantial trauma or anoxia, and (3) testing in accordance with published guidelines, the criteria for determining death by neurological examination are probably among the most reliable and valid available in medicine.[19] However, achieving this level of certainty requires adhering to quite specific protocols for determining death. The evidence to date shows that physicians are not being careful in applying these tests.[20,21] The single most important test is the test for apnea, the absence of any drive to breathe despite maximal stimulation. This is an emotionally difficult test, as the professional staff must observe the patient breathless for many minutes. The test has been reported to be performed in a minority of cases in which death is declared on neurological grounds.[22–24] If this is generally true, and especially if the other criteria are similarly disregarded, then the accuracy of the determination of death in practice could be quite seriously error prone.

Similar inattentiveness undoubtedly attends the determination of death on circulatory criteria. Physicians are rarely taught how to determine "routine" death, and it is very difficult to locate a discussion of the topic in the medical literature. Probably many people are declared dead without adequate observation or assessment, although reliable and accurate determinations would be possible just by waiting a minute or two longer before pronouncing death.

Of course, in the highly visible circumstances of organ donation immediately after death, the physicians involved are not likely to make any of these errors of failing to follow a reasonable protocol. These problems are much more likely to arise in "routine" dying, where nothing important turns on the exact minute of death. Nevertheless, all who deal with these issues would be well served to expand the data base for evaluating the criteria so that there are more gold-standard cases and therefore more reliability in the testing, more adequate guidelines, and more precise compliance with published guidelines in the determination of death.

Unitary versus Binary Criteria of Death

Obviously, this discussion would be more straightforward if death were consistently and explicitly held to be the irreversible cessation of the functioning of the brain, which can be known by appropriate examination of neurological functions (and observation period and other tests) or can be known indirectly by having ineffective circulation for a critical period of time.[25] At present, the major statutes and discussions construe the situation as if there are two separate ways to know that death has occurred and make no particular connection between the two. This gives rise to the troubling conception that one might be dead by one set of criteria and not dead by the other. For example, a body could have irreversible cessation of neurological function of the brain, but still have circulation and therefore seem not to be really dead.

There would be advantages to a unitary standard of death holding that irreversible cessation of all function of the entire brain is the death of the person and that one can know that indirectly by circulatory cessation or directly by examination of the brain and its functioning. Then the error would be obvious for those who wrongly believe that cessation of spontaneous heartbeat for 2 minutes allows them to declare the person dead and to place the body on artificially supported circulation.

Conclusion

Research priorities include the need for better evidence of when spontaneous or treatment-induced restoration of circulation is not possible, about what functions of the brain are irrelevant to the determination of death, and about the standards of certainty for cardiovascular or direct neurological examination. Probably society also should address the practices of physicians who are not in compliance with defensible standards. Optimal practices then need to be placed into a serviceable social context, complete with rituals that support the family and the care-giving staff. We have been singularly inattentive to the cultural meanings of this work.

Death is not primarily a medical event. It is primarily a human and family event of the most profound significance. Public policy demands a highly reliable means to determine its having occurred, but public well-being demands more sensitivity and meaning and more support for those involved. The demands for usable organs for transplantation should be heard, but should take a lower priority.

References

1. Guidelines for the determination of death: A report of the medical consultants on the diagnosis of death to the President's Commission for the Study of the Ethical Problems in Medicine and Biomedical and Behavioral Research. *JAMA* 1981;246:2184.

2. Uniform Determination of Death Act. In: President's Commission for the Study of Ethical Problems in Medicine and Biomedical and Behavioral Research. *Defining Death.* Washington, DC: Government Printing Office, 1981, 119.

3. Ivan LP. Time sequence in brain death. In: Morley TP (ed). *Moral, Ethical, and Legal Issues in the Neurosciences.* Springfield, IL: Charles C Thomas, 1981.

4. Cranford RE. Minnesota Medical Association Criteria. Brain death: Concept and criteria. *Minn Med* 1978;61:561,600.

5. Grenvick A, Powner DJ, Snyder JV, et al. Cessation of therapy in terminal illness and brain death. *Crit Care Med* 1978;6:284.

6. Koostra G, Wijnen R, van Hooff JP, van der Linden CJ. Twenty percent more kidneys through a non-heart beating program. *Transplant Proc* 1991;23:910–11.

7. Heineman E, Daemen JHC, Kootstra G. Non-heart-beating donors: Methods and techniques. *Transplant Proc* 1995;27:2895–97.

8. Youngner SJ, Landefeld CS, Coulton CJ, et al. "Brain death" and organ retrieval: A cross-sectional survey of knowledge and concepts among health professionals. *JAMA* 1989;261:2205–10.

9. DeVita MA. The death watch: How and when physicians certified death using cardiopulmonary criteria. Presented at Defining Death in a Technological Age; November 1995; Cleveland, Ohio.

10. Waters DJ, Belz M, Lawse D, Ulstad D. Portable cardiopulmonary bypass: Resuscitation from prolonged ice-water submersion and asystole. *Ann Thorac Surg* 1994;57:1018–19.

11. Thompson DA, Anderson N. Successful resuscitation of a severely hypothermic neonate. *Ann Emerg Med* 1994;23:1390–93.

12. Shewmon DA. Caution in the definition and diagnosis of infant brain death. In: Monagle JF, Thomasma DC (eds). *Medical Ethics: A Guide for Health Professionals.* Rockville, MD: Aspen, 1988, 39.

13. Hanley JA, Lippman-Hand A. If nothing goes wrong, is everything all right? Interpreting zero numerators. *JAMA* 1983;249:1743–45.

14. Fiser DH, Jiminez JF, Wrape V, et al. Diabetes insipidus in children with brain death. *Crit Care Med* 1987;15:551–53.

15. Keren G, Barzilay Z, Schreiber M, et al. Diabetes insipidus indicating a dying brain. *Crit Care Med* 1982;10:798–99.

16. Schroder R. Later changes in brain death: Signs of partial recirculation. *Acta Neuropathol (Berl)* 1983;62:15–23.

17. Outwater KM, Rockoff MA. Diabetes insipidus accompanying brain death in children. *Neurology* 1984;34:1243–46.

18. Task Force for the Determination of Brain Death in Children. Guidelines for the determination of brain death in children. *Arch Neurol* 1987;44:586–88.

19. Guidelines for the determination of death: Report of the medical consultants on the diagnosis of death to the President's Commission for the Study of Ethical Problems in Medicine and Biomedical and Behavioral Research. *JAMA* 1981;246:2184–86.

20. Mejia RE, Pollack MM. Variability in brain death determination practices in children. *JAMA* 1995;274:550–53.

21. Norton DJ. Clinical applications of brain death protocols. *J Neurosci Nurs* 1992;24:354–58.

22. Earnest MP, Beresford HR, McIntyre HB. Testing for apnea in brain death: Methods used by 129 clinicians. *Neurology* 1986;36:542–44.

23. Ropper AH, Kennedy SK, Russell L. Apnea testing in the diagnosis of brain death: Clinical and physiological observation. *J Neurosurg* 1981;55:942–46.

24. Schafer JA, Caronna JJ. Duration of apnea needed to confirm brain death. *Neurology* 1978;28:661–66.

25. Bernat JL, Culver CM, Gert B. On the definition and criterion of death. *Ann Intern Med* 1981;94:389–94.

III

Revisiting Statutes
on Brain Death

THE PHILOSOPHICAL AND scientific disputes about the determination
of death have raised questions about our current public policy. In this
section, Alexander Capron explains and defends the current legal standard, and Robert Veatch and Norman Fost offer alternatives that call for
greater pluralism and flexibility.

Capron summarizes the current law and its development. When intensive care technology was first introduced, the courts ruled inconsis-
tently about the determination of death from jurisdiction to jurisdiction.
As a result, pressure developed to establish one clear and consistent legal
standard through legislation. Although serious consideration was given
to establishing a single criterion based on brain function, a bifurcated
standard (recognizing brain-based and cardiopulmonary criteria
equally) became the law of the land. Capron argues that the law has
worked well; he adopts a pragmatic posture of "If it ain't broke, don't
fix it."

Veatch argues that the current law violates our society's basic precepts
of liberal pluralism. When individuals have different beliefs about when
life ends and acting on these beliefs does not result in harm to others,
the state should allow individual choice. Given that there are several
possible definitions of death, Veatch concludes that "a tolerance of pluralism may be the only way to resolve the public policy debate." Opera-
tionally this means that the state would choose a default position (Veatch
opts for the "middle of the road" whole-brain criterion) and then indi-

viduals would choose more conservative or liberal criteria according to their own philosophical or religious views. For Veatch, reasonable alternatives include cardiopulmonary, whole-brain, or higher-brain criteria. Health care providers would elicit individuals' preferences (à la the Patient Self-determination Act) through advance directives or surrogates.

How many persons would avail themselves of alternative choices under Veatch's proposal is not known. Moreover, while Veatch's proposal may have theoretical appeal, its social costs are far from clear. As Capron and other critics ask: Will standards for homicide, insurance policies, and health care payment be as easily individualized as patients' beliefs about death? Will health professionals be able to distinguish between surrogates who are accurately communicating the patient's moral beliefs and those who use the choice to support their own agendas—for example, extending life because they cannot accept the patient's death? Will the reasons behind a choice be subject to scrutiny, as are claims of conscientious objection to military service, or will they be accepted at face value? Will conservative elements in society agree to a range of choice that allows a personal determination of death for permanently unconscious but spontaneously breathing patients?

Rather than endorsing personal choice in defining death, Fost challenges the usefulness of drawing a line between life and death as a means of solving social problems. He argues that the social problems—forgoing treatment and procuring organs—could have been solved without legislation on brain death. After all, we have evolved to a point at which we forgo life-sustaining treatment for patients who are clearly alive, and, he argues, brain-death legislation really did very little to increase organ procurement. Moreover, says Fost, this legislation encouraged the false belief that a physician needs legal protection to forgo life-sustaining treatment, promoted a whole-brain criterion that turned out to be scientifically and conceptually untenable, and further sanctified the dead-donor rule.

7

The Bifurcated Legal Standard for Determining Death

Does It Work?

Alexander Morgan Capron, LL.B.

The Terminology and Scope of This Discussion

The title of this chapter invokes five terms—*bifurcated, legal, standard, determining,* and *death*—that deserve comment before I elaborate on them as part of the general discussion.

Bifurcated: This term refers to the fact that most statutes proposed and adopted in the United States on this subject over the past 25 years have used two standards by which death is determined, one based on measurement of circulatory and respiratory functions and the other based on brain functions. For example, the Uniform Determination of Death Act (UDDA), which is the law in 36 U.S. jurisdictions,[1] provides that "an individual who has sustained either (1) irreversible cessation of circulatory and respiratory functions, or (2) irreversible cessation of all functions of the entire brain, including the brain stem, is dead. A determination of death must be made in accordance with accepted medical standards."[2]

Bifurcated does not mean that the thing being determined (namely, death) is divided into distinct parts. Rather, it is the method by which death is to be determined that forks into two branches. However, standards like the UDDA have been criticized because they are bifurcated. This pejorative connotation may be partly deserved, because the relationship of the two branches (heart and brain) incorporated into statutes like the UDDA is not made clear by the statute. The true object of most criticism is not the twin standards for determining death but rather the content of those standards, particularly the so-called brain-death standard.

Legal: This chapter addresses the legal as distinct from the medical or philosophical aspects of the topic of "defining" death, as the task is commonly (albeit perhaps misleadingly) described.[3] This distinction does not suppose that a useful legal rule can be created or maintained without reference to philosophical or medical views, merely that the task of framing a legal rule is not necessarily coincident with those other tasks. The legal standard in question is a matter of positive law, whether manifested in judicial decisions (as in the United States until 25 years ago, with the common law definition of death, and as remains true at least in part even today in four states), in legislation (as is generally the norm today), or in regulations (as is true in New York State). Positive law is arbitrary in the sense of resulting from a human act rather than being necessitated by the nature of the matter to which the law is addressed. In the case of standards for determining death, however, it seems unlikely that positive law that failed to accord with what most people regarded as the reality of death would be accepted or allowed to persist.

Standard: The law might have addressed the topic of death at any of several levels. The four levels widely used range from basic *concepts* of death, through general physiological *standards,* to operational *criteria* and specific *tests and procedures.*[4] Although concepts, such as "departure of the animating or vital principle" or "irreversible loss of personhood," may be too abstract to be useful in the practical task of declaring death, the concept(s) chosen will shape the more focused standards actually adopted; conversely, one can derive a conceptual statement from the standards, criteria, and tests in use. It is also true that philosophical issues arise not just in the details of a standard but in the very choice "to define death in terms of organ systems, physiological functions, or recognizable human activities, capacities, and conditions,"[5] such as "irreversible cessation of spontaneous respiratory and circulatory functions" or "irreversible loss of the ability to respond or communicate." The UDDA establishes general standards for determining death and then leaves to the medical profession, applying what the UDDA calls "accepted medical standards" (a somewhat confusing term in this context), the articulation of criteria and tests to implement the standards. (In some countries, the law incorporated the criteria and tests, which risks either freezing the law at existing technical capacities or necessitating repeated amendments.) When the UDDA was proposed, a group of medical advisors to the President's commission published a statement on how death should be determined in patients older than 5 years that still guides determinations of death in most institutions in the United States.[6]

Determining: No word is more important than *determining* because it reinforces the central point that what is at issue is the process of reaching a decision about whether death has occurred rather than a statutory attempt to explain life and death. The word *determining* also conveys two other essential features. First, it underlines that what is involved is a human determination, rather than a discovery, of a particular status. Second, the making of determinations is an activity associated with "findings" and "consequences," in this case, adjusting the relationship of a formerly living person (now determined to be dead) to other entities, with consequent changes in rights and responsibilities.

Death: This final term might not seem to need any introductory explanation, but recent resurrection of the old debate about whether death is a process or an event makes it advisable to emphasize what is addressed within this chapter. First, the deaths of interest are those of human beings, which can be expected to affect the way the concepts, standards, and so forth are worked out; at the same time, the concept of human death has long been grounded in biological functions that are common to all mammals. Second, the determination of death relates to an actual entity; the death of a particular human body may coincide with other things, such as the loss of personhood or the departure of a specific Jane Doe whose existence gave special meaning to that body. The fact that measurements—and ultimately a determination—are being made about a body reveals that it is merely playing with words to object that "there is no state of death," since once life ceases "there is no being in any state or space."[7] A "person" and the interests that he or she possessed during life may well be said to become nonexistent when life ceases. Yet because the personality or personhood of the individual who is constituted in a body may wane (and sometimes wax again) before the human being dies does not (for reasons elaborated below) make those prior states "death" in any sense other than the metaphorical. Whatever the standards for determining death may be (and the current ones are not carved in stone), once they have been met, the organism is dead. The precise moment when this occurs may not be easily ascertained and usually does not matter enough to require minute precision. But a moment does indeed exist when a living human being becomes a being in the "state of death."[8]

This chapter addresses three issues: (1) How did the law come to recognize both cardiopulmonary and whole-brain standards or criteria? (2) How well has the law worked in practice? (3) What challenge do new protocols for procuring organs from non-heart-beating cadavers pose to existing law?

How Did the Law Come to Recognize the Bifurcated Standard?

Medical—and Other—Interests in Changing the Law

The development in the 1950s, and ever wider use over succeeding decades, of intensive methods to resuscitate and support victims of head trauma, stroke, and other neurological injuries (with barbiturates, respirators, vasopressors, and feeding/fluids by tube) left some physicians unsure about the legal status of patients/bodies whose circulatory and respiratory functions were dependent on artificial support. When such means were used on other sorts of injuries, such as those involving muscular paralysis, their use was for a limited period, was accompanied by the continuation of consciousness, or both. Patients in this new category were profoundly comatose—indeed, beyond coma in the description of French physicians[9]—and when their bodies eventually stopped functioning, postmortem examination of their brains revealed extensive necrosis and autolysis, which demonstrated that their brains had ceased functioning prior to the collapse of their other, artificially supported organs.

Although relatively rare, such patients did pose a problem for physicians and families in determining what care was appropriate for—or even owed—them. Today these patients might well be lumped together with others who, physicians are considerably certain, have underlying medical problems that could not be reversed or whose mental functioning could not be restored. Analysis of this type, though now standard, was then not generally used, however, so that the decision to forgo life-sustaining interventions for seriously ill and dying patients was regarded as much more difficult than the decision to discontinue intervention once a patient had been declared dead. Thus, medical interest in modernizing the law on death determination rested in part on an interest in narrowing the number of situations in which a (perhaps agonizing) decision on whether to allow a patient to die needs to be made.

Had physicians been content to let the law and their own practices evolve slowly, perhaps no legislation would have been needed. The number of artificially supported patients whose brain had completely ceased functioning was small (and concentrated in tertiary centers) and the risk of legal liability from forgoing life support was virtually nonexistent, however fearful the medical community may have been.[10] But progress in organ transplantation, and particularly the first human-to-human heart transplant in 1967, brought greater urgency to the question of which artificially supported patients qualified as potential donors. The Uniform Anatomical Gift Act (UAGA), which was proposed at this time and quickly became the most widely adopted uniform act in the history of the National Conference of Commissioners on Uniform State Laws (NCCUSL), treated the occurrence of death as a straightforward, settled matter to be left in physicians' hands. Many physicians, however, recognized that the existing legal definition of death, framed by judicial decisions (there then being no statutory law on the subject) in terms of irreversible loss of *all* vital functions, did not take account of contemporary medical capabilities.

Finally, the legal system itself faced problems. Not only did the new medical technology complicate the determination of death in the rare case where its occurrence and timing might be important, but the decision by physicians to utilize a "dead" body as an organ donor could (and did) give rise to tort claims by the donor's relatives as well as objections by criminal defendants that their victims' deaths were caused not by the defendants but by the surgeons who removed the hearts. Although defenses of this sort ultimately failed on appeal, they continued to be raised and were sometimes accepted by lower courts.

All of these factors played a role, but the greatest pressure apparently came from physicians who wanted to avoid even a possibility of criminal or civil liability, especially in the context of organ donation. As the drafter of the first statute "defining" death explained, that law was believed necessary to protect transplant surgeons against the risk of "a criminal charge, for the existence of a resuscitated heart in another body should be excellent evidence that the donor was not dead [under the then-existing common-law standard] until the operator excised the heart."[11]

Why the Two-Part Standard?

By the late 1960s, it was obvious that a change had to occur. The report of the Harvard ad hoc committee in 1968—perhaps reflecting Henry Beecher's general preference to leave ethical adjustments in medical practice in the hands of the "conscientious physician"[12]—concluded that the law would not need to be changed, but that view was soon rejected, with other physicians taking the lead. Once the issue had been clearly posed, there were only four alternatives, the first two of which had hardly any support.

First, the common-law view could be maintained. Into the early 1970s, some courts were continuing to read existing law to mean that all vital functions, even those supported by artificial means, had to have ceased irreversibly before death could be declared. If this view prevailed, transplant surgeons would have to restrict themselves (as some, at least in the kidney field, were apparently willing to do) to non-heart-beating cadavers; this course would certainly pose a major problem for cardiac transplantation, as well as for decision making about discontinuing support for the even larger number of patients without brain functions who were not potential organ donors.

Second, the common-law rule could be maintained but simply disregarded by physicians when determining death in potential organ donors. Although feasible (and perhaps even legitimate under one reading of Section 7 of the UAGA), this alternative would lead to treating patients in identical states differently, based on whether they were potential organ donors; the only way to have a relative disconnected from life support might be to agree to him or her being an organ donor. It would also give the medical profession—and, indeed, individual physicians—the authority to frame the standards on which the basic civil status of people would be determined, either as living persons with many rights or as dead bodies with only the right to be handled respectfully and buried.

The other two alternatives involved changing the law either by replacing the existing legal standard with a brain-based standard or by supplementing the existing standard with a brain-based standard. The latter gives rise to the present concern with bifurcation. The first enacted statute, adopted in 1970 in Kansas, followed the latter route and was immediately criticized because its two standards were presented without explanation, implying that brain death was a distinct form of death. This was only reinforced by the Kansas statute's explicit mention of organ transplantation in the section on determinations based on "the absence of spontaneous brain function" when "further attempts at resuscitation or supportive maintenance will not succeed." Despite such criticism, the Kansas statute was adopted in four additional jurisdictions (although it remains on the books only in Virginia).

Partially in reaction to the concerns, however, two of the four model acts that appeared in the following years took the first tack and based death determinations *solely* on "irreversible cessation of all functioning of the brain, including the brain stem" (Uniform Brain Death Act, proposed in 1978) or "irreversible cessation of total brain function" (American Bar Association model 1975 act). Although two states adopted the former and five states the latter, all but Illinois (which retains the ABA statute in the definitional section of its UAGA)[13] have since replaced these brain-only statutes with the UDDA. One reason they were replaced, or failed to receive wider adoption, is that they do not explain the relationship between brain-based determinations of death and determinations when brain functioning is not measured.

The NCCUSL did include a comment on the UBDA that the "Act does not preclude a determination of death under other legal or medical criteria, including the traditional criteria of cessation of respiration and circulation. Other criteria are practical in cases where artificial life-support systems are not utilized." Such commentary is not part of the statute and is unlikely to come to the attention of most persons trying to implement the statute. The greater difficulties, though, are that it creates an open-ended category of "other" unspecified criteria (which does little to establish a legal standard) and that it does not relate these criteria to the statutory criteria. In other words, even with the commentary included, the UBDA amounted to the sort of uncoordinated dual standard that the critics of the Kansas law found troublesome.

As an alternative to the Kansas statute, in 1972 Leon Kass and I proposed a model statute that attempted to meet head on the concern about "two deaths." Prior to the UDDA, it was the most widely adopted statute:

> A person will be considered dead if in the announced opinion of a physician, based on ordinary standards of medical practice, he has experienced an irreversible cessation of respiratory and circulatory functions, or in the event that artificial means of support preclude a determination that these functions have ceased, he has experienced an irreversible cessation of total brain functions. Death will have occurred at the time when the relevant functions ceased.[14]

This statute was premised on the conclusion, reached in discussions of the Hastings Center's research group on death and dying, that for the foreseeable future most deaths would be diagnosed through measurements of heart and lung activity and the statute ought explicitly to recognize this fact. The primary reason that the drafters of the UDDA chose not to drop the traditional heart-lung criteria in favor of measuring only the loss of brain activity, beyond wishing to avoid the confusing term *brain death* was that the statute was not intended to "define" death but to recognize the means through which it can be determined to have occurred. Irreversible cessation of either circulatory/respiratory functions or all brain functions provide such means, and the description of the two means does not suggest that either the old or the new "vital signs" are themselves death; they are merely the means by which a skilled practitioner, using the standards of medical practice, can ascertain that death has occurred.

To have limited the statute's scope to one of the useful measures would have had one of several odd results: (1) force clinicians actually to measure brain functions in all cases, hugely wasting valuable resources; (2) force clinicians falsely to state that they have determined that brain functions have ceased even though they have not measured those functions; or (3) allow clinicians to state that they have established permanent cessation of circulatory and respiratory functions and from that are presuming the cessation of brain functions because the latter functions do not persist after a relatively brief period of anoxia. Of these, the third is the only plausible one, and once it is recognized that the circulatory and respiratory measures are going to be the ones applied in close to 95 percent of all determinations of death, it seems odd to make them subsidiary to a statutorily recognized standard of measuring the absence of brain functioning. If the continued legitimacy of circulatory and respiratory measures is thus accepted, how much more straightforward and less confusing it is to recognize them explicitly in the statute and to tie their use to the same standards of medical carefulness as apply to determinations that are based on actually measuring cessation of brain functions.

What Does the Brain-based Standard Convey?

A decision to continue recognizing the loss of the traditional cardiopulmonary vital signs for determining death is on its face less debatable than the decision to add a new set of vital signs, especially ones that are employed precisely because the old vital signs are still manifest in the patient. The question, which can only be answered by skilled practitioners typically employing sophisticated equipment, is whether these signs lack their usual significance because they are mere artifacts of medical intervention. Although the use of brain-based criteria and tests for death was unfamiliar at first for medical professionals as well as for the general public, it has come to be accepted legally as well as medically, although confusion and discomfort among some clinicians has been reported.[15]

In addition to physicians' and families' dismay over the prospect of having to support indefinitely bodies that would otherwise be recognized as corpses, acceptance of the brain-based method of determining death rests on two factors. First, careful observation and analysis established that, correctly applied, the criteria and tests employed to determine death based upon absent brain functions were at least as reliable as those that relied on the loss of cardiopulmonary functions. Second, these studies also confirmed the existing concept of death as a phenomenon diagnosable by the two alternative methods, for the autopsy results in bodies determined to be dead by brain criteria indicated that they would have been incapable of spontaneous respiration or circulation. The circle of integrated functioning was broken, however it was assessed.

These findings were particularly important with regard to organ donors because of the special concerns that arise when a heart removed from a dead body goes on to function in another patient. Perhaps the easiest way to think of this is to use a comparison invoked in some of the talmudic commentary on brain death, which describes it as "physiological decapitation."[16] In actual decapitation, the head plainly ceases functioning as part of an integrated organism; by analogy, the loss of brain functions not only deprives the patient of consciousness but also of the brain's central place in the nervous integration of bodily functions. At the moment of decapitation, other organs (including the heart) remain capable of functioning. In the case of actual decapitation, they could conceivably be used immediately in transplantation. In medical practice, however, physiological decapitation is less obvious and hence, to be established, requires careful measurement over a period of time. While this is occurring, the organs must be artificially maintained. While the organs remain in the donor, they function because of the support that the donor's (dead) body receives; when they are transplanted, they continue to function because they are now part of another, integrated organism. Organ transplantation thus does more than provide a situation in which the brain-based standard is used to determine death; it also

crystalizes the contemporary understanding of death because it illustrates how some of an organism's vital parts remain functional even
though the organism has died, namely, lost its ability to perform as an
integrated whole because some essential element (typically, the brain)
can no longer function and cannot be replaced.

Why Legislation?

If legal change was inevitable by the early 1970s, why was it desirable for
change to come about through legislation rather than through judicial
decision? In brief, problems of principle and practicality emerged in
relying primarily on the courts to reformulate the standards for determining death.

First, like the medical profession, the judiciary may be too narrowly
based for the task. It has no means for actively involving the public in its
decision-making processes. Second, judge-made law has been most successful in factual settings embedded in well-defined social and economic
practices, with the guidance of past decisions and commentary. Third,
courts operate within a limited compass—the facts and contentions of a
particular case—and with limited expertise; they have neither the staff
nor the authority to investigate or to conduct hearings to explore such
issues as public opinion or the scientific merits of competing definitions.
Consequently, a judge's decision may be merely a rubber-stamping of
the opinions expressed by the medical experts who appear in court.
Moreover, testimony in an adversary proceeding is usually restricted to
the two sides of an issue and may not fairly represent the spectrum of
opinion held by authorities in the field.

In the cases in which parties first argued for a redefinition, the courts
were unwilling to disturb the existing legal definition. Such deference
to precedent is understandable (because everyone needs to be able to
rely on predictable legal rules in managing their affairs) and cannot
always be overcome by arguments on the merits of a new rule. As late as
1968 a California appellate tribunal, in a case involving an inheritorship
issue, declined to redefine death in terms of brain functioning despite
the admittedly anachronistic nature of an exclusively heart-lung definition.[17] As already described, the unsettled state of the common-law definition of death in the 1970s led to unfortunate consequences not only
for patients and physicians but even for prosecutors. Courts had to grap-
ple not only with civil suits (such as *Tucker v. Lower,* a 1972 Virginia case
against a surgeon who had removed the heart of a donor who was not

dead under the common-law standard, in which the jury returned a defense verdict after the judge, without explanation or clarification of the law, permitted the jurors to find that death had occurred when the brain ceased functioning irreversibly),[18] but also with criminal prosecutions (including several cases in which defendants tried, ultimately without success, to escape a charge of homicide on the grounds that their victims were alive when physicians removed them from their respirators).[19]

In contrast, the legislative process permits the public scrutiny of and participation in lawmaking and admits a wider range of information. This is important if basic and perhaps controversial choices among alternative policies must be made. Because they provide prospective guidance, statutory standards have the additional advantage of dispelling public and professional doubt, thereby reducing both the fear and the likelihood of cases for malpractice or homicide against physicians. Finally, greater uniformity among states arises from statutes than from judicial lawmaking.

By 1980, when the President's commission began its work and took up its mandate to address "the advisability of developing a uniform definition of death,"[20] the major impediment to statutory progress was the multiplicity of statutory models—Kansas, Capron-Kass, ABA, AMA, and UBDA. Despite differences in language, the models were consistent in their aims. Yet the differences in wording confused legislators who were reluctant to take sides among the competing sponsoring groups. Accordingly, the President's commission, together with the three major sponsors—the ABA, the AMA, and the NCCUSL—drafted a single model bill that could be proposed in all jurisdictions. The resulting statute, the UDDA, was proposed in 1981 and is now law in 36 jurisdictions.

Several principles lie behind the UDDA. First, the phenomenon of interest to physicians, legislators, and the public alike is a human being's death, not the "death" of his cells, tissues, or organs. Indeed, one of the problems with the term *brain death* is that it wrongly suggests that an organ can die. Second, a statute on death will resolve the problem of whether to continue artificial support in only some of the cases of comatose patients. The cessation of treatment for patients who are alive but for whom further treatment is considered (by the patients or others) to be pointless or degrading is a separate matter. As Leon Kass and I argued from the outset, the question of "when to allow to die" is distinct from "when to declare death."[21]

Third, the merits of a legislative definition are judged by whether its purposes are properly defined and by how well the legislation meets those purposes. In addition to its cultural and religious importance, society needs a definition of death for decisions having legal consequences; besides terminal medical care or transplantation, these include homicide, damages for the wrongful death of a person, property and wealth transmission, and determination of insurance benefits, taxes, and marital status. While some commentators have argued that a single definition was inappropriate because different policy objectives might exist in different contexts,[22] it has been generally agreed that a single definition of death is capable of fulfilling the needs of the law in a wide variety of contexts, just as the traditional definition was generally applied.[23] The need for special, separate standards is most often advanced as a means to facilitate organ transplantation, but

> the question whether the benefits conferred by transplantation justify the risks associated with a broader "definition" of death should be addressed directly rather than by attempting to subsume it under the question "what is death?" Such a direct confrontation with the issue could lead to a discussion about the standards and procedures under which organs might be taken from persons near death, or even those still quite alive, at their own option or that of relatives, physicians, or representatives of the state. The major advantage of keeping the issues separate is not, of course, that this will facilitate transplantation, but that it will remove a present source of concern: it is unsettling to contemplate that as you lie slowly dying physicians are free to use a more "lenient" standard to declare you dead if they want to remove your organs for transplantation into other patients.[24]

Furthermore, "calling the same person 'dead' for one purpose and 'alive' for another would engender nothing but confusion."[25]

Fourth, although dying is a process (since not all parts of the body cease functioning equally and synchronously), a line can and must be drawn between those beings who are alive and those who are dead. The ability of modern biomedicine to extend the functioning of various organ systems may have made knowing which side of the line a patient is on more problematic, but it has not erased the line. The line drawn by the UDDA is an arbitrary one in the sense that it results from human choice among a number of possibilities, but not in the sense of having no articulated, defensible, and, indeed, widely accepted rationale.

Fifth, the standards must be uniform for all persons. It is, to say the least, unseemly for a person's wealth or potential social utility as an organ donor to affect the way in which the moment of his or her death is determined. Sixth, and of great importance in light of the challenges discussed in Part IV below, the UDDA was framed on the premise that it is often beneficial for the law to move incrementally, particularly when matters of basic cultural and ethical values are implicated. Incremental movement is not so much slow (which it usually is) as deliberate, making only those changes that are necessary to deal with the problem at hand. In the present case, the problem was not that people had doubts about the validity or meaning of the established definition of death. Rather, the problem was that the means customarily employed to diagnose death were rendered unusable by medical interventions. Therefore, the statute provides a modern restatement of the means for determining death as it is traditionally understood as a biological phenomenon, whether one is speaking of a person or any other animal. It was not necessary to redefine death, which is just as well, since no consensus would have existed on how to do so.

Finally, in making law in a highly technological area, care is needed that the definition be at once sufficiently precise to determine behavior in the manner desired by the public and yet not so specific that it is tied to the details of contemporary technology. The UDDA achieves this flexible precision by confining itself to the general *standards* by which death is to be determined, while leaving to the continually developing judgment of biomedical practitioners the establishment and application of appropriate *criteria* and specific *tests* for determining that the standards have been met. For this reason, the President's commission assembled the group of leading neurologists, neurosurgeons, pediatricians, anesthesiologists, and other authorities on the determination of death mentioned previously, who prepared the medical guidelines that were published in *JAMA* in 1981, coincident with the release of the commission's report *Defining Death*.

How Well Has the Law Worked in Practice?

If It Ain't Broke

Though not without its problems, the UDDA exemplifies what Daniel Wikler has described as "a remarkable consensus, bordering on unanimity, . . . among the world's medical and legal experts on the definition of death."[26] Certainly, from a practical viewpoint, the standards set forth in the UDDA seem to have worked well, and the fact that, unlike the Capron-Kass model, the statute does not explain the relationship between the two standards has not proven a problem. When the standard has been challenged in court, it has been upheld.[27] Furthermore, courts have understood that the standard for determining death imposes no limitation on the separate decision to terminate life support in a terminally ill patient who does not meet the standard.[28] The judicial resolution of the issue of death has plainly been more straightforward in states with the UDDA (and Capron-Kass statute)[29] than in those without statutes or than I expect would prove the case were any state to adopt a "conscience clause" of the type urged by Robert Veatch.[30] Even the less sweeping "opt-out" provisions adopted by New Jersey in 1991 may prove problematic.[31] By providing that the neurological standard should not be applied when a physician has reason to believe that a brain-based declaration of death would "violate the personal religious beliefs" of the patient (in which case "death shall be declared, and the time of death fixed, solely upon the basis of [the] cardio-pulmonary criteria" specified elsewhere in the statute), the New Jersey law sows confusion and invites litigation. For example, it sets up the prospect that, when a dispute arises over the religious beliefs of a respirator-supported patient, a single set of findings (e.g., that all functions of the brain have ceased irreversibly) could produce oscillating results (alive, not dead, not alive, and so forth) depending upon fluctuations in the resolution of the dispute.

The logical conclusion from the foregoing is "If it ain't broke, don't fix it." Theoretical objections of philosophers notwithstanding, the UDDA, with its "bifurcated" reliance on circulatory/respiratory and whole-brain standards for determining death, seems to work fine. A return to the "cessation of all vital signs" rule of the common law would have a great many bad results.

Do Problems with Clinical Measures Mean Problems with the Statute?

Some commentators have suggested that we "rethink brain death" because several clinical tests of the phenomenon are not in accord with the standard of "irreversible loss of all functions of the entire brain."[32] Specifically, they note that some patients diagnosed dead on neurological grounds retain hypothalamic-endocrine function and others show cerebral electrical activity or responsiveness to the environment. They also note that some may have spinal reflexes.

For the first category, there is a sequence of reasoning that should be applied to clinical findings observed now or in the future in patients diagnosed dead. In each case, one needs to ask:

1. Are such findings observed among patients diagnosed through both alternative means of diagnosing death? For example, if people who are diagnosed dead on heart-lung grounds routinely have hypothalamic-endocrine function, cerebral electrical activity, environmental responses, or spinal reflexes, then their presence in neurologically diagnosed patients is not cause for concern.
2. Are such findings inconsistent with the irreversible loss of integrative functioning of the organism? Is the presence, for example, of hypothalamic endocrine function inconsistent with an irreversible loss of integrated functioning of the organism? The question then becomes whether, for example, the secretion of arginine vasopressin is so physiologically integrative (compared with other functions whose cessation is an accepted part of the diagnostic criteria for death) that it must be irreversibly absent for death to be declared.
3. Do such findings relate to functions that when lost do not return and are not replaceable by external means (as a respirator substitutes for lungs that no longer function spontaneously)?

The answers to these points will determine whether it is appropriate (or perhaps mandatory) to, for example, add measurements of arginine vasopressin to the tests performed in diagnosing death or, conversely, whether the findings from such new (and perhaps complicated and expensive tests) fail to add any essential information.

The existence of spinal reflexes is different. Unlike the other observations, it was fully acknowledged by all involved in the process of framing the standards, the criteria, and the tests for brain-based determinations of death. Truog and Fackler can easily point to physiological definitions of the brain as the entire central nervous system, but the term *brain* in the so-called brain-death definition explicitly excluded the nervous system below the brainstem because activity there did not contradict the theoretic premises of the diagnosis.

In sum, I see no problem with modifying the clinical criteria to incorporate the outcomes of tests and procedures that have meaning and significance consistent with existing criteria.

What Challenge Do NHBC Protocols Pose to Existing Law?

One final challenge to the UDDA has been presented by the non-heart-beating cadaver protocols that highlight the significance of the irreversibility requirement regarding the cessation of relevant functions. They raise the question, "If a decision is made not to attempt reversing the loss of a function, can one say that the loss is irreversible?"

Under the Pittsburgh protocol, for example, a patient dependent on life-support technology who desires to be an organ donor is taken to the operating room and disconnected from the life support, leading (usually) to cardiac arrest. After 2 minutes of asystole, death is declared based upon the UDDA's first alternative, "irreversible cessation of circulatory and respiratory functions," and organs can be removed for transplantation. To the objection that the body is not dead because brain functions doubtless remain, it is answered that the UDDA defines death as established by alternative criteria.

The Pittsburgh protocol seems less a challenge to the UDDA than simply a contradiction of it. The failure to attempt to restore circulatory and respiratory functions in these patients prevents lawfully declaring that death has occurred because *irreversibility* must mean more than simply "we chose not to reverse, although we might have succeeded." It is certainly true that circumstances will dictate whether a reversal can be attempted or will succeed. A cardiopulmonary arrest in a modern American operating suite has different implications for determining death than one that occurs in the wilderness. But even though the absence of medical technology in the wilderness would mean that a statement of finality could perhaps be made sooner than in the operating suite, the actual point in each case at which it becomes impossible to reverse the loss of functions would be unaffected.

If a bystander in the wilderness setting were to say "It's irreversible, he's dead" when all that he meant was "There is no way to reverse the cessation of breathing and heartbeat given the circumstances"—in other words, "It's hopeless"—he would be confusing a prognosis for a diagnosis. Yet this confusion would be of little significance for three reasons. First, any theoretical possibility of reversal would be only brief. Damage to the brain from the anoxia would very quickly render the cessation of cardiopulmonary activity irreversible if it wasn't already. Second, no action comparable to the removal of organs in the operating room is likely to occur during this brief period. These two reasons relate to fair and appropriate treatment of the individual. There is also a third, more social reason why the potential misstatement uttered in the wilderness is of little significance: it is invisible and hence not subject to being generalized.

In contrast, the decision to follow a Pittsburgh-style protocol would inevitably affect other cases. The reason for alternative standards for determining death is not that we believe there are two kinds of death. On the contrary, there is one phenomenon that can be viewed through two windows, and the requirement of irreversibility ensures that what is seen through both is the same or virtually the same thing. Disregarding the requisite of irreversibility as it applies to either standard is as destructive of the process of determining death as it would be to ignore the requisite of cessation.

Thus, replacing "irreversible cessation of circulatory and respiratory functions" with "we choose not to reverse" flies in the face of the UDDA's underlying premise. In the absence of establishing circulatory/respiratory irreversibility, one has no reason to suppose that brain functions will have ceased irreversibly at the point when the patient was declared dead and used as an organ donor. If a transplant team wants to rely only on the circulatory/respiratory standard, rather than conduct tests of brain function, to determine death in patients who are discontinued from life support, then it will have to explain why the resumption of cardiac function in a heart removed from a patient thus diagnosed as dead does not show the falsity of the diagnosis. Unlike the removal of a still-functional heart or other vital organ from a body determined to be dead because of a loss of brain functions, the break in the circle under the Pittsburgh protocol (in which brain functions are not assayed) is said to be in circulatory/respiratory functions, which is prima facie incompatible with the heart or other vital organ manifesting continued functional ability.

Notes

1. The UDDA has been adopted by legislatures in 31 states, the District of Columbia, and the U.S. Virgin Islands and is also incorporated into the definition section of the Health Care Surrogate Act in Illinois, the only state that retains the American Bar Association's model "brain death" act (as part of its version of the Uniform Anatomical Gift Act); in addition, the UDDA provides the legal standard in New York by incorporation into a 1987 State Department of Health

regulation (which also requires hospitals to establish and implement a policy that makes "reasonable accommodation" for an individual's "religious or moral objection to [such] determination") and in Washington State (in the form of a 1982 decision of the state's supreme court). See A. M. Capron and F. H. Cate, "Death and Organ Transplantation," in M. G. Macdonald, R. M. Kaufman, A. M. Capron, and I. M. Birnbaum, eds., *Treatise on Health Care Law* (New York: Matthew Bender, 1991, May 1995 Suppl.), 21–29 to 21–32 and 21T-1 to 21T-4 (table).

2. The UDDA also contains language, standard to such acts, about the name of the statute and about uniform construction and application among enacting states.

3. See, e.g., R. E. Cranford, "Death, Definition and Determination of: I. Criteria for Death," in W. T. Reich, ed., *Encyclopedia of Bioethics*, rev. ed. (New York: Simon & Schuster Macmillan, 1995), 529–34, and K. G. Gervais, "Death, Definition and Determination of: II. Philosophical and Theological Perspectives," ibid., 540–49.

4. See A. M. Capron and L. R. Kass, *A Statutory Definition of the Standards for Determining Human Death: An Appraisal and a Proposal,* 121 U. Pa. L. Rev. 87, 102–4 (1972). James Bernat, Charles Culver, and Bernard Gert utilize three levels of terms, without explaining the advantage of such a scheme over the four-level model; they use the generic term. Bernat JL, Culver CM, Gert B. "On the Definition and Criterion of Death." *Annals of Internal Medicine* 94 (1981): 389–90.

5. Capron and Kass, *Statutory Definition,* 102.

6. Medical Consultants on the Diagnosis of Death to the President's Commission for the Study of Ethical Problems in Medicine and Biomedical and Behavioral Research, "Guidelines for the Determination of Death," *Journal of the American Medical Association* 246 (1981): 2184–86.

7. L. L. Emanuel, "Reexamining Death: The Asymptotic Model and a Bounded Zone Definition," *Hastings Center Report* 25 (1995): 27 n. 4.

8. "Death should be viewed not as a process but as the event that separates the process of dying from the process of disintegration." Bernat, Culver, and Gert, "Definition of Death," 389.

9. P. Mollaret and M. Goulon, "La coma depasse," *Revue Neurologique* 101 (1959): 3–15.

10. See, e.g., *Bacchiochi v. Johnson Memorial Hospital,* No. 256126 (Hartford/ New Britain Super. Ct., March 13, 1981) (declining to "update" common law but providing reassurance that no liability will follow discontinuation of interventions on patients without brain functions).

11. Taylor, "A Statutory Definition of Death in Kansas," *Journal of the American Medical Association* 215 (1971): 296 (letter to the editor).

12. In a landmark article published shortly before the work of the Harvard ad hoc committee, Dr. Beecher, having documented dozens of unethical experiments with human subjects, concluded that, rather than regulation, a "more reliable safeguard" for ethical research was "provided by the presence of an

intelligent, informed, conscientious, compassionate, responsible investigator."
H. K. Beecher, "Ethics and Clinical Research," *New England Journal of Medicine*
274 (1966): 1354, 1360.

13. Ill. Comp. Stat. Ann. ch 755, § 50/2(b)(1995). As described in Note 1
above, Illinois is also unusual in having made the UDDA part of its Health Care
Surrogate Act, Ill. Comp. Stat. Ann ch. 755, §40/10 (1995), which orders the
termination of interventions in the event of the patient's death. The net result
is that, in Illinois, determinations of death under statute are limited to organ
donors and persons covered by the surrogate law; in fact, Illinois physicians apparently have generalized and apply the UDDA standards in all circumstances,
without legal problems.

14. A. M. Capron, "Legal Definition of Death," *Annals of the New York Academy
of Sciences* 315 (1978): 349 (setting forth a somewhat simplified version of the
Capron-Kass proposal).

15. S. Youngner, C. Landefeld, C. Coulton, B. Juknialis, and M. Leary, "'Brain
Death' and Organ Retrieval: A Cross-sectional Survey of Knowledge and Concepts
among Health Professionals," *Journal of the American Medical Association* 261
(1989): 2205.

16. M. D. Tendler, "Cessation of Brain Function: Ethical Implications in Terminal Care and Organ Transplant," *Annals of the New York Academy of Sciences* 315
(1978): 394, 395.

17. *In re* Estate of Schmidt, 261 Cal. App.2d 262, 67 Cal. Rptr. 847 (1968).

18. *Tucker v. Lower,* No. 2231 (Richmond, Va. L. & Eq. Ct., May 23, 1972).

19. See, e.g., *People v. Saldana,* 47 Cal. App.3d 954, 122 Cal Rptr. 243 (1975);
State v. Brown, 8 Ore. App. 72, 491 P.2d 1193 (1971).

20. 42 U.S.C. §1802 (1978).

21. Capron and Kass, *Statutory Definition,* 111.

22. See, e.g., R. B. Dworkin, *Death in Context,* 48 Ind. L.J. 623 (1973).

23. The general applicability of the "definition of death" does not preclude
the use of additional triggers for the same actions. For example, marriage may
be terminated by divorce as well as by death. "Presumed death" is another trigger
that applies in many areas, such as marital status and distribution of assets; such
presumptions, based upon a showing of unexplained absence for a specified
number of years, are not true "definitions of death," however, which accounts
for the protections built into such statutes to readjust many of the steps taken if
the "dead" person shows up again. See generally A. M. Capron, *The Purpose of
Death: A Reply to Professor Dworkin,* 48 Ind. L.J. 640, 643–45 (1973).

24. Capron and Kass, *Statutory Definition,* 107–8 (citations omitted).

25. President's Commission for the Study of Ethical Problems in Medicine
and Biomedical and Behavioral Research, "Defining Death: A Report on the
Medical, Legal and Ethical Issues in the Determination of Death," 60 (1981),
citing F. Fabro, *Bacchiochi vs. Johnson Memorial Hospital,* 45 Conn Med. 267 (1981),
which describes the uncertainties created by the statute Connecticut then had

on "brain death," which applied only to organ donors; physicians were unwilling to declare dead a patient who had suffered irreversible loss of total brain functions because she was not an organ donor.

26. D. Wikler, "Brain Death: A Durable Consensus?" *Bioethics* 7 (1993): 239–41.

27. See, e.g., *Alvardo v. New York City Health & Hospitals Corp.*, Index No. 20767/89 (N.Y. Co. Sup. Ct., Oct. 18, 1989). To the extent that courts have had anything critical to say, the Kansas model (with its obvious deficiencies) has been the one in question. See, e.g., *Fredella v. Farrelly,* 28 V.I. 90, 95 (Territorial Court of the Virgin Islands, 1993) (finding the territory's Kansas-model statute "woefully inadequate" because it failed to explain when either of its two "definitions" of death applied). Thereafter, the legislature of the Virgin Islands repealed its statute and replaced it with the UDDA.

28. See, e.g., *In re* Colyer, 660 P.2d 739, 741 (Wash. 1983); *Barber v. Superior Court,* 147 Cal. App. 3d 1006 (1983).

29. See, e.g., *Crobons v. Wisconsin National Life Insurance Company,* 594 F.Supp. 379 (E.D. Mich. 1984), aff'd, 790 F.2d 475 (6th Cir. 1986); *In re* Rosebush, No. 88–349180 Az (Oakland Co. Cir. Ct., Mich., July 29, 1988). Even the modified Capron-Kass statute in Florida (which recognizes neurologically based determination but allows unspecified standards to be used for non-"brain death" determinations) was read sensibly by the Florida Supreme Court, which limited determinations in patients not supported by respirators to the circulatory-respiratory one recognized by UDDA. *In re* T.A.C.P., 609 So. 2d 588 (Fla. 1992) (declining to create an additional common law standard of death for anencephalic infants).

30. R. Veatch, *Death, Dying and the Biological Revolution* (New Haven: Yale University Press, 1976), 72–76, under which an individual (or family members, should the individual already be incompetent) could specify the (apparently unbounded) standards to be used for determining death, based on the individual's personal or religious views.

31. L. 1991, ch. 90, N.J.S.A. 26:6A-1 to 6A-8 (Supp. 1995).

32. R. D. Truog and J. C. Fackler, "Rethinking Brain Death," *Critical Care Medicine* 20 (1992): 1705–13.

8

The Conscience Clause

How Much Individual Choice in Defining Death Can Our Society Tolerate?

Robert M. Veatch, Ph.D.

ON THE MORNING OF March 1, 1994, a blue 1978 Chevrolet Impala pulled next to a van as it began to cross the Brooklyn Bridge. The van was carrying 15 students from the Lubavitch Hasidic Jewish sect returning from a prayer vigil in Manhattan. As the car neared the van, a lone gunman fired at least five rounds of bullets from two separate semi-automatic weapons into the side of the van while reportedly yelling, "Kill the Jews." Four students were injured, two critically. One, 15-year-old Aaron Halberstam, was "declared brain dead, but he remained on life support."[1]

New York has adopted a brain-oriented definition of death through administrative regulation of the State Hospital and Planning Council and with the endorsement of the State Health Commissioner, which reads, "Both the individual standard of heart and lung activity and the standard of total and irreversible cessation of brain function should be recognized as the legal definition of death in New York."[2] That would seem to imply that Mr. Halberstam was dead once the diagnosis of the death of the brain was confirmed. However, the parents, following widely held Jewish beliefs, insisted that the individual does not die when the brain dies. They would accept only a criterion based on respiratory function. The rabbis for the Halberstam family were reported to have said that Mr. Halberstam should be kept on support systems as long as his heart could beat on its own.[3] The physician, honoring the parents' wishes, refused to pronounce the death. Depending on interpretation, this may have been legal. A sentence in the regulation permits (but does not require) physicians to accommodate family views on the definition of death.

One can hardly imagine what the result would have been had the family placed their ventilator-dependent, brain-dead, but not legally pronounced dead son in an ambulance and driven him through the Holland Tunnel to New Jersey. When they arrive in New Jersey, they are in a jurisdiction with an even more complex legal situation. New Jersey has a whole-brain-oriented criterion of death, but the law explicitly permits religious objectors to object to the use of that criterion in their own cases, thus making the patient alive until cardiac function ceases irreversibly.[4] Had Mr. Halberstam been known to hold such views, he would clearly be alive in New Jersey, assuming the law applies to minors. The present law, however, does not explicitly permit family members to choose a cardiac criterion of death based on their own religious beliefs. Thus, unless his own views were known or the law were extended to permit surrogate decision making, he could not have been treated as alive.

The New York case is not the only one that has raised these complex issues surrounding religious and other dissent from the legal definition of death. In California on March 27, 1994, two students whose parents live in Japan and who had been shot in a senseless act of violence were declared "brain dead." According to the report, they were diagnosed as brain dead, taken off respirators, and then pronounced dead even though the family was from a culture that still does not recognize brain criteria for death pronouncement.[5] They were not given any discretion to opt for a criterion of death that was preferred in their culture.

At about the same time in Florida, 13-year-old Teresa Hamilton, a severe diabetic who had been left in a coma, had been diagnosed as brain dead. Although Florida, like California, has a law stating that people with dead brains are dead people, the parents were insisting she was still alive and demanding that she be kept on what was called life support.[6] Although the hospital was insisting that the patient was dead and its personnel wanted to stop ventilatory support on the body, they yielded to the family wishes that her body be treated as if it were alive. They pressed for a plan to send the girl home on the ventilator without

pronouncing her dead. Here the family got its wishes in spite of the
Florida law.

The Present State of the Law

The New Jersey law is unique in the world. A few countries have not yet
adopted a whole-brain criterion of death.[7] They continue to use the traditional cardiac definition. All other jurisdictions except New Jersey have
adopted a whole-brain-oriented definition without any provision for individuals to conscientiously object for religious or other reasons. The
New York regulation appears to introduce some discretion, based on
family objections to a brain-oriented definition, but actually gives the
discretion to the physician who is contemplating death pronouncement
based on a brain-oriented concept of death. A family could express dissent to one physician who is willing to accommodate, but, if they happen
to be dealing with another physician, that physician could refuse the
request to refrain from pronouncing death.

The law in most American jurisdictions specifies that if the criteria for
measuring the irreversible loss of all functions of the entire brain are
met, "death shall be pronounced." In other jurisdictions, the law actually
reads "death may be pronounced." This seems to imply that the physician has the discretion, as in New York, except that the discretion is
actually broader. The physician could refuse to pronounce based on his
or her own personal values, economic considerations, or other factors
in addition to family wishes. Clearly, these laws seem defective if they
give the physician the opportunity legally to choose whether to pronounce death based on the physician's values. The problem under consideration in this chapter is whether such discretion could be tolerated
by the society if the dissent comes from the patient or the patient's next
of kin.

The common wisdom has been that such discretion makes no sense.
After all, being dead seems to be an objective matter to be determined
by good science (or perhaps good metaphysics) rather than by individual
conscientious choice. Concern is often expressed that such discretion
not only makes no sense but would produce public chaos leading to
situations in which some patients are dead while medically identical patients are alive. I will make the case for the legitimacy of a conscientious
objection to a uniform definition of death, a conscientious objection

that permits patients to choose, while competent, an alternative definition of death provided that it is within reason and does not pose serious public health or other societal concerns. In cases in which the patient has not spoken while competent (in cases of infants, children, and adults who simply have not expressed themselves), I will argue that the next of kin should have this discretion within certain limits.

Concepts, Criteria, and the Role of Value Pluralism

The Early Fact-Value Distinction

Early in the debate over the definition of death, commentators insisted that a basic distinction be made between two elements of the discussion. What at first appeared to be one question turned out to include at least two separate issues. First, there was a question that seemed primarily scientific: How can we measure that the brain has been irreversibly destroyed (that it has "died")? That seems like the kind of question that those skilled in neurology could answer. The neurological community, sometimes aided by others, has offered many sets of criteria with associated tests and measures for determining that the brain will never again be able to conduct any of its functions.[8] We have come to understand this as primarily a question for competent medical scientists.[9]

The second question is quite different in character. It asks whether we as a society or as individuals ought to treat an individual with a dead brain as a dead person. This question is clearly not something about which the neurological community can claim expertise. No amount of neurological study could possibly determine whether those with dead brains should be considered dead people. This is a religious, philosophical, ethical, or public policy question, not one of neurological science.

When society determines that someone is dead, many social behavioral changes occur. The medical team may stop treating the patient if previously a decision had been made to treat aggressively to the very end of life; health insurance coverage will cease, while life insurance will pay off; if the patient is married, the spouse becomes a widow or widower; grieving can begin in a way that was not appropriate previously; and, if the deceased was president of the United States, the vice president automatically assumes the presidency. A great deal is at stake in determining exactly when someone dies. Wills will be read, assets distributed, and the timing of the occurrence of the death, which may be critical for determining inheritance, prosecution of crimes, and other things, will be established. These are not neurological issues; they are social, normative issues about which all citizens may reasonably voice a position relying on their personal religious, philosophical, and ethical view of the world. I have been pressing for this distinction between concept and criteria and some critical implications that follow since the late 1960s.[10]

Democratic Pluralism and Value Variation

In a democratic, pluralistic culture, we have great insight into how to deal with religious, philosophical, and ethical issues about which there are strongly held views and unresolvable controversy. At the level of morality, we agree to tolerate diverse opinion, and we even let a person act on those opinions, at least until the effects on the lives of others become intolerable. This is the position we take regarding religious dissent.

Religious and Other Positions

To the extent that the disagreement is a religious or quasi-religious disagreement, toleration of pluralism seems the appropriate course. It permits people with differences to live together in harmony. And at least one major source of division over the definition of death is surely theological. The case with which this chapter opened seems not only to have been caused by tensions between Jewish people and Muslims; the moral disagreement about whether to declare Mr. Halberstam dead also has religious roots. Judaism has long been known to include persons who oppose brain criteria for death pronouncement. Not that all Jews oppose it. Rabbi Moses Tendler, a well-known moral commentator, has supported it.[11] But many Orthodox rabbinical scholars strongly oppose it, maintaining that where there is breath there is life.[12] Japanese, influenced by Buddhist and Shinto belief systems, see the presence of life in the whole body, not just in the brain.[13] Native Americans reportedly sometimes hold religious beliefs that oppose a brain-oriented definition of death.[14] Fundamentalist Christians, sometimes associated with the right-to-life movement, and some Catholics focusing on pro-life issues press for a consistent pro-life position by opposing death pronouncement of brain-dead individuals.[15]

On the other hand, mainstream Christians, both Protestant[16] and Catholic,[17] support a brain-oriented definition, claiming that being pro-life does not foreclose being clear on when life ends. One Christian theological argument supporting brain-oriented definitions starts with the ancient Christian theological anthropology that sees the human as the integration of body and mind or spirit. When the two are irreversibly separated, then the human is gone. This view, as we shall see, places many Christian theologians in the higher-brain camp. These theologians sometimes differentiate themselves from secular defenders of higher-brain concepts. The latter group, under the influence of Derek Parfit,[18] stresses mentalist conceptions of the person that sometimes lead to support of a higher-brain conception that focuses exclusively on the irreversible loss of mental function without concern about the separation of mind from body.[19] By contrast, those working within Christian theology are more likely to insist on the importance of both mind and body.[20]

There are, of course, also many secular persons who support a cardiac definition of death. One, now somewhat dated, survey found that about a third continued to support a cardiac definition.[21] The only plausible conclusion is that the definition of death is heavily influenced by theological and metaphysical beliefs, along with theories of value. We have learned that, in a pluralistic society, it is unrealistic to expect unanimity on such questions. Hence, a tolerance of pluralism may be the only way to resolve the public policy debate.

This conclusion seems even more inevitable when one realizes that there are not just two or three plausible definitions (cardiac, whole-brain, and higher-brain definitions); there are literally hundreds of possible variants. Some insist on irreversible loss of anatomical brain structure at the cellular level; others only on irreversible loss of function. Some insist on loss of function at the cellular level, while others insist only on irreversible loss of supercellular functions or integration of bodily function. Some might insist on loss of all central nervous system functions, including spinal cord function (an early position of Henry Beecher, the chair of the Harvard ad hoc committee), while others draw a line between spinal cord and brain. Among defenders of the higher-brain concept, there are countless variations on what counts as "higher": everything above the brainstem, the cerebrum, the cerebral cortex, the neocortex, the sensory cortex, and so forth. Some, insisting on loss of all brain functions, ignore electrical functions, limiting their attention to clinical functions.[22] Some are even willing to ignore functions of "nests of cells," claiming they may be "insignificant."[23]

When all the possible variants are combined, there will be a large number of positions; no group is likely to gain the support of more than a small minority of the population. The only way to have a single definition of death is for those with power to coerce others to use their preferred definition. If that single definition were the current "whole brain" one with a requirement that literally all functions of the brain must be gone before death is pronounced, the result could be disastrous. No one really believes that every last function of the entire brain must be irreversibly lost for a brain to be dead. That would include all electrical functions, all neurohumoral functions, and cellular functions. Since clinicians would necessarily have to exercise discretion in deciding which functions are to be ignored, patients would be at the mercy of the discretion of the clinician who happens to be present when the question of pronouncing death arises. Even if we were willing to let some ride roughshod over others, it is very unlikely that any one position could gain majority support; in fact, it is unlikely that any single position could come close to a majority. There may be no alternative but to tolerate multiple views.

Constitutional Issues

Once the choice of a definition of death is cast in terms of theological or philosophical issues, the necessity for conscientious choice among the definitions seems more plausible. The constitutional issue of separation of church and state presses us in the direction of accepting definitions with religious groundings. Of course, the constitutional provision prohibiting the establishment of religion does not give absolute freedom of religious action.

Nevertheless, the burden on the state to justify interference with religious practice is great. Defenders of compulsory imposition of a single definition of death on a large group of religious conscientious objectors to that definition would have to be supported by significant social harms to other parties. I argue below that such harms cannot be demonstrated. Thus, the New Jersey law authorizes religious objection to the state's default definition of death when there is a religious basis for objecting to the whole-brain definition.

Problems Limiting Conscientious Objection to Religious Objectors

A state limiting conscientious objection to religious objectors, as New Jersey has done, is likely to face potentially difficult constitutional challenges. We learned from laws permitting religious conscientious objection to service in the military that restricting objection to certain types may be legally indefensible. During the Vietnam war era, some objectors had views that were clearly moral or philosophical, but they had a hard time accepting or demonstrating to others that they were religious. Especially if *religious* is defined as involving belief in a Supreme Being, many individuals whose objections seemed very similar to religious objections could not qualify. Even members of certain groups often classified as *religions* could not meet the belief in a Supreme Being test: Buddhism, Confucianism, Native American belief systems, all look much like religions but fail the Supreme Being test. Gradually, the restriction of conscientious objection to religious objection was challenged and was found to be discriminatory. The concept of religious objection was gradually broadened to include many belief systems that may not, at first, appear to be overtly religious.

Some scholars who have studied the New Jersey criterion of death law (including some most closely involved with the drafting of the law) believe that restriction of the beliefs supporting objection to the brain-oriented definition of death to those that were narrowly religious would be interpreted to include more broadly moral objections as well. That, at least, is the opinion of Robert Olick (personal communication, October 23, 1996), an attorney who served as the executive director of the commission that developed the New Jersey law.[24] The only reason that the New Jersey Commission on Legal and Ethical Problems in the Delivery of Health Care and the New Jersey legislature limited its provision to religious objection was political. Even during the debates before passage, some commentators were saying that objections that were not religious, if religion is narrowly construed, would be sustained in a legal challenge.

There are enormous practical as well as moral problems with attempts to limit the law to religion narrowly construed. At a practical level, enforcement officials would have to establish mechanisms for verifying whether an objection was truly religious. A nonpracticing Jew who had a nonreligious objection to a brain-oriented definition of death could cite his religious background, and it would be almost impossible for the state to establish whether his objection was religious. Morally, the principle of equal respect would seem to require that, if religious objections were permitted, equally sincere and equally deeply held nonreligious philosophical objections would be equally acceptable. If little is at stake in terms of public interest, little is lost by accepting both on equal terms.

Assuming that the case is made that individuals should be able to exercise religiously or nonreligiously based conscientious choice of an alternative definition of death, should that discretion be extended to surrogate decision makers in the manner of decisions to refuse treatment by patients with terminal illness? I see no reason to limit the choice to competent and formerly competent persons who have executed advance directives.

Consider a formerly competent adult or adolescent who has never formally written a document choosing an alternative definition of death, but who has left an oral record or a life-style pattern that appears to the surrogate to favor an alternative. Mr. Halberstam was returning from an Orthodox Jewish prayer service when he was shot. Assuming that he has not written an instruction stating a preference for a cardiac-oriented definition of death, should parents (or other next of kin) be permitted formally to choose it for Mr. Halberstam (as, in fact, Mr. Halberstam's did through the informal decisions in New York)? It appears that he had continued to live the religious life of his parents, and I see no reason to doubt that he would choose as they did. Just as the next of kin can presently exercise substituted judgment in decisions to forgo treatment, his parents likewise should be permitted to choose on his behalf based on the values he is most likely to have held.

Some might claim that this subordinates the interests of the patient or society to the whim of the idiosyncratic beliefs of the next of kin. Below I shall argue that there is little at stake for the society. As for Mr. Halberstam's interests, presently as an unconscious individual he seems to have no explicit contemporaneous interest. If it can be said that he has any residual interests, it surely must be to have his prospective autonomy preserved. Insofar as the parents can deduce what he would have autonomously chosen had he been able to exercise such judgment, surely they must be permitted, indeed required, to exercise that choice on his behalf.

But suppose we had no idea what Mr. Halberstam's wishes were about which definition of death should be used in his case. Or suppose he suffered his injury when he was 1 year old rather than 15 or 21. Clearly, in these cases respecting autonomy is out of the question. The only moral alternative is to use what is considered the best concept of death. But should it be the concept of death considered best by the society—perhaps some version of a whole-brain-oriented death, assuming that is the law of the state—or should it be the concept considered best by his next of kin? In the context of decisions to forgo treatment, I have long argued that the discretion should go to the next of kin under the doctrine of what I have called *limited familial autonomy*.[25] Just as the individual has an autonomous right to choose a definition of death (or a treatment plan), so likewise families are given a range of discretion in deciding what is best for their wards. They select the schooling and religious education that so dramatically shapes the system of values and beliefs of the child. They are expected to socialize the child into some value system. In a liberal pluralistic society, we do not insist that the familial surrogate choose the best possible value system for their wards; we expect them to exercise discretion, drawing on their own beliefs and values. As long as the ward's interests are not jeopardized too substantially and the interests of the society are not threatened, parents should not only be permitted, but actually be expected to make a choice of a definition of death for their wards.

Limits on the Range of Discretion

In my early writing on the subject of individual choice of a definition of death, I assumed without stating it that the range of choice would be limited among a range of tolerable alternatives. If the risks to the society became too great, surely a limit would have to be placed. Hence, probably, no one should be able to decide that he or she should be treated as alive if cardiac, respiratory, and brain function have all completely and irreversibly ceased. At least such choice should be foreclosed if it would pose public health problems or be grossly unfair to spouse and beneficiaries. Likewise, I believe no one should be able to choose to be considered dead when he or she retains all of these functions. Also, for pragmatic reasons a state should choose a default definition, leaving it up to individuals to exercise conscientious objection if they disagree with the default. What I now make explicit is that the choice must be within a range of reasonable or tolerable alternatives.

Whole-Brain versus Cardiac Conceptions of Death

The New Jersey law gives the narrowest of options: between the default whole-brain-oriented definition and the single alternative of a cardiac definition. That would be a clearly acceptable choice assuming there are no significant societal or third-party consequences. The New Jersey plan would seem to offer a minimal range of choice.

The Inclusion of Higher-Brain Concepts of Death

For over 20 years I and many other people have argued that it is no longer plausible to hold to a literal whole-brain definition in which every last function of the entire brain must be dead before death can be pronounced.[26] A case can be made that some versions of higher-brain formulations of a definition of death should be among the choices permitted. Under such an arrangement, a whole-brain definition might be viewed as the centrist view that would serve as the default definition, permitting those with more conservative views to opt for cardiac-oriented definitions and those with more liberal views to opt for certain higher-brain formulations. Of course, this would permit people with brainstem function including spontaneous respiration to be treated as dead. Organs could be procured that otherwise would not be available (assuming the dead-donor rule is retained), bodies could be used for research (assuming proper consent is obtained), and life insurance would pay off.

Some might be concerned that this would give surrogates the authority to have their wards treated as dead while some brain and cardiac functions remain. They see this as posing risks for unacceptable choices, for ending a lingering state of disability, for example. Assuming that the only cases that could be classified as dead by surrogates would be those who have lost all capacity for consciousness (i.e., who have lost all higher-brain functions), the risks to the individual classified as deceased would be minimal. We must keep in mind that surrogates are already presumed to have the authority to terminate all life support on these people. Often such decisions by surrogates to terminate life support would mean that the patient would soon be dead by the most traditional definitions of death. Death by traditional cardiac and whole-brain criteria would occur within minutes in many cases if the surrogate exercised his or her authority to forgo life support. The effect on inheritance and insurance would be trivial if these cases were simply called dead before stopping medical support rather than stopping prior to pronouncing death. Even for those vegetative or comatose patients who had sufficient lower-brain function to breathe on their own, a suspension of all medical treatment would lead to death fairly soon.

Adding a higher-brain option to the range of discretion would have only minimal effect on practical matters and would be a sign that we can show the same respect to the religious and philosophical convictions of those favoring the higher-brain position as we do now in New Jersey for the holders of the cardiac position. If there are actually scores of potential definitions of death within the range from higher-brain to cardiac positions, then only a relatively small minority is likely to be in agreement with the default position. The wise thing to do seems to be to pick some intermediary position and permit people to deviate to both somewhat more liberal and somewhat more conservative positions. The choices would probably have to be limited to this range. Both public health and moral problems become severe if the scope of choice is expanded much further.

The Problem of Order: Objections to a Conscience Clause

All of this, of course, depends on my as-yet-undefended claim that there are no significant societal or third-party harms from permitting conscientious objection to a default definition within the range I have specified. The President's Commission for the Study of Ethical Problems in Medicine and Biomedical and Behavioral Research prepared an important report in 1981 reviewing the debate on the definition of death.[27] In that report the commission examined the cardiac, whole-brain, and higher-brain options. In spite of the fact that their two philosophical consultants on the issue endorsed versions of a higher-brain formulation, the commission endorsed the whole-brain position. They gave serious consideration to the higher-brain position before rejecting it for a number of reasons, most of which can be summarized under the heading of the problems that would be created for social order.

Death as a Biological Fact

One preliminary objection that was not dwelt on by the commission but that arises in many discussions of the issue is the claim that death is not a matter of religious or philosophical or policy choice, but rather a matter of biological fact.[28] It is now generally recognized that the choice of a concept of death (as opposed to formulation of criteria and tests) is really normative[29] or ontological.[30] We are debating when as a matter of social policy ought we to treat someone as dead. No amount of biological research can answer that question at the conceptual level. Of course, many people could still hold that, although the definition of death is a normative or ontological question, there is still only one single correct formulation. That seems to me to be a very plausible position, but we are not discussing the issue of whether there can be only one true definition of death; we are discussing whether society can function for public policy purposes while tolerating differences in beliefs about the true definition. Tolerating a Jew's or Native American's belief in a definition that is perceived as wrong is no different from having a society tolerate more than one belief about whether abortion or forgoing life support in the living is morally correct. We are asking whether society can treat people as dead based on their own beliefs rather than whether people are really dead, really conform to some metaphysically correct conception of what it means to be dead, in such circumstances. (It is possible to hold that there is one and only one metaphysically correct concept of death, but that society can treat some people who conform to this meaning of death as if they were alive.)

Policy Chaos

One of the consistent themes in the criticism of higher-brain definitions, especially with the conscience clause I am defending, is that its adoption would lead to policy chaos. Presumably critics have in mind stress of health professionals, insurers, family members, and public policy processes, such as succession of the presidency. But a very similar substituted-judgment and best-interest discretion is already granted surrogates regarding decisions to forgo life support on still-living patients. One would think that the potential for abuse and for chaos would be much greater granting this discretion. It remains to be seen what chaos would be created from conscientious objection to a default definition of death. If each of the envisioned policy problems can be addressed successfully, then we are left with a religious/philosophical/policy choice for which we should be tolerant of variation if possible and no good social reasons to reject individual discretion. Some of the rebuttal against the charge of policy chaos has already been suggested.

Problems with the Stoppage of Treatment

One concern is that life-sustaining medical treatment would be stopped on different people with medically identical conditions at different times if conscientious choice among definitions of death is permitted. That assumes, however, that decisions to stop treatment are always linked to pronouncement of death. We now know that normally it is appropriate to consider suspension of treatments in a manner that is decoupled from the question of whether the patient is dead.[31] A large percentage of in-hospital deaths now occur as a result of a decision to stop treatment and let the patient die. Presumably any valid surrogate who was contemplating opting for a higher-brain definition of death would, if told that option were not available, immediately contemplate choosing to forgo treatment, letting the patient die. In either case the patient will be dead within a short period.

The decoupling of the decision to forgo treatment from that of the pronouncement of death has led some (including Brody and Fost in this volume) to further decouple what I have called *death behaviors,* leaving agreed-upon points for various behaviors such as initiating grief, procuring organs, and terminating insurance coverage. I considered such decoupling in the 1970s before rejecting it for two reasons.

First, even if we further decouple death behaviors, different people with different cultural beliefs and values will still consider different times appropriate for each of the behaviors. Some will consider widowhood to begin with loss of higher-brain function, others only with the death of the whole brain or the cessation of circulatory and respiratory function. We would still need a conscience clause, but now we would need one for the societally defined point for each of the list of death behaviors.

Second, even though some death behaviors surely must be decoupled (such as deciding to forgo treatment), we should not underestimate the importance of having something resembling a moment of death. Socially and psychologically, we need a moment, no matter how arbitrary, that loved ones can identify as a symbolic transition point, at least for a large cluster of these death behaviors. Relatives cannot send flowers one at a time as each moment arrives during a drawn-out process of death involving many different death-related behaviors. Kass won the 1970 argument about whether death was a process or an event. Although dying might be a process, death is not. There must be one defining moment of transition to which at least many of the death-related behaviors may attach.

Abuse of the Terminally Ill

For the same reasons the risk of abuse of the terminally ill should not be a problem. There could be more concern about a family member dependent on the terminally ill person's pension opting for a cardiac definition of death. That, however, seems remote. There is no record of that having occurred in New Jersey, where the option for a cardiac definition is available. If the problem did arise, the procedures currently available for review of suspected patient abuse would be available so that the next of kin could be removed from the surrogate role, just as they would be now if a surrogate refused life support in a situation where the motive seemed to be the financial gain of the surrogate.

Health Insurance

I have already mentioned the potential impact on health insurance if someone chooses a definition of death that would have the effect of making someone alive longer—if, for instance, a cardiac definition were chosen. (If some version of a higher-brain definition were chosen, the effect would more likely be a savings in health insurance.) There is good reason to believe that the effect on health insurance would be minimal. A relatively small number of people would actively make a pro-treatment choice based on their preference for a cardiac definition or any alternative that would require longer treatment. The small costs would probably be justified to preserve respect for individual freedom on religious or philosophical matters. If the problem became significant, a health insurance policy could easily address the problem. Any health insurance policy must have some limits on coverage. Cosmetic surgery is usually not covered; there are often limits on the number of days of inpatient care for psychiatric services. Many marginal procedures including longer days of stay in the hospital will be rejected. If an insurer were worried about unfair impact on the subscriber pool if its funds were used to provide care for patients without brain function who had selected a cardiac definition of death, they could simply exclude care for living patients with dead brains.

Life Insurance

The concern by life insurance companies is exactly the opposite. Insisting on a cardiac definition would simply delay payment, which would be in the insurer's interest; however, selecting a higher-brain definition would make the individual dead sooner, potentially quite a bit sooner. However, most living persons with dead brains die fairly soon either because such patients are hard to maintain or because an advance directive or surrogate opts for termination of treatment.

Inheritance

As in the case of pensions and life insurance, some surrogate might be inclined to manipulate the timing of death to gain an inheritance more quickly. This could lead to choosing a higher-brain definition. However, the same surrogate already has the power to decline medical treatment, which would theoretically expose the patient to similar risks, and such cases are exceedingly rare. If a surrogate is suspected of abusing a patient by choosing an inappropriate concept of death, such a surrogate can always be challenged and removed. If one compares the risk of abuse from surrogate discretion in deciding to forgo treatment with that from deciding on a variant definition of death, surely the discretion in forgoing treatment is more controversial and more subject to abuse. Yet that has not proved to be a significant problem.

Spousal or Marital Status

Another social practice that can be affected directly by the timing of a death is the marital status of the spouse. Spouses may want to retain their status as spouses rather than become widows or widowers for various psychological and financial reasons. Or they may want to become widows or widowers so that they can get on with their lives. Conceivably, some may be ready to remarry. For example, a spouse who had been caring for a PVS patient for years may have already separated psychologically from his or her mate even though that mate was not actually dead. This person could be ready to remarry, which could be done legally once the spouse were deceased. This problem seems quite far-fetched, but it could happen. Such spouses would probably already have contemplated refusing life support and could be removed as inappropriate surrogates if it is clear that they are motivated for non-patient-centered reasons.

Organ Transplantation

One significant effect of the definition of death is the availability of organs for transplant. If someone insists on a cardiac-based definition of death, that person would not be able to donate organs when heart function remains even though brain function has ceased. However, anyone who selected a cardiac definition of death would be unlikely to be a donor of organs if he or she were forced to be pronounced dead based on brain criteria in any case. On the other hand, a person who chose to be considered dead even though lower-brain function remained would be a potential organ source. Someone who wanted to have organs procured when his or her higher-brain functions were irreversibly lost potentially could have his or her organs procured earlier by selecting a higher-brain definition. As long as this were limited to cases where an active choice were made in favor of the higher-brain formulation, it is hard to see why there would be strong objection. With the evolution of protocols for the non-heart-beating cadaver, such persons could accomplish something similar by refusing life support to the point of death, followed by organ procurement. The outcome would be similar except that the donor would be forced to participate in the use of a concept of death that he or she rejected and the quality of the organs might be jeopardized. As long as the cases are limited to those in which there is a valid choice for a higher-brain definition, I cannot see why moral or societal concern should be raised.

Many people have pressed for a law authorizing organ procurement from living anencephalic infants.[32] Most recently the AMA's Council on Ethical and Judicial Affairs endorsed such a view,[33] although the council later rescinded it. If we mean by death nothing more than being in a condition in which it is appropriate for others to engage in death-associated behaviors, including procuring organs, then anyone who is an appropriate candidate for donating so-called life-prolonging organs is dead.[34] By this logic, to be consistent those who believe it is acceptable to procure organs from an anencephalic infant with brainstem function should claim that such infants are already dead (or, more accurately, have never been alive). In effect, they have adopted some version of a higher-brain-oriented definition of death and should really be claiming that it is acceptable to procure organs from anencephalic infants because they are dead (or have never been living, in the social policy sense of the term).

Succession to the Presidency

Another potential implication of choosing an alternative definition of death is that succession to the presidency or to other roles could be affected. In the United States, the vice president automatically is elevated to the presidency upon the death of the president. Similar policies affect monarchies in which the successor is automatically made king. A president who chose a cardiac definition of death could thereby end his term of office at a different time than one who chose a whole-brain or higher-brain definition. Since one in certain circumstances can retain cardiac function for years, the succession of the vice president could be delayed.

Obviously, this reflects a flaw in the succession law. Under present law a permanently vegetative president is not dead and there would be no automatic succession. But as soon as a permanent vegetative state is diagnosed, there should be immediate succession, regardless of whether the president is dead. One could imagine a next of kin being pressured to choose a definition with an eye toward timing the succession. That could happen now in an effort to delay succession in New Jersey. It could happen elsewhere if discretion were permitted. The possibility of this happening seems extremely remote. A constitutional amendment provides a mechanism for temporary assumption of the office, but once a president is known to be permanently incapacitated, he or she clearly should be replaced.

The Effect on Health Professionals

A final potential problem with authorizing conscientious choice is the possible effect on health professionals providing care for the patient. Nurses will be required to suffer potential emotional stress at having to continue care or cease care at a time they believe inappropriate. Physicians will face similar problems. But this is hardly a problem unique to a choice of a definition of death. Some living patients or their surrogates refuse life-supporting therapy before the nurse or physician believes appropriate. The health professional is simply obliged to stop according to laws about informed consent and the right to refuse treatment. More recently, health professionals have been disturbed about requests for care the clinicians deem futile. Patients who insisted on not being pronounced dead until their heart stopped potentially could insist on hospital-based treatment even though their brains were dead. That is potentially the situation in New Jersey now. But the responsibility of the health professional to deliver care deemed futile against his or her will is already a matter of considerable controversy. It will have to be resolved whether or not other states adopt the New Jersey conscience clause. Most patients demanding such care are clearly not dead by any definition. The resolution could be the same for patients with dead brains as it is for terminally ill or vegetative patients, or it could be different. The law could determine, for instance, that conscious patients would have a right of access to normatively futile care (perhaps with the proviso that they have independent funding), but that permanently unconscious patients or those with dead brains would have no right of access. In any case, the effect on care givers is not a problem unique to patients who might exercise an option for an alternative definition of death.

The Implementation of a Conscience Clause

The procedural implementation of a conscience clause would require some additional planning, but the problems would not be novel. Most are addressed in the existing Patient Self-Determination Act and required response laws. The former requires that someone inquire about the existence of an advance directive upon admission to a hospital and provide assistance in executing an advance directive if the patient desires. The latter requires that the next of kin be notified of the opportunity to donate organs in suitable cases. The most plausible way to record a choice of something other than a default concept of death would be in one's advance directive. That is the kind of document that ought to be on the minds of those caring for a patient who is near death. An addition specifying a choice of an alternative concept of death would be easy; it would be crucial in the case of those who are writing an advance directive demanding that life support continue even though the brain is dead. It would be a simple clarification in the case of one asking that support be forgone when the patient is permanently unconscious. A sentence choosing a higher-brain concept of death (and perhaps donating organs at that point) would be a modest addition.

Whether the new definition-of-death laws authorizing a conscience clause should also impose a duty on health professionals to notify patients or their surrogates of alternative concepts of death is a pragmatic question that would have to be addressed. I do not think that would be necessary. Just as Orthodox Jews presently carry the burden of notifying others of their requirements for a kosher diet and Jehovah's Witnesses carry the burden of notifying about refusal of blood transfusions, so those with alternative concepts of death would plausibly carry that burden. Something akin to the subjective standard for informed consent would apply. According to that standard, health professionals, when they negotiate a consent, are required to inform the patient of what the patient would reasonably want to know, but they are not expected to surmise all unusual views and interests of the patient. According to this approach, they would be expected to initiate discussions on alternative definitions of death only when they knew or had reason to know that the patient plausibly would have an interest in such a discussion. A clinician who knew his patient was an Orthodox Jew and knew that many Orthodox Jews prefer a more traditional concept of death would have such an obligation, but there would be no obligation if he or she had no reason to believe the patient might be inclined toward an alternative concept.

Some might claim that adding a conscience clause is unnecessary because only a small group of people would favor an alternative. In fact, a not insignificant number seem to prefer a more traditional cardiac or respiratory concept of death (Jews, Native Americans, Japanese, and others who are still committed to the importance of the heart or lungs). If a higher-brain-oriented concept of death were among the options, a much larger minority would have an interest in exercising the conscience clause. In fact, there have been court cases and anecdotal reports of families objecting to the use of whole-brain-based concepts. It seems reasonable to assume that these represent only a fraction of the total number of cases in which patients or families would prefer either a more traditional or a more innovative concept of death.

Even if it could be shown that few people would care enough about the concept and criteria of death used to pronounce them or their loved ones dead, this is still an important issue to clarify. It is important if only the rights of a small minority are violated. It is also important as a matter of conceptual clarity and of principle. The knee-jerk revulsion to a conscience clause for alternative concepts of death probably reflects lingering belief that deciding when someone is dead is a matter of biological fact (for which individual conscience seems irrelevant). But insisting that the choice of a concept of death be treated as a matter of philosophical and theological dispute seems to follow naturally once one realizes the true nature of the issues involved. Getting people to think why a conscience clause is appropriate for this issue has an important teaching function and serves to respect the rights of minorities on deeply held religious and philosophical convictions.

Conclusion

Once one grasps that the choice of a definition of death at the conceptual level is a religious/philosophical/policy choice rather than a question of medical science, the case for granting discretion within limits in a liberal pluralistic society is very powerful. There seems to be no basis for imposing a unilateral normative judgment on the entire population when the members of the society are clearly divided. When one realizes that there are many variants and that no one is likely to receive the support of a majority, pluralism seems to be the only answer. Having a state choose a default definition (probably the whole-brain, middle-of-the-road position) and then granting individuals a limited range of discretion within the limits of reason seems to be the only defensible option. There is no reason to limit this discretion to religiously based reasons and no reason why familial surrogates should not be empowered to use substituted judgment or best-interest standards for making such choices, just as they presently do for forgoing treatment decisions that determine even more dramatically the timing of death. A default with an authorization for conscientious objection seems the humane, respectful, fair, and pragmatic solution.

References

1. Man charged in shooting of Jewish students. *New York Times*, March 3, 1994, A1, A6.

2. Failure of brain is legal "death," New York says. *New York Times*, June 19, 1987, A1, B4.

3. In hospital hallways, family and friends pray for victims. *New York Times*, March 3, 1994, B4.

4. The New Jersey Declaration of Death Act, signed April 8, 1991. It reads, in part: "The death of an individual shall not be declared upon the basis of neurological criteria . . . of this act when the licensed physician authorized to declare death, has reason to believe, on the basis of information in the individual's available medical records, or information provided by a member of the individual's family or any other person knowledgeable about the individual's personal religious beliefs that such a declaration would violate the personal religious beliefs of the individual. In these cases death shall be declared, and the time of death fixed, solely upon the basis of cardio-respiratory criteria."

5. Slaying suspects share a past marred by crime. *New York Times*, April 1, 1994, A24.

6. Florida hospital seeks to end life support of comatose girl. *New York Times*, February 13, 1994, A24; Brain-dead Florida girl will be sent home on life support. *New York Times*, February 19, 1994, 9.

7. Kimura R. Japan's dilemma with the definition of death. *Kennedy Inst Ethics J* 1991;1:123–31.

8. Harvard Medical School. A definition of irreversible coma: Report of the Ad Hoc Committee of the Harvard Medical School to Examine the Definition

of Brain Death. *JAMA* 1968;205:337–40; Task Force on Death and Dying, Institute of Society, Ethics and the Life Sciences. Refinements in criteria for the determination of death: An appraisal. *JAMA* 1972;221:48–53; President's Commission. Report of the medical consultants on the diagnosis of death to the President's Commission for the Study of Ethical Problems in Medicine and Biomedical and Behavioral Research. In: *Defining Death: Medical, Legal and Ethical Issues in the Definition of Death.* Washington, DC: Government Printing Office, 1981, 159–66; Cranford RE. Minnesota Medical Association Criteria: Brain death—concept and criteria. Part I. *Minn Med* 1978;61:561–63; Law Reform Commission of Canada. *Criteria for the Determination of Death.* Ottawa, Canada: Minister of Supply and Services, 1981; Walker AE, and colleagues. An appraisal of the criteria of cerebral death: A summary statement. *JAMA* 1977;237:982–86.

9. More recent analysis has challenged the blatant fact/value dichotomy implied in this separation of the criteria question as one for medical science and the concept question as one of religious, philosophical, or public policy. See Veatch RM. *Death, Dying, and the Biological Revolution.* Rev ed. New Haven: Yale University Press, 1989, 43–44.

10. See, e.g., Veatch RM. Brain death: Welcome definition or dangerous judgment? *Hastings Cent Rep* 1972;2:10–13; and Veatch RM. *Death, Dying, and the Biological Revolution.* New Haven: Yale University Press, 1976.

11. Tendler MD. Cessation of brain function: Ethical implications in terminal care and organ transplant. In: Korein J (ed). *Brain Death: Interrelated Medical and Social Issues.* New York: New York Academy of Sciences, 1978, 394–97; Veith FJ, Fein JM, Tendler MS, Veatch RM, Kleiman MA, Kalkinis G. Brain death: I. A status report of medical and ethical considerations. *JAMA* 1977;238:1651–55.

12. Bleich JD. Establishing criteria of death. *Tradition* 1973;13:90–113; Bleich JD. Neurological criteria of death and time of death statutes. *Jewish Bioethics.* New York: Sanhedrin Press, 1979, 303–16; Rosner F. The definition of death in Jewish Law. *Tradition* 1969;10(4):33–39.

13. Kimura R. Japan's dilemma with the definition of death. *Kennedy Inst Ethics J* 1991;1:123–31.

14. President's Commission for the Study of Ethical Problems in Medicine and Biomedical and Behavioral Research. *Defining Death: Medical, Legal and Ethical Issues in the Definition of Death.* Washington, DC: Government Printing Office, 1981, 41.

15. Byrne PA, O'Reilly S, Quay PM. Brain death—an opposing viewpoint. *JAMA* 1979;242:1985–90.

16. Hauerwas S. Religious concepts of brain death and associated problems. In: Korein J (ed). *Brain Death: Interrelated Medical and Social Issues.* New York: New York Academy of Sciences, 1978, 329–38; Potter RB. The paradoxical preservation of a principle. *Villanova Law Rev* 1968;13:784–92; Ramsey P. On updating death. In: Cutler DR (ed). *Updating Life and Death.* Boston: Beacon Press, 1969, 31–53.

17. Haring B. *Medical Ethics*. Notre Dame, Ind.: Fides Publishing, 1973, 131–36.

18. Parfit D. *Reasons and Persons*. Oxford: Clarendon Press, 1984.

19. Green MB, Wikler D. Brain death and personal identity. *Philos Public Affairs* 1980;9(2):105–33.

20. Ramsey P. *The Patient as Person*. New Haven: Yale University Press, 1970, xiii; Veatch RM. *Death, Dying, and the Biological Revolution*. New Haven: Yale University Press, 1976, 42.

21. Charron WC. Death: A philosophical perspective on the legal definitions. *Washington Univ Law Q* 1975;4:979–1008.

22. Ashwal S, Schneider S. Failure of electroencephalography to diagnose brain death in comatose patients. *Ann Neurol* 1979;6:512–17.

23. Bernat JL. How much of the brain must die on brain death? *J Clin Ethics* 1992;3(1):21–26.

24. Olick RS. Brain death, religious freedom, and public policy. *Kennedy Inst Ethics J* 1991;1(December):275–88. Also see Goldberg CK. Choosing life after death: Respecting religious beliefs and moral convictions in near death decisions. *Syracuse Law Rev* 1988;39(4):1197–1260 (see esp. 1256).

25. Veatch RM. Limits of guardian treatment refusal: A reasonableness standard. *Am J Law Med* 1984;9(4):427–68.

26. Veatch RM. The whole-brain-oriented concept of death: An outmoded philosophical formulation. *J Thanatol* 1975;3:13–30; Engelhardt HT. Defining death: A philosophical problem for medicine and law. *Am Rev Respir Dis* 1975; 112:587–90; Bernat JL. How much of the brain must die on brain death? *J Clin Ethics* 1992;3(1):21–26; Haring B. *Medical Ethics*. Notre Dame, Ind.: Fides Publishing, 1973, 131–36.

27. President's Commission for the Study of Ethical Problems in Medicine and Biomedical and Behavioral Research. *Defining Death: Medical, Legal and Ethical Issues in the Definition of Death*. Washington, DC: Government Printing Office, 1981.

28. For a discussion, see Gervais KG. *Redefining Death*. New Haven: Yale University Press, 1986, 45–74; Lamb D. Diagnosing death. *Philos Public Affairs* 1978; 7:144–53; Becker LC. Human being: The boundaries of the concept. *Philos Public Affairs* 1975;4:334–59.

29. Veatch RM. *Death, Dying, and the Biological Revolution*. Rev ed. New Haven: Yale University Press, 1989.

30. Green MB, Wikler D. Brain death and personal identity. *Philos Public Affairs* 1980;9(2):105–33.

31. The general problem of decoupling of behavioral correlates of pronouncing death is the subject of Norman Fost's Chapter 9 in this volume and will not be examined in detail in this chapter.

32. Harrison M. The anencephalic newborn as organ donor. *Hastings Cent Rep* 1986;16(April):21–23; Fletcher J, Robertson J, Harrison M. Primates and

anencephalics as sources for pediatric organ transplants. *Fetal Ther* 1986;1(2–3): 150–64; Walters J, Ashwal S. Organ prolongation in anencephalic infants: Ethical and medical issues. *Hastings Cent Rep* 1988;18(October-November):19–27.

33. American Medical Association, Council on Ethical and Judicial Affairs. The use of anencephalic neonates as organ donors. *JAMA* 1995;273(20):1614–18.

34. Of course, some organs (single kidneys and liver lobes) can be procured from living people—we do not insist on people being declared dead in these cases—if proper consents have been obtained.

9

The Unimportance of Death

Norman Fost, M.D., M.P.H.

The effort devoted to defining death is wasted at best, counterproductive at worst . . . The most basic question [is]: What difference does it make whether somebody is dead? That question places the issue of death into the only posture in which it can be of relevance to the law—the posture of context or consequences.

—Roger Dworkin, 1973

IN THIS CHAPTER I revisit an argument made originally by Roger Dworkin in 1973 and in the early 1980s by myself and by Susan Brennan and Richard Delgado;[1-3] namely, that statutes on brain death are unnecessary and have predictable unwelcome complications. My purpose here is to reaffirm and expand that view in the light of our experiences since then. The central points are as follows:

—The social purposes for declaring a patient dead (e.g., cessation of treatment, organ removal, settling estates, burial, etc.) can be justified in other ways. It was and is not necessary to conclude that a patient is dead to accomplish those social goals in a morally and legally satisfactory way.
—The points in the life cycle at which these decisions are optimally made are not the same. Therefore, a single definition of death does not ideally serve all of these social purposes.
—Even if it were desirable to define or declare a patient dead to

achieve those goals, whole-brain death was and is not the only, best, or most desirable way to define death.

—The movement to adopt the present legal definition(s) of death has had adverse effects that are expanding.

In summary, I do not believe it is necessary to know whether or not brain-dead patients are truly dead, nor is it knowable. Similar views have been presented more recently by Halevy and Brody,[4] Arnold and Youngner,[5] and Emanuel.[6]

What Is the Question?

Several separate questions are under review: When is a person dead? What is the "real" or "right" definition of death? If whole-brain death is the preferred or "right" definition of death, how can we ascertain when it has occurred? And, finally, what is the social purpose of having a policy on these issues?

Others in this volume address the conceptual and medical issues. It is my view that the pursuit of definitive answers to these questions is fruitless and not necessary for the development of sensible policy. Although discussion of the definition of death may inform the development of policy, there is no right answer to its definition, and the alleged consensus surrounding a brain-death-oriented definition is increasingly unstable.

It is not surprising that the definition of death should be elusive. Death is not an entity, a substance, or the presence of something.[6,7] It is the absence of something—namely, life—whose definition is elusive, not objective, and not susceptible to consensus. The U.S. Supreme Court has acknowledged the futility of trying to define life.[8] A panel of distinguished scientists claimed that they had expertise on the subject in testifying at congressional hearings on a Human Life Amendment,[9] but predictably could not agree.[10] As Morison pointed out long ago,[7] death is a process, not an event, and the concept encompasses the loss of many functions, not just one. Some of the important moments in this process include the following:

—*Traditional death*, which refers to irreversible cessation of spontaneous cardiac and respiratory function. This results in brain death unless treatment is instituted to maintain perfusion of the brain.

—*Brain death,* which refers to irreversible loss of all brain function. This relies on loss of integrating functions of the brain.
—*Personal death,* which refers to death of the person, or loss of personal identity, generally thought to depend on the higher brain, or cerebral cortex.
—*Reproductive death,* which refers to death in the sense of irreversible loss of the ability to reproduce one's self. This would seem an important point if death is considered a biological issue, since the traditional biological notion of when life begins (or began) depends on the appearance of a self-replicating entity.
—*Genetic death,* which refers to the loss of all means of identifying the genetic make-up of the individual.
—*Biological death,* which refers to the loss of all biological activity that can be traced to an identifiable individual.
—*Legal death,* which refers to death in the sense of conforming to relevant statutory and case law.

A single definition of death might rely on any one of these concepts. None of these versions of death would be a right or wrong definition of death. None is sufficient as a single basis for policies that need to provide guidance for discontinuing treatment, removing organs, settling estates, and burial. Each refers to the loss of something that is relevant for some purpose. Traditional (cardiorespiratory) death is still considered important for deciding when it is appropriate to commence an autopsy or bury a person. Brain death has been a useful concept in deciding when it is appropriate to remove organs for transplantation. Personal death is helpful in deciding when it is appropriate to discontinue life-sustaining treatment. But none of these definitions or concepts of death serves all these purposes equally well. There are other policy issues for which none of these definitions of death may be useful or ideal; for example, when can wills be effected and estates settled? When can a body be used for research or training purposes, with or without the consent of the person?

A single definition of death is also unnecessary. We can find moral and legal justifications for removing organs, discontinuing life support, implementing wills, and settling estates without addressing or resolving the question of whether the patient is dead or in which of these many senses of the term he or she is dead. As Dworkin said, "It would be odd indeed if all these different situations were susceptible to resolution by one definition of death. They involve different consequences and resolutions of different policy questions."[1]

Moreover, attempting to use death as the keystone for resolving the policy questions makes the task more difficult and aggravates other social problems. To understand how we went astray and to suggest an alternative approach, let us go back to the beginning of the movement to redefine death.

What Was the Need for a Revised or More Explicit Definition of Death?

In the late 1960s, three troublesome issues stimulated discussion and suggestions for rethinking the definition of death.[11] First, the evolving ability to maintain bodily functions despite failure of the respiratory center was forcing clinicians and others to make decisions about whether to withhold or withdraw life support, particularly mechanical ventilation. Although only a minority of ventilator-dependent patients, then and now, had irreversible destruction of the whole brain, these were the clearest candidates for withholding or withdrawing treatment. If they were defined as dead, there would be little controversy, on either ethical or legal grounds.

Second, in a small number of cases the traditional definition of death threatened successful prosecution of homicide charges. In the typical case, an assailant caused severe brain injury that progressed to what we now call *brain death,* but the victim would be rescued before cardiorespiratory death could occur and be placed on mechanical ventilation. The assailant claimed that, if the physicians had continued to treat the patient by providing necessary ventilator assistance, feeding, and so forth, the patient would not have necessarily died,[12] leaving the assailant vulnerable to a charge of assault but not homicide.

Third, and most importantly, there were rapid advances in organ transplantation causing concern about an emerging imbalance between demand and supply. The growing number of ventilator-dependent patients who were "certain" to die (in the traditional sense) created the opportunity to remove organs before cardiorespiratory arrest and organ damage due to loss of warm perfusion. Since there was reluctance to remove vital organs from a living patient, declaring such patients dead would facilitate "harvesting" of usable organs. Although the expanding interest in kidney transplantation might have been sufficient to stimulate this movement, the discovery that hearts could also be transplanted accelerated interest in revising the definition of death, since removal of the heart would otherwise constitute homicide.

It is important to note that the redefinition of death was an optional exercise. It is not the case that experts in philosophy, law, and religion revealed a discovery—namely, the true definition of death. The major impetus was an explicitly utilitarian exercise by a Harvard committee consisting primarily of physicians, who had the candor to state that their "primary purpose" was "to define irreversible coma as a new criterion for death. There are two reasons why there is a need for a definition: . . . Obsolete criteria for the definition of death can lead to controversy in obtaining organs for transplantation."[11]

None of These Problems Required a Redefinition of Death

The claim that legal cover was needed to withhold or withdraw ventilator support from patients with severe brain damage rested on the most persistent and important misunderstanding in the management of seriously ill patients—namely, that there was or is legal liability for such actions. The simple fact is that there has never been a single physician in the history of the United States found liable, in a criminal or civil proceeding, for withholding or withdrawing any kind of life-sustaining treatment from any patient for any reason.[13] Although this historical record of absolute legal deference to medical judgment in this area should be reassuring, it cannot, of course, give absolute reassurance about the future. It is plausible that some day a physician will be successfully sued or criminally prosecuted for withholding or withdrawing life-sustaining treatment from a patient. But it is not plausible that this case will involve a patient who is brain dead.

Many legal actions have been initiated, onerous for all concerned and much to be avoided. There are many ways to reduce that risk close to zero,[14] but immunity against the initiation of a lawsuit or prosecution is not possible. Statutes on brain death do not protect physicians against charges of negligence.[15]

The claim that a statute was needed to prevent assailants from escaping homicide charges was also misplaced and proven wrong by the litigated cases. Courts consistently concluded that traditional death was an inevitable consequence of an assault that caused brain death, and the assailant, not the physician, was therefore legally responsible for the death. Even Capron, the father of the Uniform Determination of Death Act,[16] acknowledged this point: "Courts do not necessarily have to adopt brain-based criteria of death in order to hold defendants responsible for committing homicide. Defendants may be held responsible on the grounds that they caused the victim's death."[17]

The final claim, and the driving force behind the redefinition of death, was based on the need for more efficient procurement of viable organs for transplantation, particularly kidneys at the time of the Harvard report. Capron acknowledged that "most commentators have been careful to point out that organ transplantation concerns alone are not sufficient to justify a revised or special purpose definition of death."[17] Indeed, the Uniform Anatomic Gift Act does not contain a definition of death.[18]

The alleged necessity for a redefinition of death is belied by the experience in Wisconsin—the country's leader in organ procurement.[19] Wisconsin, one of the last states to enact a brain-death statute, had been retrieving organs, mainly kidneys, from brain-dead patients for more than 10 years without the benefit of statutory protection. The Wisconsin experience is noteworthy in another regard. Although many of the patients from whom organs were taken were brain dead by prevailing standards, many were not. These were patients who were terminally ill, commonly due to heart or lung disease, and about whom a decision had been made, by family and providers, to discontinue life support and allow the patient to die. With consent of the appropriate relatives, life support was discontinued in the operating room rather than on the clinical unit, so that organs could be removed promptly after cessation of heart function and declaration of death on traditional (heart-lung) criteria. This practice was "rediscovered" and became known as the Pittsburgh protocol after a conference that stimulated some controversy.[20]

There was no legal challenge in Wisconsin to removal of organs from either brain-dead patients or patients who had died by heart-lung criteria despite the absence of a statute covering either practice. I am not aware of any controversy or complaint about it from any source. Controversy arose only when a brain-death statute was introduced, based on the manifestly false claim that the absence of such a statute was interfering with organ procurement.

Although Wisconsin and other states were successfully removing organs without the benefit of a brain-death statute, it might be argued that they were not successful enough. Organ supply lags behind demand, and it is possible that uncertainty about the legality of removing organs may have inhibited requests in some cases. The weight of the evidence, however, is that the legal framework plays a minimal role in the success of organ procurement. There are several lines of evidence supporting that view.

The Effect of Statutory Changes on Organ Procurement Rates

One of the basic assumptions behind the statutory redefinition of death was that the law was a major barrier to organ procurement or, more to the point, that changing the law would change behavior. Organ procurement rates are the result of many factors besides the legal background, including attitudes and beliefs of potential donors and their next of kin, the motivation and effectiveness of those who are in a position to request donation, the organizational skill and effort of transplant centers and procurement organizations in educating the public and professionals, and the availability of transplant surgeons and their colleagues in responding to calls. Although organ procurement has increased since the establishment of brain death as a criterion for legal death, it is not clear that legislation, among the many possible factors, is a primary cause. There is some evidence that legislation may not have much effect on procurement rates.[21]

The most permissive laws, in the sense of facilitating organ procurement, are so-called presumed consent statutes, which authorize hospitals to remove organs in specified circumstances unless the patient explicitly refuses. Such laws have been in effect in France, among other countries, with little apparent effect on procurement rates.[22] Even though the family's consent or refusal is legally irrelevant, in practice they are routinely asked, and organs will not be removed without family permission.

Similarly, the enactment in the United States of a national "required request" law has had minimal effect on the rate of kidney procurement.[23] This legislation was the result of a concerted effort by Caplan, who argued that "there is not a shortage of givers, but a shortage of askers," but he has acknowledged that the law did not have the expected effect.[24]

Finally, the enormous disparity in organ procurement rates across the United States today, despite uniform statutes, suggests that there are more powerful factors in procurement rates. Prottas, a longtime analyst of procurement effectiveness, has concluded that "cultural, social and professional differences are quite overwhelmed by organizational differences."[22] Wisconsin offers a striking example. There are two organ procurement organizations (OPOs) in the state, each centered around major academic centers. Working under identical statutes, the two OPOs have had consistently different procurement rates.[19]

These observations suggest that statutes which should plausibly affect organ procurement do not predictably do so. It is possible that the redefinition of death was an exception. We can only say that there is no clear evidence that, among the many factors that affect procurement rates, the redefinition of death played a major role.

Even if we concede that statutory help was necessary or desirable to promote organ retrieval, redefining death was not the only way or the best way to achieve that goal. A more direct statute would have simply stated as its purpose the promotion of organ transplantation. Toward that end, a state could have declared removal of organs from a brain-dead patient, so diagnosed by appropriate medical standards, to be legally authorized, with appropriate standards for informed consent, record keeping, regulation, and so on. Such a statute would effectively have provided immunity from civil or criminal charges for organ removal from brain-dead patients under the same circumstances as exist today. It is not my task to construct such a statute here or to claim that it would be problem-free. But it would have the advantage of being narrowly constructed to achieve its purpose, and it would be more candid regarding its purpose. It would have the advantage, as I will discuss later, of making it easier to justify removal of organs from other patients, who are not brain dead, but whose interests would not be violated by such removal.

The Predictable Adverse Consequences of Redefining Death

If the redefinition of death had no costs or adverse effects, then arguments about its efficacy would be academic. But no intervention is without undesirable and unintended consequences. I believe the redefinition of death has contributed to conceptual confusion on related issues and aggravated efforts to have a more rational policy on organ procurement involving a much broader population of patients than those who are brain dead. I believe it has also aggravated efforts to develop coherent and sensible policies and practices on withholding and withdrawing life support from a wide range of patients.

Exacerbation of the False Belief That Legal Protection Is Needed When Withholding or Withdrawing Life-sustaining Treatment

If one of the reasons for the adoption of statutes on brain death was to facilitate discontinuation of life support, then it was logical to assume that legislative guidance was even more urgently needed for more complicated cases. Brain death is the clearest and least controversial justification for stopping life ventilator support. If physicians needed legislative guidance on the simplest cases, some reasoned, then discontinuation of life support in more complex cases must be even more problematic.

In the years immediately after Wisconsin's adoption of a brain-death statute,[25] I experienced a surge in consultations from physicians and hospitals who felt paralyzed by the law in the management of dying patients. The simplest but most disturbing manifestation was the false belief that the legislature had defined and limited the circumstances under which life support could be terminated. This confusion has now passed in most hospitals, but the view that management of life-sustaining treatment was now a concern of the legislature has not passed, and the false belief that legislative protection was needed expanded greatly in the years after widespread adoption of brain-death statutes. The federal government intruded itself when the Reagan administration promulgated the infamous Baby Doe rules, which created widespread belief among neonatologists that they were prohibited from discontinuing treatment on a wide range of seriously ill infants.[26] Hospital attorneys commonly persuaded physicians that the law required maximum treatment of patients in a prolonged vegetative state, even though there had never been any finding of civil or criminal liability.[27]

Many other factors contributed to legislative action, many revolving around plug-pulling cases in which physicians, hospitals, or hospital attorneys solicited judicial protection. As noted earlier, all of these were unnecessary if the purpose was to protect the physician from liability. The plea for brain-death statutes was not the only example of a request for unneeded protection, but it was an early and important example.

The false fear of legal oversight has worsened in some sectors. In New York State there is continuing fear of discontinuing life support on hopelessly ill infants and other incompetent patients based on the belief that clear and convincing evidence of the patient's wishes are an absolute prerequisite for such actions. But worse: even brain-dead patients—legally dead in New York, as elsewhere—are now sometimes maintained for prolonged periods. Various statutes and court rulings might suggest that, in theory, physicians are so constrained, but the law in practice suggests otherwise, as physicians who ignore these rulings have been immune to findings of liability.

Confusion Created by Conflating Three Separate Issues

As Veatch pointed out,[28] the report of the Harvard committee created and reflected the continuing confusion over three related but separate issues—when coma is irreversible, when the whole brain is dead, and when the patient is dead. The title of the report, "A Definition of Irreversible Coma," suggests an appropriate investigation for a committee consisting primarily of physicians: identifying the clinical and laboratory variables that predict that coma is irreversible. The subtitle, however, raised a different subject—brain death—by describing their project as the "Report of the Ad Hoc Committee of the Harvard Medical School To Examine the Definition of Brain Death." Since a patient can be irreversibly comatose and not be brain dead, these are separate issues, though still the appropriate subjects of inquiry by medical experts.

But the opening sentence states yet another purpose, beyond medical expertise. It states that the purpose of the committee is to create public policy by encouraging physicians, and legislatures if necessary, to declare such patients as dead, in apparent defiance of the traditional legal standard of cessation of cardiac and respiratory activity. Here they lurched, apparently unwittingly, into complex questions of philosophy and religion, as if such questions could be resolved by a committee, and a committee consisting primarily of physicians.

The confusion about death that was set in motion by the Harvard committee has persisted. Journalists state that patients are dead but are being kept alive by physicians.[29] Doctors who work in intensive care settings commonly misunderstand the concept and misapply the criteria.[30,31] For the layperson, the statement that a brain-dead relative is dead, when she or he looks no different from other patients in the intensive care unit, is often difficult to understand. Among the most informed scholars in medicine, philosophy, and law, there is increasing disagreement, as this volume documents. In the United States, loss of all brain function is considered to be the *sine qua non* of death of the person; in Great Britain, death of the brainstem is sufficient. Some scholars, including Robert Burt in Chapter 20 of this volume, suggest that the lack of consensus could be so distressing to the public that suppression of the debate should be considered.

Dependence on Legislatures to Resolve Philosophical and Religious Issues

The redefinition of death created the false belief that legislatures could resolve, or were the best place to resolve, complex philosophical and religious issues, such as the definition of life and death. Other chapters in this volume address in more detail the complexities inherent in defining death, summarized above. While the President's commission, scholars, and public discussions wrestled with some of these distinctions, legislatures hardly noted them. Nor should they. Legislatures exist to address practical social problems, not to resolve unresolvable philosophical and religious questions. They are clearly acting within their appropriate purpose when they enact a law whose purpose is to facilitate (or inhibit) plug pulling, to facilitate organ retrieval, or to ensure that criminals are appropriately punished. They are not designed to resolve unresolvable abstract questions, nor need they.

Inviting legislative involvement in abstract philosophical and religious questions risks broader activities. If they can define death, they should be equally competent to define life. As discussed earlier, the U.S. Supreme Court had the wisdom to acknowledge their inability to resolve such questions, but Congress did not shrink from the temptation to draft a Human Life Amendment, defining for the nation when life begins.

The Invitation to Redefine Death Again for Utilitarian Purposes

The Harvard committee was explicitly and candidly utilitarian in their proposal to redefine death. The opening statement declares that they did not see themselves as making a discovery, as the President's commission seemed to do, but as achieving a social purpose. "Our primary purpose," they declared, "is to define irreversible coma as a new criterion for death" and then go on to explain the social benefits of this move.

Some critics expressed concern at the time that, if death could be redefined for utilitarian purposes, it could be redefined again at a later time, possibly threatening more vulnerable groups, such as those with severe brain damage but not brain death, or the demented, or the retarded. This prediction came true when efforts to retrieve organs from anencephalic infants met legal obstacles, since brainstem activity in such infants renders them legally alive.[32,33] Proponents of organ retrieval in such cases tried to persuade legislatures to redefine such infants as dead or outside the scope of the brain-death law, so their organs could be retrieved.[34]

These observations do not imply that it would be ethically wrong to remove organs from anencephalic infants while they are still living. My own view is that no interests of such infants would be violated by such removal.[35] My point is that, as with all ethical controversies, the justifications should be the right ones. It may be acceptable to remove organs from anencephalic infants and other patients who are not brain dead, but the reason is not because they are dead.

Reliance on a Medically Flawed Concept

It is now clear that brain death, as it has been diagnosed for the past two decades, has been based on false medical assumptions. Many patients who meet acceptable criteria for whole-brain death in fact have residual brain function, including hypothalamic function.[4] More refined diagnostic techniques have disclosed that other parts of the brain continue to function after the patient appears to have met the criteria for whole-brain death.

The Dead-Donor Rule

The reliance on death as a necessary condition for removal of organs has made it more difficult to justify removing organs from anencephalic infants, patients in a persistent vegetative state, and many others. The movement to redefine death, primarily as a mechanism to improve organ procurement, was predicated on and locked into place the unexamined reliance on the so-called dead-donor rule.[36] This principle is often posited as a starting point for discussions about organ retrieval, as if its rationale were self-evident. According to this principle, a patient must be dead before his or her organs can be removed. My contention is that there is ample precedent in the law and good moral justification for removing organs from persons who are not legally dead.

One purpose of the dead-donor rule is to ensure that no interest of the potential organ donor is threatened. But there are many patients who are not dead in any sense whose interests would not be violated by allowing removal of vital organs before death. Consider, for example, a patient in a permanent vegetative state, with no prospect for recovery of any cognitive function, for whom a decision had been properly made to discontinue life-sustaining treatment, such as mechanical ventilation. In such a case, with appropriate consent, kidneys and liver could be removed prior to discontinuation of the ventilator. Such removal would not immediately cause death. The cause of death would be the same as traditionally occurs, namely, respiratory failure leading to irreversible loss of cardiac function.

There are other patients from whom organ retrieval could be justified on the grounds that it violates no discernible interests—patients for whom planned death is considered the morally preferred course, particularly when death is expected to follow discontinuation of life-sustaining treatment. The justification for organ retrieval would be strongest in patients who had explicitly requested that their organs be removed in this way. Examples would include patients with advance directives that included specific instructions about organ donation. A survey of young adults with cystic fibrosis revealed that 30–50 percent were interested in having their organs removed *before they died* as part of their terminal care.[37] From a moral perspective, these patients would seem to be ideal organ donors. Their death is commonly anticipated for many years, allowing ample time for reflection and truly informed consent, a rare event in organ removal from brain-dead patients; they could truly be donors. The possibility of having their one healthy solid organ serve others after their death is likely to be experienced as a positive experience. I mention these patients to emphasize the point, and highlight the irony, that organ removal is most persuasively justified when it serves the interests and true desires of the patient from whom it is taken, yet our current policies exclude precisely these morally ideal donors.

The much-discussed Pittsburgh protocol constituted a thoughtful effort to allow organs to be taken in a morally justified way from patients who would not meet brain-death criteria but were expected to die from other causes.[38] The most troublesome feature of this protocol is the awkward requirement, imposed by the dead-donor rule, that patients be declared dead when they are not dead by either brain-death criteria or the old-fashioned definition, irreversible cessation of cardiorespiratory activity. (See Chap. 18.) Such patients are declared dead within a specified number of minutes after heart function ceases, since resuscitation is precluded by a valid do-not-resuscitate order. In most jurisdictions, statutes stipulate that determining death by cardiac criteria requires that the loss of cardiac function be irreversible, but in many such patients cardiac function undoubtedly could be restored and has, therefore, not been irreversibly lost. This apparent inconsistency with the statutes as written is no different from the declaration of death in ordinary clinical settings, when organ retrieval is not under consideration. There, too, death is declared even though the loss of cardiac function is often not yet irreversible. Contrary to the innuendo in a report by the television show *60 Minutes* on this issue, such protocols do not create a new definition of death or deviate from traditional definitions in any way.

Exposing the ambiguities of the current ways in which death is defined risks a public reaction that could adversely affect the fragile trust necessary for more traditional forms of organ donation. It is possible that brain death itself evokes a similar, though lesser, discomfort among relatives asked to consent to donation. Many have noted that grieving relatives look skeptical when told that their loved one is dead. Eighteen years after the Harvard report, despite uniform state laws, it is still contrary to the intuition of many, including myself, to call someone dead whose normal bodily functions continue.

If the dead-donor rule were reconsidered, it would even be possible to consider removal of the heart from terminally ill patients who were not brain dead. Under present statutes, this would constitute causing death, but others have argued that the distinction between causing death and allowing to die in this setting is of little moral weight. Legally, immunity against a homicide charge would be necessary. An immunity statute could be crafted, or death could be redefined in a way that required only loss of cortical functions, with acknowledgment that the brainstem has little to do with our notion of personal identity.[39] Some might object to redefining death again for utilitarian purposes, but that is exactly what was proposed by the Harvard committee, with what is now nearly universal public acceptance. Utility, of course, is not the only or even the most compelling reason for such a change. A stronger argument would be based on respect for patient autonomy in a setting where no interest of the patient was being jeopardized.

Conclusion

Organ removal should be considered justified when no apparent interest of the patient is violated and appropriate permission has been obtained.

A redefinition of death was not necessary for the claimed social purposes, nor has the redefinition been effective in achieving the stated goals. The original social problems—facilitating termination of treatment and improving organ supply—are more prevalent today. Overtreatment—the continuation of life-sustaining treatment on patients who have no reasonable prospects for meaningful survival and often no clear interest in or desire for such treatment—seems far more widespread today than in 1968, when the redefinition was proposed as the solution to that problem. Organ supply lags further and further behind demand, and the redefinition of death, required-request laws, and even more permissive statutes have not had the desired effect.

Not only did brain-death statutes not solve these problems, the problems have become worse despite the widespread adoption of brain-death statutes. My suggestion—today, as in 1983—is that we abandon the dead-donor rule and recurrent redefinitions of death. Instead, I suggest we find more narrow justifications and legal rationales for the removal of organs, the discontinuation of life support, and the other social goals for which death has ill served us.

I do not pretend that this reformulation of policy, divorcing law and regulation from the question of whether or when a person is dead, would be without problems or other unwelcome consequences. No policy is without adverse effects. But it would have the virtue of no longer claiming that we know something that is beyond our expertise or capacity to know—namely, when a person is dead. We would no longer be making false medical claims—that the whole brain has ceased to function in patients who meet clinical criteria for brain death. We would no longer have to ask next of kin to use or accept a word—*death*—in situations where it makes little intuitive sense. Instead, we would be facing our dilemmas more candidly: how can we reduce the spreading practice of overtreatment, and how can we reduce the imbalance between demand and supply of organs in a way that satisfies widely shared views of respecting the interests of patients?

Finally, I do not address here the important role that declaring death plays in the ritual of saying good-by and grieving for a loved one who is passing on. I believe it is helpful and desirable to select a point in time where it is appropriate to say, "He is dead," not because it is true, or because we are expert on such questions, or because it facilitates organ retrieval, but because it is helpful.

References

1. Dworkin R. Death in context. *Ind Law J* 1973;48:623–39.
2. Fost N. The new body snatchers: On Scott's *The Body as Property. Am Bar Fdn Res J* 1983;3:718–32.
3. Brennan SL, Delgado R. Death: Multiple definitions or a single standard. *South Calif Law Rev* 1981;54:1323–55.
4. Halevy A, Brody B. Brain death: Reconciling definitions, criteria, and tests. *Ann Intern Med* 1993;119:519–25.
5. Arnold RM, Youngner SJ. The dead donor rule: Should we stretch it, bend it, or abandon it? *Kennedy Inst Ethics J* 1993;3:273–78.
6. Emanuel L. Reexamining death: The asymptotic model and a bounded zone definition. *Hastings Cent Rep* 1995;25(4):27–35.
7. Morison RS. Death: Process or event? *Science* 1971;173:694–98.
8. *Roe v Wade* 410 US 113 (1973).
9. Human Life Bill: A bill to provide that human life shall be deemed to exist from conception: Hearings on S.158 before the Subcommittee on Separation of Powers of the Senate Committee on the Judiciary, 97th Cong, 1st Sess (1981).
10. Only Leon Rosenberg had the wisdom to acknowledge that his expertise as a scientist and geneticist gave him no special insight into the complex religious, legal, and philosophical questions surrounding the definition of when life begins.
11. A definition of irreversible coma: Report of the Ad Hoc Committee of the Harvard Medical School To Examine the Definition of Brain Death. *JAMA* 1968;205:337–40.
12. Of course, the patient would eventually die, most likely from complications of his head injury, but no one knew then or now how long that death might be postponed. Few have tested the limit of our ability to maintain a brain-dead patient. One patient has allegedly been maintained for 5 years (Cranford R, personal communication). The precise claim, then, might have been that, if treatment were continued, death need not have occurred by the time of the assailant's trial.
13. It is difficult to prove a negative, and I would be open to be proven wrong on this point. I have made the statement repeatedly, in meetings and in print, for 20 years to audiences including most of the country's leading health lawyers and bioethicists, without refutation. A thorough legal search could not uncover any jury convictions of a physician for active euthanasia. Stone TH, Winslade WJ. Physician-assisted suicide and euthanasia in the United States: Legal and ethical observations. *J Leg Med* 1995;16:481–507. Jack Kevorkian could not be convicted for recurrently violating a statute created explicitly for the purpose of stopping his repeated involvement in assisting suicide.
14. Hafemeister T, Hannaford PL. *Resolving Disputes over Life-sustaining Treat-*

ment: A Health Care Provider's Guide. Williamsburg, Va.: National Center for State Courts, 1996.

15. A negligence action was brought in Wisconsin against a physician for withdrawing ventilator support from a patient who was unarguably brain dead, over the objections of a relative. The relatives were divided, and the litigant claimed emotional damages. An arbitration panel voted against the physician (2–1), but the trial court ruled in favor of the physician.

16. Uniform Determination of Death Act, 12 U.L.A. 236 (Supp. 1983).

17. Areen J, King PA, Goldberg S, Capron AM. *Law, Science and Medicine.* New York: Foundation Press, 1984, 1067.

18. Uniform Anatomic Gift Act 8 U.L.A. 15 (1968).

19. Annual Report of the United States Scientific Registry of Transplant Recipients and the Organ Procurement and Transplantation Network. U.S. Department of Health and Human Services, Health Resources and Services Administration, 1995.

20. Arnold RM, Youngner SJ, Schapiro R, Spicer CM. *Procuring Organs for Transplant: The Debate over Non-Heart-Beating Cadaver Protocols.* Baltimore: Johns Hopkins University Press, 1993. Most of the conference proceedings are also available in Arnold RM, Youngner SJ (eds). Ethical, psychosocial and public policy implications of procuring organs from non-heart-beating cadavers. *Kennedy Inst Ethics J* 1993;3(2).

21. The acceptance of brain death as a criterion for death was obviously necessary for progress in heart transplantation, since removal of the heart would otherwise be the cause of death. Assuming the requirement that the donor must be dead, then heart transplantation required some other definition of death than the traditional heart-lung criteria. This discussion applies primarily to the claim that higher rates of kidney transplantation required a redefinition of death, which seemed to be the major consideration at the time of the Harvard committee report.

22. Prottas JM. Organ procurement in Europe and the United States. *Milbank Mem Fund Q* 1985;63(1):94–126.

23. Siminoff LA, Arnold RM, Caplan AL. Public policy governing organ and tissue procurement in the United States: Results from the National Organ and Tissue Procurement Study. *Ann Intern Med* 1995;123:10–17.

24. Caplan AL. Are required request laws working? Altruism and the procurement of organs and tissues. *Clin Transplant* 1989;3:1–7.

25. Wisconsin statutes 146.71, Definition of Death (1981).

26. Kopelman LM, Irons TG, Kopelman AE. Neonatologists judge the "Baby Doe" regulation. *N Engl J Med* 1988;318:677–83.

27. Fost N. Do the right thing: Samuel Linares and defensive law. *Law Med Health Care* 1989;17(4):330–34.

28. Veatch R. The whole-brain-oriented concept of death: An outmoded philosophical formulation. *J Thanatol* 1975;3:13–30.

29. Youngner SJ. Some must die. In: Youngner SJ, Fox R, O'Connell L (eds). *Organ Tranplantation: Meanings and Realities.* Madison: University of Wisconsin Press, 1996.

30. Youngner SJ, Landefeld SC, Coulton CJ, et al. "Brain death" and organ retrieval: A cross-sectional survey of knowledge and concepts among health professionals. *JAMA* 1989;261(15):2205–10.

31. Wikler D, Weisbard AJ. Appropriate confusion over "brain death." *JAMA* 1989;261(15):2246.

32. Shewmon DA, Capron AM, Peacock WJ, et al. The use of anencephalic infants as organ sources: A critique. *JAMA* 1989;261(12):1773–81.

33. Walters JW, Ashwal S. Organ prolongation in anencephalic infants: Ethical and medical issues. *Hastings Cent Rep* 1988;18(5):19–27.

34. Harrison MR. The anencephalic newborn as organ donor. *Hastings Cent Rep* 1986;16(2):21–23.

35. Fost N. Organs from anencephalic infants: An idea whose time has not yet come. *Hastings Cent Rep* 1988;18(5):5–10.

36. Robertson JA. Relaxing the death standard for organ donation in pediatric situations. In: Matthieu D (ed). *Organ Substitution Technology: Ethical, Legal and Public Policy Issues.* Boulder, Colo.: Westview Press, 1988, 69–76.

37. Fost N, Bernstein G. Organ donation from young adults with cystic fibrosis. Department of Pediatrics and Program in Medical Ethics, University of Wisconsin, Madison. Unpublished study.

38. Nothing new under the sun. The Wisconsin program had been using a similar protocol for nearly two decades. In fact, the majority of kidneys transplanted in that program were from patients who died of cardiorespiratory failure, not brain death. (Robert Hoffman, personal communication, 1997).

39. Green D, Wikler D. Brain death and personal identity. *Philos Public Affairs* 1980;9(winter):105–33.

IV

Public Attitudes about Brain Death in the United States

Given the controversies described in the previous chapters, one might expect active, even acrimonious, debates in the lay press over the current methods of defining death. Compared with the fascination the American public has shown over when life begins, however, there has been little public discussion about when life ends. The following chapters by Siminoff and Bloch, Campbell, and Rosner attempt to summarize what we know or can discern regarding public attitudes toward the definition of death.

Siminoff and Bloch, in Chapter 10, survey empirical data regarding health care provider and lay public attitudes, with an emphasis on opinions regarding brain death. The review is as remarkable for what it does not find as for what it finds. Despite an exhaustive review, the authors were unable to find one population-based survey of public attitudes toward the current definition of death. Most of the studies of public opinion are small and suffer from methodological flaws that limit their generalizability. The studies of health care providers, while larger and more recent, are also limited. Much of the data concentrate on attitudes about organ procurement and are only tangentially related to what people think the definition of death is or should be. It seems that the public is poorly informed about the controversies related to determining death. Many of the families involved in decisions regarding organ donation seem unaware that there is any controversy about defining death and do not know the clinical criteria for brain death or their medical and legal implications. What people say they do know about brain death is often factually incorrect. And despite their scientific training, health care providers are not clear about these concepts either.

Another way to understand the public's attitudes toward defining death is by examining religious organizations' views. The most common religious denominations in the United States—Catholicism, Protestantism, and Judaism—are generally supportive of the view that one may be declared dead using either neurological or cardiopulmonary criteria. However, this support is not unanimous. Campbell and Rosner examine the views of two conservative and influential wings of mainstream religion: fundamentalist Christians (Chap. 11) and Orthodox Jews (Chap. 12), respectively.

Campbell offers a scholarly examination of fundamentalist Christian views in light of their more general views toward medical science and modern, secular bioethics. Rather than portraying fundamentalists as having an irrational adherence to, and interpretation of, the Bible, Campbell describes their internally coherent world view and how religious commitments frame their understanding of secular issues. Fundamentalists view death as primarily a spiritual rather than biological event. Instead of directly questioning the current definitions of death, fundamentalists have focused on changes that would "be the wedge to qualitative assessments of human life and value, rather than affirming a sanctity of life assessment under the dominion of God." Thus, they have spoken out against higher-brain definitions of death, the definition of anencephalics as dead, and active euthanasia. They also object to the University of Pittsburgh Medical Center's attempt to define cardiovascular criteria of death within its non-heart-beating organ donor policy because they believe the policy subverts the sacredness of human life for consequentialist gerrymandering "and compromises the biblical commitment of care to the dying person." But they have been quietly supportive of whole-brain definitions of death.

Rosner describes a critical theological debate within the Orthodox Jewish community over the meaning of the pivotal biblical passage (and its talmudic interpretation), "In whose nostrils was the breath of the spirit of life" (Gen. 7:22). One orthodox school argues that the irreversible cessation of respiratory function is the primary physical sign of death and thus that whole-brain death with loss of respiration is equivalent to death; others believe that respiration is a surrogate for cardiac function and thus that death requires loss of cardiac function. Despite their relatively small numbers, the debate within Orthodox Judaism has had important public policy ramifications; largely in response to lobbying by Orthodox Jews, New Jersey passed a law defining death that allows family members to require that death be declared using cardiopulmonary criteria if the patient had religious objections to brain death. In Chapter 8 of this volume, Robert Veatch points to this policy as an example of how pluralism can be respected in definitions of death.

What conclusions can we draw from these essays? First, the current definition of death seems to be accepted for the most part, if somewhat misunderstood, by both health care providers and the general public. In fact, many analysts view the definition of death as one of the few areas in bioethics in which there is a social consensus. The push to review again how death is defined is driven by theoretical arguments from a small group of academicians.

Second, the academic discussion has not been informed by adequate data about public knowledge and opinion. We simply need better empirical data about what people think. How death is defined and clinically determined affects everyone, yet the debate has occurred almost exclusively among a small group of bioethicists. The philosophical critiques and countercritiques of public policy regarding death may (or may not) reflect public opinion. As Richard Rettig commented at the Cleveland meeting on defining death:

> My concern is with a process, dominated by experts, of almost constant tinkering with the legal framework of death [and] dying . . . over more than two decades. This process is not informed by deep knowledge and understanding of public attitudes, values, and beliefs about death. It is a process that may be counterproductive to the development of a broad-based, deeply-rooted, and settled view on these matters by the general public. Instead, the constant tinkering . . . may engender confusion and may increase, not diminish, the distance between expert opinion and general public opinion.

10

American Attitudes and Beliefs about Brain Death

The Empirical Literature

Laura A. Siminoff, Ph.D., and Alexia Bloch, Ph.D.

NORTH AMERICAN attitudes toward death have changed significantly in accord with shifting socioeconomic, demographic, and technological aspects of society. In earlier eras, death was primarily governed by ritual as dictated by the family and religious or ethnic affiliation. Since the beginning of this century, institutions such as hospitals have increasingly regulated and organized death. While these institutions are products of society, they are not necessarily closely allied with individual family traditions. Most importantly, advanced technologies, such as life-sustaining equipment, have expanded the time to death and changed our technical and legal definitions of death. The need to obtain potentially life-saving organs for transplantation from cadaver sources has also encouraged expansion of our definition of death beyond traditional cardiopulmonary criteria.

Is it the case that in the course of these changes the medical community has diverged far from the public's views surrounding death and the human body? What attitudes do Americans have toward the new definitions of death? There is more we do not know than do know about the general public's attitudes toward and understanding of these new conceptions of death. This chapter explores contemporary attitudes toward death in the United States, particularly focusing on attitudes toward and the understanding of brain death.

The existing research on general attitudes Americans have toward death consists of a hodgepodge of studies from various academic disciplines. In general, there is a consensus that America is a death-denying society. Americans are viewed as fearful of death.[1-6] Yet, even as Americans have put death further away from the public eye, there have been radical changes in the American symbolic and legal notions of what death is.

Variations in Criteria and Acceptance of Brain Death

Following the 1968 report by the Harvard committee and later the report by the President's commission in 1981,[7,8] states were incorporating brain death into their legal definition of death. Even as this was occurring, the public and many in the medical community were raising concerns about it. Papers appeared in both the popular press and scholarly journals questioning the theoretical and moral bases of neurological death. During the 1970s a growing awareness of life-extending and death-delaying technologies made Americans more concerned about how they died in addition to why death occurred.

One article in a 1974 issue of *Harper's* magazine calls into question the rapid adoption of the 1968 Harvard criteria for neurological death.[9] The author intimates that the new definition of death was intended to avoid the issue of euthanasia while granting the right to "pull the plug," thus facilitating the harvesting of organs. The author tellingly states that "the heart may have been reduced by the new definition of death to merely another organ" (26).

Other authors expressed a deep uneasiness with organ donation itself. A 1973 article in *Hastings Center Studies* refers to the process of procuring organs for donation as the "disbursement of the body and 'picking up leftovers.'"[10] Yet another article, published in 1979, expressed concern about the varying, and sometimes nonspecific, statutory definitions of death. While pointing out that there was a strongly entrenched cardiac definition of death, the author concludes that brain-death criteria had become a generally accepted standard of death by the medical, and indeed most, if not all, members of society.[11] The truth of this last statement is currently a matter of conjecture.

There is still much conceptual uncertainty regarding the meaning of *brain death*. Many people are ambivalent about the status of a patient whose brain has ceased functioning but whose attachment to mechanical support systems keeps his or her heart beating. This is evidenced by anecdotal reports of how people talk about death, distinguishing between "brain death" and "real death," that is, cardiopulmonary death. Surprisingly few studies have examined, in a systematic fashion, how either the public or the health care community has responded to this formal reworking of the legal definition of death. None of the public opinion polls that examine American attitudes toward death in general have focused specifically on Americans' attitudes toward, or understanding of, brain death.

A 1968 report in the *Journal of the American Medical Association* reviewed public understanding of the diagnosis of death in conjunction with organ donation and the use of life-support systems. The authors noted that, in their informal survey of hospital house staff, not one person could remember receiving formal instruction on the requirements for the diagnosis of death. A second, small survey of public attitudes toward death ($n = 112$) reported that two-thirds of those surveyed thought that death occurred when the heart stopped beating, when breathing ceased, or both.[12] Only 9 percent thought of death in terms of brain function. A few years later another survey, this time of 100 laypersons, 100 physicians, and 70 first-year medical students, still found a sizable number of Americans uncomfortable with a neurological definition of death. Sixty percent of lay people, 42 percent of medical students, and 46 percent of physicians interviewed did not consider brain death an adequate definition of death.[13]

More recent studies have found a somewhat greater acceptance of brain death. Yet, as Youngner recently pointed out,[14] the persistence of the term *brain death* in our language and the continued debate over whole-brain versus higher-brain definitions of death signal that American society is still confused and divided over this newer definition of death.

A 1984 study of 200 neurosurgeons and 100 neurologists indicated substantial diversity in the criteria used to declare brain death and in attitudes toward it.[15] Although 88 percent required the absence of pupillary reflex, only 61 percent required an absent cough reflex. Further, in response to a hypothetical situation in which the family of a brain-dead patient did not want death declared, 78 percent reported that they would continue ventilatory support; however, one-third of these respondents reported that they would declare the patient dead while doing so.

A more detailed examination of health care professionals' knowledge about brain death found that even those who should have intimate knowledge of the brain-death criteria are often misinformed. For example, a study of 195 physicians and nurses likely to be involved in organ procurement found that only 35 percent could correctly identify the legal and medical criteria for determining brain death.[16] In yet another study, roughly one-half of nurses in intensive care units (ICUs) believed that physicians were unsure of organ donor eligibility criteria and one-third reported that nurses were also unsure of the criteria.[17]

Studies of the public, including families of brain-dead patients, also show that the concept of brain death is not widely understood. An Australian self-administered survey of 69 families of brain-dead patients reported that one-third claimed to know something about brain death before the patients' admission, and a little over half were judged to have a good or adequate understanding of brain death.[18] One study of 94 consenting donor families reported that 14 of the families still had no clear understanding of brain death even after they had donated.[19]

At the 1996 Annual Meeting of the Division of Transplantation, a report was delivered on a study of 164 donor and nondonor families. The study found significant gaps in families' understanding of brain death despite the fact that 95.7 percent were made aware of brain death by their relatives' physicians. Forty-five percent equated brain death with coma, and 31.7 percent believed that a brain-dead individual could recover.[20]

Our own recent studies have examined health care providers' and laypersons' understanding and acceptance of the concept of brain death. These populations, obtained in separate studies, were asked a series of identical questions concerning their knowledge and attitudes surrounding organ procurement and brain death. The first was a general survey of American attitudes drawn from a sample of Americans in three geographic regions using a random digit dial telephone technique. This sample of the general public was not found to be totally accepting of the concept of brain death. Twenty percent of those asked agreed with the statement that a person is dead only when the heart stops.[21]

The second study is examining a sample of 400 donor and nondonor families. Data analysis of 80 respondents from the sample reveals that 90 percent of respondents were informed that their relative was brain dead and 75 percent understood that an individual who was brain dead had no hope of recovery. However, on the basis of extensive interviews with respondents, it was determined that only 32.5 percent had a satisfactory understanding of brain death. Among the most common misconceptions volunteered by subjects were beliefs that the patient was still alive but not able to function without the aid of the machines (37.9 percent) and that the machines were keeping the patient alive (27.3 percent). Some respondents also explicitly confused brain death with a coma or vegetative state (19.7 percent). Furthermore, when directly asked when they considered the patient had died, 40 percent thought their brain-dead relatives were not dead until the machines had been turned off or admitted that they were confused as to exactly when the patient had actually died.[21]

The health care providers who spoke with these families about organ donation were also interviewed. They were asked questions about what they told the family about brain death, whether they agreed with proposals that would presume all patients would be donors unless they explicitly opt out (presumed consent), and if they agreed with the statement that a person is dead only when the heart stops. Only a small number of health care providers accepted only cardiopulmonary criteria for death. Of the 209 health care provider respondents, only 4.8 percent agreed with the statement that a person is dead only when the heart stops. Of the 168 respondents who discussed brain death with family members, no more than 5.4 percent gave families misinformation. Interestingly, despite a significantly better understanding of brain death than that of the general public or the families of organ-eligible patients, only 37.6 percent favored a presumed consent policy for obtaining organs.

One of the few larger studies of the general public examined the understanding of brain death of 946 college students using a true/false series of questions. This study found that most students were seriously misinformed about brain-death criteria.[22] Using an experimental word association method, another study found that subjects tended to misunderstand brain death, viewing it as less than terminal.[23]

Some sizable minority communities within the United States do not accept the concept of brain death. Rosner's close analysis in Chapter 12 of this volume highlights the intense rabbinic debates within the Orthodox Jewish community in regard to brain death. He notes that, although cerebral death is not acceptable in Judaism as a definition of death, some rabbis recognize brainstem failure because of the brainstem's role in controlling respiration. Rosner introduces Jewish perspectives on physiological decapitation to support the view that brain death is seen as death in Judaism. However, he notes that this view is countered by a rabbinic view that requires both cessation of respiration and cardiac standstill as evidence of death. The definition of death among various Jewish communities and among other ethnic minorities is clearly important for those dealing with misunderstandings surrounding brain death. Members of any one community do not necessarily agree about the acceptability of brain death.

There is also a growing body of literature on cross-cultural attitudes toward brain death, which can help us understand how certain ethnic populations in the United States may view death. One example is work on the resistance that the concept of brain death has met in Japan.[24] The traditional Shinto view of the moment of death as ambiguous and uncertain is not compatible with the concept of brain death, where death is determined by quite distinct medical characteristics.[25] In fact, in a 1984 poll,[26] almost 40 percent of the Japanese population was strongly opposed to recognizing brain death as a definition of death. In Chapter 14 in this volume, Lock notes that from 1983 to 1992 the proportion of Japanese recognizing brain death increased from 29 percent to 55 percent. Such research can potentially be extrapolated to Japanese Americans and perhaps to other Asian-American populations.

Clearly, much more research is needed to understand how the general public conceptualizes brain death. The discomfort of health care professionals (especially nurses) and the public when participating in organ retrieval or the withdrawal or withholding of therapy from patients is intuitively linked to their beliefs about what constitutes our "knowing" when someone is really dead. An unease with organ donation may be related to several factors, including culture, religion, or simply a misunderstanding or lack of acceptance of the concept of brain death as equating with death. An understanding of this issue is crucial if we are to come to grips with the intensifying debates surrounding care at the end of life and euthanasia or are to increase the procurement of organs.

Conceptions of Death and Views on Organ Donation

Organ donor rates have remained low while the number of patients needing organs continues to swell the waiting lists. In 1992, 24,791 people were on transplant waiting lists; by January 1996 these numbers had almost doubled, with 43,937 patients on the list.[27] Nonetheless, despite extraordinary efforts to convince the American public to donate organs, the rate of donation has remained unchanged nationally.

The reasons for this imbalance are unclear, as public opinion surveys show that over 95 percent of Americans are aware of transplantation and the need for more organs. Moreover, between one-half and three-quarters say they would be willing to donate an organ after their death.[28,29]

People are generally willing to donate in theory, but they do not take the necessary actions to ensure that the organs can be procured. In a telephone survey of 2,056 respondents, 94 percent of the respondents had heard of organ transplantation, but only 19 percent carried donor cards.[30] Another study found that only about 23 percent of Americans had signed organ donor cards or indicated on their driver's licenses their willingness to donate organs or tissues after their deaths.[31] Indeed, in Texas, which recently implemented a de facto mandated choice system, only 20 percent of state residents applying for a driver's license chose to check the "donor" option.[32] The largest study yet examining the actual donation decisions of families asked to donate ($n = 827$) found that 46.5 percent of organ-eligible families, 34.5 percent of tissue-eligible families, and 23.5 percent of cornea-eligible families agreed to donation.[33] A variety of explanations have been given for the discrepancy between the public's positive attitudes and their aversion to signing donor cards or donating. These explanations include people's fear of their own mortality, their fears about organ procurement and the possibility of being declared dead too soon, concern about the fairness of the organ distribution system, concerns about the effect that donation might have on funeral arrangements, and deeply held beliefs about the integrity of the body after death.

We actually know little about why families do or do not donate organs. Some have posited that an unwillingness to accept the patient as dead or to accept brain-death criteria leads many to refuse to donate. Pearson et al. conducted one of the few studies that has explicitly linked beliefs about brain death with organ transplantation.[18] This survey of 69 families of brain-dead patients found that there was a significant relationship between lack of knowledge on the part of the families about brain death and the reluctance to donate the organs of family members. In addition, 55 percent of the respondents felt that being better informed about the illness of their relative would have put them in a position to make a different decision. However, it is also noted that it is not easy to overcome the inability of many people to accept that a warm body is actually dead. Two-thirds of the respondents said they accepted the death intellectually but had doubts about it emotionally.

Conclusion

Culture, as Geertz writes,[34] is created and perpetuated through the "webs of meaning" with which the beliefs, behaviors, and fears of given groups take form and are passed on from generation to generation. Thus, the subculture of biomedicine is not necessarily shared by lay people from the same society, although those belonging to the subculture of biomedicine (health care professionals) will share the broader webs of meaning of American culture with a lay population. In fact, the formal understandings as propounded by academic medicine may not even be shared by a majority of health care professionals. Several studies indicate that health care providers differ little from the general lay population in the disparity between their apparent desire to donate their organs and their lack of preparation to do so. For instance, studies have found no difference between the percentage of physicians and intensive care nurses and that of lay people who carry a donor card.[30,35,36]

The degree to which dominant cultural themes of biomedicine find their way into the broader cultural webs of meaning in the United States is only beginning to be critically examined.[37] Making connections between attitudes toward brain death and attitudes toward organ donation for diverse populations in the United States starts to clarify where webs of meaning are shared and where they differ for lay people and health care professionals. Furthermore, making these types of connections starts to clarify where, even for health care professionals, these meanings still have not penetrated beyond the formal ideology of medicine.

The rapidly changing technological aspects of death in the United States play a crucial role in shaping contemporary views of death. While there are a multitude of traditional and distinct views held by different communities in the United States, all of these communities are faced at some point with biomedical concepts of death which emphasize a dichotomy between life and death.

Lay and medical concepts of brain death are particularly crucial to study as biomedicine moves to expand the options for organ donation, including cold perfusion, non-heart-beating donation, use of anencephalics as donors, and other even more obscure techniques. What each has in common is that it asks both health care professionals and the general public to expand or somehow revise their definition of what death is and when someone is "really" dead.

It is clear that lay and medical concepts do not always correspond, and therefore it is necessary to extend research efforts to explore further how different sociodemographic variables (particularly gender, social status, religion, and ethnicity) affect concepts of death (and especially brain death). More research is needed among individuals who have actually confronted the option of organ donation, the withdrawal of life-support therapy, or the withholding of treatment for family members. Also, explicit measurement of health care professional and lay attitudes toward death in varying contexts and especially of how and if people differentiate between death and brain death is needed. Studies would benefit from moving past simple surveys or the administration of psychometric scales on death to college sophomores. Research that combines the best in both qualitative and quantitative techniques is needed to understand this complex phenomenon. Additional research could assist in improving communication and creating more common ground for lay and health care professionals to understand the implications of the technological changes and developments in biomedicine which are affecting us all.

References

1. Aries P. *Western Attitudes toward Death from the Middle Ages to the Present.* Baltimore: Johns Hopkins University Press, 1974.

2. Aries P. Death inside out. In: Steinfels P, Veatch R (eds). *Death Inside Out: The Hastings Center Report.* New York: Harper & Row, 1975, 9–24.

3. Lester D. Re-examination of Middleton's data: Sex differences in death attitudes. *Psychol Rep* 1970;27:136.

4. Lester D. Attitudes toward death today and thirty-five years ago. *Omega* 1971;2:168–73.

5. Kastenbaum R. Reconstructing death in postmodern society. *Omega* 1993; 27:75–89.

6. Dyer KA. Reshaping our views of death and dying. *JAMA* 1992;267:1265–70.

7. Ad Hoc Committee of the Harvard Medical School To Examine the Definition of Brain Death. A definition of irreversible coma. *JAMA* 1968;205:337–40.

8. President's Commission for the Study of Ethical Problems in Medicine and

Biomedical and Behavioral Research. *Defining Death: Medical, Legal and Ethical Issues in the Determination of Death*. Washington, DC: Government Printing Office, 1981.

9. Gaylin W. Harvesting the dead. *Harper's* 1974;249(1492):23–30.

10. May W. Attitudes toward the newly dead. *Hastings Cent Studies* 1973;1:3–13.

11. Green PM. The question of brain death—concepts and criteria. *Wis Med J* 1979;78:13–17.

12. Arnold JD, Zimmerman TF, Martin Daniel C. Public attitudes and the diagnosis of death. *JAMA* 1968;206:1949–54.

13. Delmonico FL, Randolph JG. Death: A concept in transition. *Pediatrics* 1973;51:234–39.

14. Youngner SJ. Defining death: A superficial and fragile consensus. *Arch Neurol* 1992;49:570–72.

15. Black PM, Zervas NT. Declaration of brain death in neurosurgical and neurological practice. *Neurosurgery* 1984;15:170–74.

16 Youngner SJ, Allen M, Barlett ET, et al. Psychological and ethical implications of organ retrieval. *N Engl J Med* 1985;313:321–24.

17. Daneffel MB, Kappes JE, Waltmire D, et al. Knowledge and attitudes of health care professionals about organ donation. *J Transplant Coordination* 1992;2:127–30.

18. Pearson IY, Bazeley P, Spencer-Plane T, Chapman JR, Robertson P. A survey of families of brain-dead patients: Their experiences and attitudes to organ donation and transplantation. *Anaesth Intensive Care* 1995;23:88–95.

19. Savaria DT, Rovell MA, Schweizer RT. Donor family surveys provide useful information for organ procurement. *Transplant Proc* 1990;2:316–17.

20. Franz H. Study of donor and nondonor families. Presented at the Annual Meeting of the Division of Transplantation, Washington, DC, February 1996.

21. Seltzer D, Siminoff LA, Arnold RM. Public opinion and attitudes toward alternative methods of organ donation. *Arch Intern Med* (forthcoming).

22. Horton RL, Horton PJ. Knowledge regarding organ donation: Identifying and overcoming barriers to organ donation. *Soc Sci Med* 1990;31:791–800.

23. Jasper JD, Harris RJ, Lee BC, et al. Organ donation terminology: Are we communicating life or death? *Health Psychol* 1991;10:34–41.

24. Feldman EA. Defining death: Organ transplants, tradition, and technology in Japan. *Soc Sci Med* 1988;27:339–43.

25. Botkin JR, Post SG. Confusion in the determination of death: Distinguishing philosophy from physiology. *Perspect Biol Med* 1992;36:129–38.

26. *Yomiuri Times*, November 22, 1984.

27. United Network for Organ Sharing. Update 12;1:26. Richmond, Va. January 1996.

28. Evans RW, Manninen DL. U.S. public opinion concerning the procurement and distribution of donor organs. *Transplant Proc* 1988;20:781–85.

29. Gallup Organization. *The American Public's Attitudes towards Organ Donation and Transplantation.* Boston: Partnership for Organ Donation, 1993.

30. McIntyre P, Barnett M, Harris R. Psychological factors influencing decisions to donate organs. *Adv Consumer Res* 1987;331–34.

31. Prottas JM, Batten HL. *Attitudes and Incentives in Organ Procurement: The Attitudes of the American Public.* Report to the Health Care Financing Administration, April 1986.

32. Texas Department of Public Safety Statistics. July 1994.

33. Siminoff LA, Arnold RM, Caplan AL, Virnig BA, Seltzer DL. Public policy governing organ and tissue procurement in the United States. *Ann Intern Med* 1995;123:10–17.

34. Geertz C. *Interpretation of Culture.* New York: Basic Books, 1973.

35. Sophie LR, Salloway JC, Sorock G, et al. Intensive care nurses' perceptions of cadaver organ procurement. *Heart Lung* 1983;12:2611–17.

36. Perkins KA. The shortage of cadaver donor organs for transplantation: Can psychology help? *Am Psychol* 1983;42:921–30.

37. Martin E. *Flexible Bodies.* Boston: South End Press, 1994.

11

Fundamentals of Life and Death

*Christian Fundamentalism and
Medical Science*

Courtney S. Campbell, M.A., Ph.D.

A FUNDAMENTALIST HAS BEEN described as a person willing to "do battle royal" for the fundamentals of the Christian faith.[1] However, fundamentalists have yet to engage in battle over the theological and jurisprudential legitimacy of brain death, which suggests the issue is currently tangential to the contemporary fundamentalist movement. Thus, this essay of necessity will be impressionistic and interpretive in seeking to develop the implications of certain theological themes central in fundamentalist and conservative Christianity for medical science, standards of death, and organ procurement.

First, I present the theological "fundamentals" within which an issue such as that of brain death would be situated in a fundamentalist Christian context. I then discuss the relevance of this perspective within a secular society that is committed constitutionally to respect for religious pluralism, but whose public rhetoric frequently vilifies religious views that resist appropriation by the secular society for its own ends. This closed public square is (from the standpoint of fundamentalism) a manifestation of secular humanism and of cultural biases against orthodox Christian faith. For reasons I develop, what would ensure direct fundamentalist engagement with the status of brain death are serious policy proposals for a higher-brain standard of death.

Biblical Fundamentals and Methodology

In the United States, the Christian fundamentalist movement began to differentiate itself from liberal Protestant theology and ecclesiology in the late nineteenth and early twentieth centuries. The central concern of early fundamentalism was to contest religious "modernism," which was viewed as forsaking the metaphysical and moral truth revealed in Christian scripture for rationalist propositions expressed in scientific postulates and secular practices. More specifically, fundamentalists indicted the modernists' optimism about human nature, which seemed to offer a theological endorsement of "progress," including technological progress, as harmonious with, and mandated by, the will of God. The theological and social ferment of this period led to a doctrinal method of religious identification, as articulated in the so-called five points of fundamentalism, which are considered "necessary and irreducible foundations of belief and therefore non-negotiable bases for Christian faith" (243).[2]

> —*Biblical inerrancy and infallibility.* The Bible contains no errors of fact; it is free of error with respect to theology, morality, history, geography, cosmology, and science,[3] although the poetic license of biblical writers may not be scientifically precise.
> —*The Deity of Jesus,* including the virgin birth
> —*The substitutionary atonement of Jesus* as punishment for the crime of human sin and the source of personal salvation
> —*The physical, bodily resurrection of Jesus*
> —*An eschatology ("end of time") of "Rapture,"* in which believers will be gathered up to heaven at the second coming of Jesus Christ. Signs of the coming of Christ are revealed in biblical prophecy, which provides for the discerning believer an accurate prediction of future events through symbols.[3,4]

These foundations of faith reflect "minimal doctrinal essentials, apart from which Christianity ceases to be Christian."[4] Compromise on these essentials amounts to betrayal or apostasy ("falling away") from truth. The "five points" provide for the fundamentalist a coherent and consoling world view, in which Scripture mediates answers to questions, guides decision making, and offers a cultural critique in which social deterioration is a prelude to eschatological rapture.

Public discourse about "Christian fundamentalism," however, seldom reflects this rigid doctrinal identification. Rather, it is often used in a broad and typically pejorative sense to refer to Christians who understand the Bible to be *the* definitive authority and guide for the moral life of the Christian and for society. This broader and evaluative public definition of fundamentalism may encompass any or all of the following movements:

1. *Literalists,* who contend not only that the revelation of God's will in the Bible is the sole *source* of metaphysical and moral truth, but also that the biblical revelation must be *interpreted* in a literal, absolute, and universal sense. Most commonly, the literal method of interpretation surfaces in disputes over creationism, sexuality, and faith healing.

2. *Evangelicals,* whose primary commitment includes not only fidelity to faith, but also an efficacious Christian witness to the *society.* The content of this witness is construed by conservative evangelicals primarily in terms of "family values," while liberal evangelicals emphasize "peace and justice" issues. The Southern Baptist Convention, the largest Protestant denomination in the United States (approximately 15 million adherents) is often designated a "fundamentalist" faith, but its own self-understanding is as a conservative evangelical faith community.

3. *Charismatic Christians,* who, while observing the moral authority of scripture, acknowledge the ongoing historical presence of the spirit of God in the Christian community, manifested especially in speaking in tongues (glossolalia) and faith healing. The "charisma" of the spirit is most commonly associated with the Pentecostal movement, whose largest denominational exemplars include the Assemblies of God, the Church of God, and the Church of Christ. In addition, charismatic congregations have recently emerged in Catholic, Episcopal, and Lutheran denominations.

4. *Right-to-Life Christians,* who affirm as "fundamental" a commitment to the sanctity and preservation of human life. This validates, at minimum, opposition to abortion and euthanasia. This movement is most well known for its political activism on these questions and less so for its theoretical justifications.

Needless to say, the public definition of *fundamentalism* is fuzzy and certainly allows for overlap among the above movements. The societal dimension of the evangelical movement, which often overlaps with the concern for the sacredness of life affirmed by "pro-life" Christians, has culminated in the most direct engagement with questions of biomedical science and medical ethics.[5,6] My use of the term *fundamentalism* throughout the rest of this chapter will reflect the kind of ethical discourse prevalent among fundamentalists and conservative evangelicals.

The theological horizons of these two movements are not limited to rescuing individual souls from sure social doom, but also encompass a positive witness to culture. Fundamentalists and conservative evangelicals understand themselves to be not merely custodians of the true faith, but also engaged in a mission to rescue a secular society from moral evil and political anarchy: "We [the faith community] are the last line of defense against a rapid descent into an evil abyss of barbarism."[7] One prominent exposition of this defensive posture is a "family values" emphasis, displayed most recently in the May 1995 "Contract with the American Family" announced by the Christian Coalition. In the context of biomedical ethics, some authors have warned that conservative Christians need to be aware that "there is a movement afoot in society to redefine death, . . . and the question for Christians is how to combat this movement."[8]

Since biblical narratives seldom address social policy questions directly, it is reasonable to inquire what hermeneutical (interpretative) principles are used to support the conclusions reached by fundamentalists and conservative evangelicals. The answer lies in the development of theological analogues to *scientific* methodologies. For example, some authors suggest that a parallel to the second law of thermodynamics exists in the moral and political realms, namely, the concept of moral entropy.[9] This moral law gives justification for the articulation of Christian theological convictions in public discourse, at least in seeking to preserve family, church, and professional moral traditions, including the Hippocratic tradition, from the perceived permissiveness of secular humanism. Moreover, scriptural interpretation involves what some theologians describe as a Baconian method: The believer identifies and organizes the facts of Scripture regarding the nature of reality and then derives general principles and underlying patterns that are coherent with these facts. For example, the biblical posture about life gradually unfolds and supports a claim about the sanctity of human life. A discerning organization of biblical evidence on human nature is expressed in the idea that persons are created in the "image of God" (Gen. 1:27–28). All of life, from beginning to end, is portrayed as subject to the sovereignty and dominion of God, who both gives breath to human beings that they may live (Gen. 2:7) and deprives them of breath when they expire (Ps. 104:29). Human beings are therefore accountable and responsible for exercise of their moral agency, often expressed in the value of stewardship.

The Fundamentals of Life and Death

These values shape certain distinctive perspectives that bear on some conceptual underpinnings of brain death, including ideas of personhood, death, and human destiny. The concept of *personhood* is from the fundamentalist perspective considered a secular reduction of the image of God. "The personhood concept is usually defined in terms of physical and mental abilities or capabilities and, thus, excludes human beings lacking those defined qualities. 'Personhood analysis' ignores the full scriptural view of humankind."[10] The fundamentalist and conservative evangelical interpretation of the image of God requires a standard for death that affirms life's sanctity rather than a qualitative evaluation of life, such as cessation of relational capacity, consciousness, or social interaction.

This perspective also critiques the modern medicalization of death: "Modern medicine defines death primarily as a biological event; yet Scripture defines death as a spiritual event that has biological consequences."[11] This "spiritual event" is the departure of the spirit, or breath of life, from the body, or as phrased biblically, "and the dust returns to the earth as it was, and the spirit returns to God who gave it" (Eccles. 12:7; cf. James 2:26). In such a theology, death is a consequence of the human fall from grace and alienation from the divine presence through sin. It cannot be embraced as a "natural" part of the life cycle nor dignified through the language or ideology of "rights."[12] Nor can death be mastered through a process of medicalization, for secular medicine has an incomplete understanding of death.

Insofar as a specific criterion of death is at issue, fundamentalist and conservative evangelical discussions invariably situate the definition of death within the context of social acceptance of *euthanasia,* rather than facilitating organ procurement.[13] The prospect that revising the definition of death is simply a way to hasten death for vulnerable but biologically tenacious patients leads to objections to policy revisions grounded in the principle of the sanctity of life. Gregory Rutecki, for example, objects to the Pittsburgh protocol on non-heart-beating cadaver donors (NHBCDs) on the grounds that the dying process is "contrived" and "hastened." Rutecki's position relies on both secular and religious reasons: The protocol represents abandonment of the dead-donor rule and denies equal treatment for the dying. Moreover, it violates the Hippocratic prohibition of intentional assistance in death and compromises the biblical commitment of care to the dying person.[14,15]

While fundamentalist and evangelical authors do not dispute braindeath criteria per se, their concerns emerge within the medical/technological and social/qualitative contexts in which a standard of brain death is applied or revised. Moreover, given the studies of Youngner et al. that there is both confusion and incoherence about the meaning and application of brain death, even among medical professionals,[16] this suspicion of secular expertise is exacerbated rather than assuaged for a lay audience rooted in biblical rather than scientific authority.

It can be questioned why such religious opposition did not emerge during prior discussions over the definition of death, such as the Report of the Ad Hoc Committee of the Harvard Medical School. The time frame is very important. One cannot speak of a politically mobilized and socially active fundamentalist movement until after the *Roe v. Wade* decision legalizing abortion in 1973, some 5 years after the report of the Harvard committee. Nor was euthanasia a realistic end-of-life option for patients until very recently. Thus, current moves to redefine death are understood within a quite different social context than that which prevailed in the 1960s; indeed, the current social ethos reflects, according to many religious conservatives, an embrace of a "culture of death."

Within this context, fundamentalist and conservative evangelicals have opted to defend whole-brain definitions of death. Such positions characteristically do not offer a theological exposition of the rationale for a whole-brain concept as much as they endeavor to expose the fallacies of a higher-brain definition. In many arguments, the whole-brain definition seems to win by default rather than to be theoretically justified by carefully developed explorations.

J. Kerby Anderson, for example, in the midst of an argument against euthanasia, claims that the spiritual view of death held by Christians requires a "rigorous medical definition for death." This supports a qualified endorsement of whole-brain death. Thus, "a comatose patient may not be conscious, but from both a medical and biblical perspective he is very much alive and treatment should be continued unless brain activity has ceased . . . A comatose patient without any brain wave activity (a flat EEG, electroencephalogram) should be removed from life-support systems; he is considered to be already dead."[11] The continual reference in conservative writings to the comatose patient as the prime example of a person whose status would be affected by a changed social understanding of death suggests that, insofar as there are objections to brain death or revising the legal standards of death, they will be based in concerns about a fear of a hastened death and the declaration of a premature end to life.

A similar case is put forward by A. A. Howsepian, whose "defense" of whole-brain death essentially consists of a critique of proposals offered by Robert Veatch.[17] Howsepian maintains that a Veatchian-type social policy will sweep persons in a persistent vegetative state, or persons with dementia, or living prospective organ donors into the category of the "dead." The "rigor" demanded by the conservative argument in defining death means that a line must be drawn against any move to a neocortical standard lest vulnerable populations be put at risk. Such fears about premature or hastened deaths or inadequate safeguards for the vulnerable may override a Christian altruistic response to donate an organ—derived from the command to love one's neighbor—to preserve life. In these concerns, the fundamentalist and evangelical perspective seems to mirror general worries of the populace, at least if public opinion surveys about reasons for refusal to sign organ donor cards are reliable.

With respect to current statutes, some fundamentalist and evangelical authors do raise questions about the meaning of "irreversibility" of entire brain function. The dispute here is not about the fallibility of technical determinations of irreversibility, but rather resides in a theological claim that, in a basic sense, the Christian cannot understand death as irreversible. Death is *not* a final exit, for it has been overcome through the literal resurrection of Christ. Religious convictions about bodily resurrection have also sometimes been cited as reasons for objection to organ donation, but in company with a gradual resolution in the 1980s of some of the medical concerns about immunology and transplant rejection, fundamentalist and evangelical discourse has begun to affirm a more positive, though not morally obligatory, stance to organ donation. Medical success has been a catalyst for reinterpreting theologies of resurrection, so that the doctrine is now portrayed as compatible with organ donation. In 1988, for example, "messengers" (representatives of autonomous congregations) of the Southern Baptist Convention approved a resolution "On Human Organ Donation":

WHEREAS, Complete resurrection of the body does not depend on bodily wholeness at death; and

WHEREAS, The values of a godless society promote self-sufficiency to such a degree that people are indifferent to the needs of others, as seen in resistance in organ donations; and

WHEREAS, Organ donation for research or transplantation is a matter of personal conscience . . .

Be it further RESOLVED, That we encourage voluntarism regarding organ donations in the spirit of stewardship, compassion for the needs of others, and alleviating suffering. [Resolution No. 15, adopted 1988, pp. 76–77.]

More recently, the love-of-neighbor imperative embedded in the biblical parable of the good Samaritan—"Go and do likewise"—has suggested to conservative evangelical scholars that "Christians of all people should be willing to give the gift of life through donating their organs and tissues." This is not seen as an impediment to bodily resurrection, for "Christians will receive a new body in the resurrection, a body of a different kind than the one that died."[18]

The point I wish to emphasize here is that the methods of fundamentalist and evangelical ethics hardly conform to the public stereotype of an illogical deduction from some biblical passage of dubious relevance to the contested issue. It is (at its thoughtful best, to be sure), rather, a complex process that uses reason to organize revelation into a coherent theme or general perspective. It involves, moreover, the appropriation of one form of pre-Enlightenment scientific methodology, which may in turn support a sharp critique of post-Enlightenment science and medicine.

The Autonomy of Science and the Exile of God

Christian fundamentalism places science squarely under the sovereignty of God, a view I will refer to as *theonomous science*. True science and orthodox belief cannot conflict, since all knowledge, empirical or revealed, is rooted in God: "Pure science is worship in that it seeks to reveal the details of the creation and perceive God's laws of the physical universe."[19] The authority of the biblical narrative provides the epistemological underpinnings for a determination of religious and scientific truth.

This does not mean that fundamentalism is necessarily antiscientific or antitechnological. The Newtonian/Baconian paradigm of scientific understanding, in which scientific methods are used to discern facts about the natural world, is embraced within fundamentalist literature as an era of pioneering discoveries of science; science discerned the natural order as designed by God,[20] and it thereby contributed to (and confirmed) humanity's understanding of theonomy. The fundamentalist complaint against science is thus directed at the autonomy of modern science.

There are two principal flashpoints for this conflict between autonomous and theonomous science. The most prominent is the natural selection evolutionary theory of Darwin. The Darwinian account presents both a theological and an ethical crisis for the fundamentalist. The theological crisis concerns the credibility of the nonnegotiable truths of the Christian faith. The Genesis creation narrative in the scientific *Weltanschauuang* is categorized as myth rather than fact. The scientific reduction of the supernatural (miracles) to naturalistic causes and explanations initiates challenges to other fundamentals, such as the virgin birth or the resurrection. Not surprisingly, then, fundamentalists perceive in evolution a potential domino effect for the authority of the entire biblical canon. Once Genesis is toppled, trust in the historical credibility of other biblical stories can no longer be validated; it assumes the status of an all-or-nothing proposition.

The second flashpoint comes in the wake of Darwin, as the biblical materials are subjected to direct scrutiny by scientific methods of literary criticism. Biblical criticism sharply distinguishes between the Jesus of history and the church-constructed Christ and offers an understanding of the Bible as a man-made book, culturally located and limited and containing historically contingent moral and religious teachings. In contrast, fundamentalists describe the Bible as "a God-breathed" document.[3,21] The metaphor of "breath" is deliberate, for it reiterates that all humanity is in a relationship of dependency upon the divine: "Then the Lord God formed man of dust from the ground, and breathed into his nostrils the breath of life; and man became a living being" (Gen. 2:7). The analogy fundamentalists propose is that the moral life of human beings in their communities no less requires a God-breathed document.

This is why the Darwinian account also precipitates an ethical crisis: The continuity between human beings and animals embedded in evolutionary theory denies human uniqueness and thereby erodes the ethic of the sanctity of life. "The whole [pro-life] debate turns on whether human life is sacred or whether human beings are merely the most sophisticated life form in the animal kingdom."[8] In the view of fundamentalists and conservative evangelicals, once the sacredness of human life is rejected, society must of necessity opt for a quality-of-life ethic, which is portrayed as merely an extension of the "survival of the fittest" maxim into the moral realm.

Although the conflicts between autonomous and theonomous science are most visible in debates over public education curricula, this dispute also has a profound bearing on the fundamentalist approach to medical science and technology. Christian stewardship involves a responsibility to "define the ethical parameters within which science must live" (209).[4] Insofar as modern science presents itself as an autonomous and alternative authority for interpretation and understanding of the world, the fundamentalist will understand it to reflect cultural acceptance of the irrelevance (or death) of God. Thus, what is really at stake in the clash with medical science is the question of an unqualified commitment to the sovereignty of God as giver and taker of life and knowledge by which to live.

This critique of autonomous medical science coincides with that popularized perception of bioethics, "playing God." For the fundamentalist Christian, the metaphor means simply that the autonomous scientist is usurping God's role and power. Playing God expresses human arbitrariness, arrogance, and the assumption of tremendous power, indeed the powers of both *creating* and of *defining or naming* life and death. Fundamentalist and evangelical writings express dismay that, in contemporary medicine, "technology becomes god," and that forms of research, such as genetic engineering "presume that we have more intelligence than God."[4] The conservative Christian seeks not to foreclose decisions about technology and research, for the ethic of stewardship enables human agency and responsibility. Rather, the issue is that the validity of these judgments hinges on whether the sacred is present or exiled from the public square.

Thus, insofar as brain-death criteria and tests involve a mediating role of technology and specialized professionals, God as giver and taker of breath-life may be relegated to the periphery of decision-making control. Modern medicine therefore embodies and reflects the exile of God that the conservative Christian takes to be so objectionable about secular humanistic culture in the first instance. The "New Medicine," writes a leading evangelical theologian, is "post-consensus, post-Hippocratic, feeding on an illusory model of autonomy which seems to be demanded by the self-consciously pluralist character of the post-Christendom soci-

ety; offering cover for a developing manipulative medical culture in
which patients are finally subservient to the 'interests' of an assortment
of other parties."[22] This view of modern medicine is why the (admittedly
few) conservative Christian discussions of brain death occur in the context of opposition to euthanasia, not support for organ donation. The
fundamentalist worry is that redefining death may be the wedge to qualitative assessments of human life and value, rather than an affirmation
of a sanctity-of-life assessment under the dominion of God.

Fundamentalism in the Culture of Disbelief

If fundamentalist and evangelical Christians find themselves so at odds
with the underlying ethos of the new medicine (and the blessings on it
pronounced by bioethicists), we need to ask what status should be given
to their moral claims? How accommodating can professionals and public
policy be of religious diversity? i conclude with some reflections that
illuminate some of the parameters of secular pluralism in its encounter
with Christian fundamentalism.

It is important first to understand that the case made by conservative
Christians for a place at the table of public discourse (and public education) is ultimately based on a claim about unequal treatment. In a
1961 U.S. Supreme Court decision in *Torcaso v. Watkins,* Justice Black
designated secular humanism as a religion.[23] The gradual secularization
of public education has, it is argued, given to the content and values of
secular humanism a privileged status vis-à-vis those of the Christian tradition. These developments have culminated in the conclusions of both
fundamentalists and evangelicals that government is hostile rather than
neutral toward Christian faith and that a pronounced violation of the
establishment clause of the First Amendment has occurred under the
guise of secularism.

This perception of political privilege and discrimination is supplemented by a concern over the medical stigmatization and marginaliza-
tion of the religiously conservative. Some brief illustrative vignettes: A
devout Pentecostal woman, in need of amputation, is assessed medically
incompetent when she refuses surgery on grounds of her religious convictions, which are deemed "madness" and "religious craziness" by
health care personnel.[24,25] The standard diagnostic reference manual for
psychiatry frequently exemplifies mental disorders and illness by reference to religious beliefs and actions.[26] A husband refuses a request by

hospital personnel to discontinue the bodily life of his comatose wife on the grounds that life and death are in the hands of God: "Physicians should not play God, that the patient would not be better off dead, that removing her life support showed moral decay in our civilization, and that a miracle could occur."[27] Yet, commentators outside the care-giving context either ignore the religious basis of the decision or disparage it as irrational.[28]

My point here is simply that when the fundamentalist or conservative evangelical looks upon political or medical institutions informed by secular values or purposes, he or she sees not a society of pluralism and tolerance but one characterized by hostility and insult. Indeed, even though the tradition of political liberalism is committed in principle to respect for diversity and for individual conscience, as Stephen Carter has insightfully suggested, the philosophical premises of secular liberalism often impose gag rules on "God-talk."[29]

Following the arguments of de Tocqueville, Carter maintains that a democratic polity functions best when a variety of intermediate associations and communities function as *independent moral voices* interposed between self and state. Faith traditions, in particular, offer sources of moral understanding and vision "without which any majoritarian system can deteriorate into simple tyranny" (16, 36). The necessity of protection from state coercion is especially important to various marginalized groups in a society who may be vulnerable to coercion and oppression. Religious commitments are therefore important in a democratic polity as "powers of resistance."

The social parameters of fundamentalist Christianity reflect just such a pattern of independence and resistance. The self-portrayal of fundamentalists is one of resistance to accommodation with the ideologies and practices of secular humanism and medicine, in contrast to the modernizing compromises that fundamentalists believe permeate other religious traditions. With respect to society, fundamentalists understand themselves to be in a basic posture of independence from and resistance against evil and social disintegration ("moral entropy").

As independent moral voices, religious traditions in general ought to resist the imposition of normative conceptions of rationality. The claim that a fundamentalist or evangelical-based religious preference is irrational, mad, or crazy presumes a tradition-free standard of rational agency, something the Enlightenment project failed to establish.[30] Rationality is given content only from within a particular tradition, narrative, or community; thus, to describe some religion-based choices in medicine as irrational per se is to appeal to an illusory standard of rational choice. It follows that it is surely valid for a conservative Christian to claim respect as a moral equal from others who think differently about religion or about the nature of the world. The attempt to censor religious discourse by the subtle imposition of gag rules such as Carter describes has ironically shown itself to be precisely the energizing force that revitalizes fundamentalists and the evangelical movement.

In conclusion I propose four parameters for public discourse on medical ethics, including brain-death criteria, that require *respect for* and impose *responsibility on* the person with fundamentalist or conservative evangelical convictions. The first, consistent with the liberal principle of respect for individual conscience, is to ensure that exemptions are permitted for persons who object to a brain-death standard for religious reasons. Such objections will be few from the fundamentalist Christian, insofar as steps have been taken to assure that death has not been hastened or declared prematurely. Nonetheless, any such objections should be respected under appropriate statutes, particularly since the state has not seen in organ procurement a compelling societal interest to require compulsory organ retrieval.

A second approach is to understand that the fundamentalist theological framework is not as antithetical to science as is portrayed in creationist stereotypes. A search for common ground on medical science *could* be undertaken between the fundamentalist and the secular ethicist. This is especially the case because fundamentalist biblical interpretation and social analysis integrate certain scientific methods or analogues.

Third, while it contravenes the ideals of liberal democracy to accept a religious understanding as the *source* of public policy, the secular state and secularized medicine can and should make room for religious, including fundamentalist, convictions in the *process* of deliberation on public or institutional policy. Given the fundamentalist antipathy to compromise with modernism and humanism, it is unreasonable to expect that such deliberations will culminate in a fundamentalist endorsement of *secular*-based standards of brain death. But it is not unreasonable to ask the fundamentalist or evangelical ethicist to delineate the *theological* convictions that support an endorsement of whole-brain death. Moreover, discussion should at least clarify some of the questions posed by the fundamentalist about medical science and brain death. For example, the central theological claim of the Christian fundamentalist presumes a question regarding the nature of *authority* for the moral and political life of a society. Even if one disagrees, as I do, that biblical authority should be the guideline for a definition of death in a technological era, it is not unreasonable to raise a question regarding the grounds and qualifications for authority of those who compose and implement such definitions. The same kind of issue should be examined with respect to the theme of *accountability* raised by the fundamentalist. Those that formulate policy on brain death should be accountable to various audiences, including conscience, professional colleagues, interested institutions, and the citizenry, which can impose certain procedural and substantive restraints on the autonomy of science.

Finally, while the conservative Christian anticipates the coming of the kingdom of God, he or she must assume the responsibilities of citizenship in a liberal democratic society. A minimal requirement is civility: It does the fundamentalist no credit as a citizen or as a believer to disparage other citizens as secular fundamentalists or to use the rhetoric of demonization to express disapproval of acts or practices in medicine. Participation in the civic life of a democratic society requires adherence to certain procedural rules, including respect for the liberty of individuals, separation of government and religious institutions, and secular justification for public policy and laws. Respect for such rules precludes, in particular, rhetorical support of a vision of a "Christian nation" and the intolerance that follows upon practical attempts to impose this vision. The fundamentalist must remember the biblical wisdom to "wait upon God," even if others see this as a wait for a Godot.

References

1. Ammerman NT. North American Protestant fundamentalism. In: Marty M, Appleby RS (eds). *Fundamentalisms Observed.* Chicago: University of Chicago Press, 1991, 2.

2. Simmons PD. Baptist-Evangelical medical ethics. In: Lustig BA (ed). *Theological Developments in Medical Ethics: 1990–1992.* Dordrecht, Netherlands: Kluwer Academic Publishers, 1993, 243–70.

3. Dobson E. Fundamentalism—its roots. *New Catholic World* 1985;228:4–9.

4. Falwell J. *The Fundamentalist Phenomenon: The Resurgence of Conservative Christianity.* Garden City, NY: Doubleday, 1981, 2–11.

5. Kilner JF, de S Cameron NM, Schiedermayer DL. *Bioethics and the Future of Medicine: A Christian Appraisal.* Grand Rapids, MI: William B Eerdmans, 1995.

6. Bouma H, Diekema D, Langerak E, et al. *Christian Faith, Health, and Medical Practice.* Grand Rapids, MI: William B Eerdmans, 1989.

7. Land RD. Life at risk: We must not fail. In: Land RD, Moore LA (eds). *Life*

at Risk: The Crises in Medical Ethics. Nashville: Broadman & Holman, 1995, 278–87.

8. Howsepian AA. *In Defense of Whole-Brain Definitions of Death,* audiotape. Bannockburn, IL: Center for Bioethics and Human Dignity, 1995.

9. Gangel KO. Moral entropy, creation, and the battle for the mind. In: Anderson JK (ed). *Living Ethically in the '90s.* Wheaton, IL: Scripture Press Publications, 1990, 18–26.

10. Lasley DM. *Euthanasia.* Nashville: Christian Life Commission of the Southern Baptist Convention, 1994, 12.

11. Anderson JK. A biblical appraisal of euthanasia. In: Anderson JK (ed). *Living Ethically in the 90's.* Wheaton, IL: Scripture Press Publications, 201,198.

12. Commission on Theology and Church Relations. *Report on Euthanasia with Guiding Principles.* St. Louis: Lutheran Church-Missouri Synod, 1979, 18.

13. Crum GE. Dying well: Death and life in the 90's. In: Land RD, Moore LA (eds). *Life at Risk: The Crises in Medical Ethics.* Nashville: Broadman & Holman, 1995, 164.

14. Rutecki GW. Blurring distinctions between the dying and the dead: A call for discernment in organ donation. *Ethics Med* 1994;10:60–67.

15. Rutecki GW. Until death shall be no more: Christian care for the dying. In: Kilner JF, de S Cameron NM, Schiedermayer DL (eds). *Bioethics and the Future of Medicine: A Christian Appraisal.* Grand Rapids, MI: William B Eerdmans, 1995, 279–89.

16. Youngner SJ, Landefeld CS, Coulton CJ, et al. Brain death and organ retrieval. *JAMA* 1989;261:2205–10.

17. Veatch RM. The impending collapse of the whole-brain definition of death. *Hastings Cent Rep* 1993;23:18–24.

18. Mitchell CB. Organ donation and the Samaritan imperative. *Commentary: The Christian Life Commission of the Southern Baptist Convention.* Nashville: The Commission, April 14, 1993.

19. Harris TR. Reflections on science, technology, and risk. In: Land RD, Moore LA (eds). *Life at Risk: The Crises in Medical Ethics.* Nashville: Broadman & Holman, 1995, 203.

20. Barr J. *Fundamentalism.* Philadelphia: Westminster Press, 1978, 93.

21. Verhey A. *The Great Reversal: Ethics and the New Testament.* Grand Rapids, MI: William B Eerdmans, 1984.

22. de S Cameron NM. Bioethics in the third milennium. In: Land RD, Moore LA (eds): *Life at Risk: The Crises in Medical Ethics.* Nashville: Broadman & Holman, 267–75.

23. *Torcaso v. Watkins* 367 U.S. 468, 1961.

24. Powell T. Religion, race, and reason: The case of LJ. *J Clin Ethics* 1995;6:73–77.

25. Dula A. LJ's religious craziness. *J Clin Ethics* 1995;6:77–80.

26. Post SG. DSM-III-R and religion. *Soc Sci Med* 1992;35:81–90.

27. Miles SH. Informed demand for non-beneficial treatment. *N Engl J Med* 1991;325:512–15.

28. Helga Wanglie's ventilator. *Hastings Cent Rep* 1991;21:23–35.

29. Carter SL. *The Culture of Disbelief: How American Law and Politics Trivialize Religious Devotion.* New York: Basic Books, 1993.

30. Engelhardt HT. *The Foundations of Bioethics.* 2d ed. New York: Oxford University Press, 1996, 32–101.

12

The Definition of Death in Jewish Law

Fred Rosner, M.D.

RAPID ADVANCES IN biomedical technology and therapeutic procedures have generated new moral dilemmas and accentuated old ones in
the practice of medicine. The vast recent strides made in medical
science and technology have created options that only a few decades ago
would have been considered to be in the realm of science fiction. New
discoveries and techniques in organ transplantation, assisted reproduction, and gene therapy, to cite but a few, have created a keen awareness
of the ethical issues that arise from humans' enhanced ability to control
their destiny.

Together with these advances has come a shift of emphasis in the
physician-patient relationship from beneficence and paternalism to the
primacy of patient autonomy and self-determination. Economic factors
and considerations also play a greater role in individual and societal
medical decision making. Religion has always been and continues to be
an important determinant of ethical decision making. This chapter presents general principles of Jewish medical ethics, the structure of Jewish
law, differences between secular and Jewish ethics, and the definition of
death in Jewish law.

The General Principles of Jewish Medical Ethics

Judaism is guided by the concept of the supreme sanctity of human life and of the dignity of man created in the image of God. The preservation of human life in Judaism is a divine commandment. Jewish law require physicians to do everything in their power to prolong life, but prohibits the use of measures that prolong the act of dying. The value attached to human life in Judaism is far greater than that in Christian tradition or in Anglo-Saxon common law. To save a life, all Jewish religious laws are automatically suspended, with the only exceptions being idolatry, murder, and forbidden sexual relations, such as incest. In Jewish law and moral teaching, the value of human life is infinite and beyond measure, so that any part of life—even if only an hour or a second—is of precisely the same worth as 70 years of it.[1-4]

In Jewish tradition a physician is given specific divine license to practice medicine. According to Maimonides and other codifiers of Jewish law, it is an obligation upon physicians to use their medical skills to heal the sick. Physicians in Judaism are prohibited from withholding their healing skills and are not allowed to refuse to heal unless their own life would be seriously endangered thereby.

Judaism is a right-to-life religion. This obligation to save lives is both individual and communal. Certainly a physician, who has knowledge and expertise far greater than that of a layperson, is obligated to use his or her medical skills to heal the sick and thereby prolong and preserve life. It is erroneous to suppose that having recourse to medicine shows lack of trust and confidence in God, the Healer. The Bible takes it for granted that medical therapy is used and actually demands it. In addition, in Judaism a patient is obligated to seek healing from human physicians and not rely on faith healing. The Talmud states that no wise person should reside in a city that does not have a physician. Maimonides rules that it is obligatory upon humans to accustom themselves to a regimen that preserves their body's health and heals and fortifies it when it is ailing.

The extreme concerns in Judaism about the preservation of health and the prolongation of life require that a woman's pregnancy be terminated if it endangers her life, that a woman use contraception if a pregnancy would threaten her life, that an organ transplant be performed if it can save or prolong the life of a patient dying of organ failure, and that a postmortem examination be performed if the results of the autopsy may provide immediate life-saving information to rescue another dying patient. Judaism sanctions animal experimentation to find the cure for human illnesses, provided there is no pain and suffering to the animal, since Judaism prohibits cruelty to animals. Judaism also allows patients to accept experimental medical or surgical treatments, provided no standard therapy is available and the experimental therapy is administered by the most experienced physicians, whose intent is to help the patient and not just to satisfy their academic curiosity.

The infinite value of human life in Judaism prohibits euthanasia or mercy killing in any form. Handicapped newborns, the mentally retarded, the psychotic, and patients dying of any illness or cause have the same right to life as you and I, and nothing may be done to hasten their death. On the other hand, there are times when specific medical or surgical therapy is no longer indicated, appropriate, or desirable for a terminal, irreversibly ill patient. There is no time, however, when general supportive care, including food and water, can be withheld or withdrawn, thereby hastening the patient's death.

The Structure of Jewish Law

The Pentateuch, or Five Books of Moses, is known as the Torah and is the fundamental source of all Jewish religious law. The Torah is sometimes referred to as the written or biblical law, as opposed to the oral law, which represents the unwritten traditions that interpreted, applied, and supplemented the written Torah.

The widely accepted reduction to writing of the legal matter of the oral law is known as the Talmud, which consists of 63 tractates of opinions and teachings of many rabbis who analyzed, interpreted, dissected, and commented on the written or biblical law. The first part of the authoritative Babylonian Talmud was redacted and written by Rabbi Judah the Prince in the second century. The Talmud was completed by Rabbi Ashi in the fifth century. The major commentary on both the Bible and the Talmud is that of Rabbi Shlomo ben Yitzchak (1040–1105), known as Rashi.

The heads of the rabbinic academies in Babylon during the sixth through ninth centuries were called *Gaonim*. They were the first to produce systematic codes of Jewish law by summarizing the conclusions of the lengthy talmudic discussions. At the beginning of the second millennium, the center of Jewish learning shifted to North Africa, where famous talmudic commentators such as Rabbenu Chananel flourished.

Rabbi Isaac of Fez, known as Alfasi (1013–1103), wrote a famous work that is a talmudic commentary and code of Jewish law at the same time.

During the eleventh to thirteenth centuries, a group of French and German rabbis known collectively as Tosafot wrote important commentaries and annotations which, in addition to that of Rashi, appear alongside the text in printed editions of the Talmud. The most illustrious Jew of the Middle Ages is the Spaniard Moses Maimonides (1138–1204), rabbi, philosopher, physician, astronomer, ethicist, and much more. His most famous work, *The Mishneh Torah,* is a monumental compilation and systematization of all biblical, talmudic, and Gaonic law. It remains to this day a classic and authoritative 14-volume Jewish legal code.

Over the next two centuries, additional commentaries on and digests of talmudic debate were composed by famous Jewish scholars such as Rabbi Moses ben Nachman (1195–1270), known as Nachmanides, Rabbi Menachem HaMeiri (1249–1315), Rabbi Solomon ben Adret (1215–1310), known as Rashba, and Rabbi Asher ben Yechiel (1250–1327), known as Rosh. The next two landmark codes were those of Rabbi Jacob ben Asher (1269–1343), known as Tur, and Rabbi Joseph Karo (1488–1575), whose work is known as *Shulchan Aruch.* Numerous commentaries by later rabbinic authorities and decisors made the *Shulchan Aruch* the accepted standard work of Jewish law, which it remains today, alongside Maimonides' *Mishneh Torah.*

The major rabbinic literature of the past four centuries consists of responsa, which are formal replies to legal queries addressed to rabbinic scholars of all generations. These responsa deal with social, political, and economic as well as legal problems and issues of their times. Hundreds of volumes of responsa have been authored by many rabbis over many centuries. This "case law" literature is part of the Jewish legal mainstream and serves as precedent authority for subsequent responsa.

Secular Ethics versus Jewish Ethics

Whereas much of the modern secular ethical system is based on rights, Judaism is an ethical system based on duties and responsibilities. "Indeed, there is no word for rights in the very language of the Hebrew Bible and of the classic sources of Jewish law. In the moral vocabulary of the Jewish discipline of life we speak of human duties, not of human rights, of obligations, not entitlement. The Decalogue is a list of Ten Commandments, not a bill of Human Rights."[5]

In Judaism, beneficence and altruism are promoted over mere non-maleficence. The physician-patient relationship is viewed as a covenant, in contrast to the notion of a relationship between freely contracting individuals.[6]

In current secular ethics, the principle of absolute autonomy for the patient takes precedence over all the other values, including beneficence and even life itself. This approach has been criticized by prominent Catholic bioethicists,[7] and it is not consonant with Jewish ethical thinking.

> Judaism restricts the notion of autonomy to actions that are morally indifferent. Where conflicting values arise, each individual is bound to act in accordance with a high standard of normal moral conduct . . . Therefore, in medical situations that involve ethical conflicts, the solution is based on the appropriate Jewish law that governs both the physician and the patient. This approach can be termed a *moral-religious paternalism* as opposed to the Hippocratic *individual-personal paternalism* of the physician.[6]

Thus, secular ethics attributes a relative value to life, whereas Judaism ascribes a supreme value to life. Therefore, in Judaism, an autonomous decision to destroy life is unacceptable, suicide is morally and legally forbidden, refusal of life-saving treatment is not respected, and active euthanasia is strictly prohibited.

Euthanasia is opposed without qualification in Jewish law, which condemns as sheer murder any active or deliberate hastening of death, whether the physician acts with or without the patient's consent. Some rabbinic views do not require the physician to resort to "heroic" methods, but sanction the omission of machines and artificial life-support systems that serve only to draw out the dying patient's agony, provided, however, that basic care, such as food and good nursing, is provided. Judaism requires the physician to do everything in his or her power to prolong life, but prohibits the use of measures that prolong the act of dying. Judaism also distinguishes between withholding (sometimes allowed) and withdrawing (never allowed) a certain treatment, whereas the secular and Catholic ethical systems do not make such a distinction.

Judaism is thus concerned with covenantal obligations and individual responsibilities, which is very different from secular ethics, which is based on individual rights, such as autonomy, liberty, and privacy. With this background on basic principles of Jewish medical ethics, the structure of Jewish law, and some of the differences between secular and Jewish ethics, one can better understand the remainder of this essay on the definition of death in Jewish law.

The Definition of Death in Jewish Law

Jewish tradition views death as inevitable and just. Judaism differentiates between the body and the soul, acknowledging resurrection for the body,[8] and immortality for the soul. The traditional view is that death occurs upon the separation of the soul from the body. Since this phenomenon does not lend itself to direct empirical observation, the classical secular definition of death has been the absence or cessation of breathing and heartbeat.

The era of organ transplantation, coupled with rapid advances of biomedical technology, led to a reevaluation of the traditional definition of death and the emergence of the concept of brain death, or whole-brain death including brainstem death. In fact, the suggestion has been made that anencephaly be equated with "brain absent" (i.e., lacking cerebral hemispheres) and be accepted as another definition of death to enable anencephalic neonates to serve as organ donors.[9] A logical extension of such thinking is to declare patients in irreversible coma or in a persistent vegetative state to be dead in order to harvest their organs. Should society stretch, bend, or abandon the dead-donor rule?[10] The American Medical Association recently withdrew its suggestion that the dead-donor rule might be broken to allow organs to be removed from anencephalics prior to death.

Judaism certainly rejects such suggestions of redefining death, since patients with spontaneous respiration and heartbeat are considered fully alive in all respects. Does Judaism, however, accept the concept of whole-brain death, whereby the patient has no spontaneous respiration but a heart that continues to beat? Cerebral death is certainly not acceptable in Judaism as a definition of death because unconsciousness does not remove the humanhood or personhood from a patient. But if the whole brain, including the brainstem, which controls vital bodily functions such as respiration, is permanently and irreversibly nonfunctional, does Judaism consider such a situation as equivalent to death? Must the patient also have asystole in Jewish law before being considered dead? One prominent Jewish bioethicist writes that:

much of the debate concerning the definition of death misses the mark. A definition of death cannot be derived from medical facts or scientific investigation alone. The physician can only describe the physiological state which he observes; whether the patient meeting that description is alive or dead, whether the human organism in that physiological state is to be treated as a living person or as a corpse, is an ethical and legal question. The determination of the time of death, insofar as it is more than a mere exercise in semantics, is essentially a theological and moral problem, not a medical or scientific one.[11]

There is at present an intense debate among rabbinic authorities as to whether Jewish law recognizes whole-brain death as a definition of death. In Judaism, the classic and primary source indicating that death coincides with irreversible cessation of respiration is a passage in the Babylonian Talmud, tractate Yoma, which enumerates circumstances under which one may or must desecrate the Sabbath in order to save a human life.[12] "Every danger to human life suspends the [laws of the] Sabbath. If debris [of a collapsing building] falls on someone and it is doubtful whether he is there or whether he is not there, or if it is doubtful whether he is alive or whether he is dead . . . one must probe the heap of the debris for his sake [even on the Sabbath]. If one finds him alive, one should remove the debris but if he is dead, one leaves him there" until after the Sabbath. The Talmud then explains as follows: "How far does one search [to ascertain whether he is dead or alive]? Until [one reaches] his nose. Some say: Up to his heart . . . Life manifests itself primarily through the nose as it is written: *In whose nostrils was the breath of the spirit of life*" (Gen. 7:22).

Rashi states that, if no air emanates from his nostrils, he is certainly dead. Rashi further explains that some authorities suggest the heart be examined for signs of life, but the respiration test is considered of greatest import. The two major Codes of Jewish law universally accepted throughout Judaism, the *Mishneh Torah* of Moses Maimonides and the *Shulchan Aruch* of Joseph Karo, both rule that, if one cannot detect signs of respiration at the nose, the patient is certainly dead.[13,14] Neither Maimonides nor Karo requires examination of the heart. Cessation of respiration seems to be the determining physical sign for the ascertainment of death. Thus, Jewish law seems to accept the concept that whole-brain death with resultant absent spontaneous respiration is equivalent to death, irrespective of the presence or absence of a beating heart. Respirator dependency in a patient with polio or amyotrophic lateral sclerosis is obviously not equated with death, since these patients clearly have brain function including brainstem function but require mechanical assistance to breathe. Death in Judaism requires permanent and irreversible cessation of respiration.

Some rabbis, however, state that the lack of respiration was thought to be indicative of prior cessation of cardiac activity. Medieval rabbis and physicians thought that warm air from the heart is expelled through the nose and cold air, which cools the heart, enters through the nose. It was thus believed that respiration without cardiac activity is impossible.[11] Furthermore, in his commentary on the pivotal talmudic passage cited above, Rashi states that "at times life is not evident at the heart but is evident at the nose." This statement, according to some writers, indicates that, if life is not evident at the nose but is evident at the heart, cardiac activity would itself be sufficient to indicate that the person is still alive.[12] These writers therefore require cessation of both cardiac and respiratory functions to confirm that a person is dead.

These two rabbinic views accepting or rejecting whole-brain death as a valid Jewish legal definition of death are thus based on different interpretations of the talmudic commentary of Rashi and on subsequent medieval and modern rabbinic interpretations of the pivotal talmudic passage and other classic Jewish sources. These diametrically opposing views, which have resulted in considerable debate and controversy in Orthodox Jewish circles over the past two decades, are not based on secular moral principles or on social policy. Rather, these views are rooted in fine points of Jewish law, which the rabbinic authorities of each generation are empowered to interpret.

To support the view that whole-brain death is equated with death in Judaism, the concept of physiological decapitation was introduced.[15] In Judaism, if a human being or animal is decapitated, they are immediately counted as dead, irrespective of cardiac or other bodily movement. The death throes of a decapitated person are not considered residual life any more than the twitching of a lizard's amputated tail. These death throes or twitchings are only reflex activities demonstrating that cellular life continues for a while after the death of the whole organism, human or animal. The decapitated state itself is recognized in Jewish law as equivalent to death. Complete destruction of the brain is said to be the equivalent of physiological decapitation and therefore a valid definition of death. Loss of the ability to breathe spontaneously is a crucial criterion for determining whether complete destruction of the brain has occurred. Thus, if sophisticated neurological examination and testing of a patient indicate irreversible total loss of the function of the whole brain, including brainstem function, the patient is as if decapitated and therefore dead, even if the heart is still beating. Judaism also recognizes the fact that, even after the organism has been pronounced dead, individual cells may continue to function for some time thereafter in various parts of the body. The movement of a severed tail of a lizard is said to be purely reflex or autonomous in nature and does not indicate that the tail is alive. A series of rabbinic responsa on organ transplants and the definition of death by the late Rabbi Moshe Feinstein strongly support this concept of physiological decapitation.

Additional rabbinic sources support the thesis of physiological decapitation. Based on a talmudic discussion in tractate Chullin, Karo's authoritative Code of Jewish Law describes individuals "who are considered dead even though they are still alive."[16] These include those whose neck has been broken. These people are considered dead in that they impart ritual defilement and render their wives widows even though they may still have spastic or convulsive movements and even have heartbeats. The reason is that the connection between the brain and the body has been severed by the severance of the spinal cord or by the severance of the blood supply to the brain. It thus seems that the death of the whole brain is the legal definition of death in Jewish law. This definition has been adopted by the Israeli Chief Rabbinate and by many but not all orthodox rabbis and orthodox Jewish physicians.[17]

Those who reject the physiological decapitation concept point to Rashi's comment in the pivotal talmudic passage in tractate Yoma, where Rashi says that the absence of respiration is conclusive "if the patient appears dead in that there is no movement of his limbs." Other medieval and more recent rabbinic authorities echo Rashi's statement. Rabbi Tzvi Ashkanazi (1660–1718), known as *Chacham Tzvi,* concludes that "there can be no respiration unless there is life in the heart, for respiration is from the heart and for its benefit."[18] Rabbi Moses Sofer (1762–1839), known as *Chatam Sofer,* states that absent respiration is equated with death only if the patient "lies as an inanimate stone and there is no pulse whatsoever."[19] Modern interpreters of Rashi's statement that the patient "appears dead in that there is no movement of his limbs," when looking at a brain-dead individual on a respirator, see a pink person. They do not see a person with the ashen blue-gray pallor classically associated with death. The person looks more like a sleeping individual.

Those who support the thesis of physiological decapitation dismiss the statement of *Chacham Tzvi* because he did not have our present knowledge of the circulatory system and, in his scheme of things, the heart was a "respiratory" organ, involved in the warming and cooling of the air. Furthermore, during the time of *Chatam Sofer*, the interval between whole-brain death and cessation of cardiac activity was a matter of minutes, since ventilators were not available to maintain blood oxygenation in the absence of an independent ability to breathe.

The controversy is ongoing. The disagreement, however, is not purely a theoretical discussion of fine points in talmudic law. Practical results and ramifications flow from the two opposing views. Those who reject the physiological decapitation hypothesis, which equates total irreversible destruction of the brain including the brainstem with death, are faced with the following problems. First, secular society, which accepts brain death, will not pay for a patient's care after death. Hence, who will pay for that care between the declaration of brain death and cessation of cardiac activity? Second, is not a brain-dead patient in an intensive care unit unnecessarily denying that bed to another living patient who needs intensive care? Is that not an inappropriate use of a scarce resource (i.e., an ICU bed)? Furthermore, how can most organ transplantations be performed if one has to wait for cardiac standstill before organ harvesting from the donor? Most organs, if not continuously perfused, cannot be successfully transplanted into needy recipients.

Those who require irreversible cardiac and respiratory arrest to pronounce a patient dead not only reject the physiological decapitation thesis, but also do not accept the thesis that cessation of spontaneous respiration is equated with death and that spontaneous respiration and life itself are one and the same. There is considerable evidence in classic Jewish sources indicating that irreversible lack of respiration and death are synonymous. The soul departs through the nostrils at death, just as it is the nostrils into which the Lord blows the soul of life at birth (Gen. 2:6). Other sources, however, indicate that life may at times continue even after respiration has ceased, suggesting "that absence of respiration is at best a sign that death may be presumed to have occurred but is not, in itself, one and the same as death."[11]

Summary and Conclusion

Judaism is guided by the principle that life is sacred, is of supreme value, and is a gift from God. Physicians and patients are obligated to heal and seek healing, respectively. The prolongation of life, where medically possible, is required, but the prolongation of dying is wrong. Physicians and patients are governed by the norms of Jewish law even if such rules and regulations occasionally conflict with the moral attitudes of a secular society.

The definition of death in Jewish law is critically important in this era of organ transplantation, since the saving of lives is an absolute Jewish mandate to individuals and to Jewish society in general. There is at present an intense debate among rabbinic authorities as to whether Jewish law (*halacha*) recognizes death of the whole brain, including the brainstem, as a definition of death. The classic definition of death in Judaism, as found in the Talmud and Codes of Jewish Law, is the irreversible absence of respiration in a person who appears dead (i.e., shows no movements and is unresponsive to all stimuli). Jewish writings provide considerable evidence for the thesis that the brain and the brainstem control all bodily functions, including breathing and heartbeat. It therefore follows that irreversible total cessation of all brain function, including that of the brainstem, is equated with death. This situation is said to be the figurative equivalent of physiological decapitation, whereby the decapitated person is certainly dead, even if the heart transiently continues to beat.

The other rabbinic view rejects the analogy of decapitation and requires cardiac standstill in addition to cessation of respiration before death can be pronounced. Proponents of both views honestly and deeply feel the correctness of their interpretation of the classic Jewish sources. How can one respect this religious diversity within the Jewish rabbinic community in a formally secular society? New York State law requires medical examiners to take into consideration the religious, cultural, and ethnic sensitivities of families before deciding on the performance of an autopsy. The separation of church and state in the constitution of the United States ensures that no physician is obligated to perform an act contrary to his or her religious convictions. No Catholic physician is obligated to perform an abortion. Similarly, no Jewish physician is obligated to remove the life-support systems from a brain-dead patient if the physician believes that the patient is still alive by virtue of a beating heart. Thus, objections to brain death within the orthodox Jewish community can inform a secular moral perspective such as the one underlying American jurisprudence or "mainstream" bioethics.

References

1. Jakobovits I. *Jewish Medical Ethics.* New York: Bloch, 1959.
2. Rosner F, Bleich JD. *Jewish Bioethics.* New York: Sanhedrin Press, 1979.
3. Feldman DM, Rosner F. *Compendium on Medical Ethics.* 6th ed. New York: Federation of Jewish Philanthropies.
4. Rosner F. *Modern Medicine and Jewish Ethics.* 2d ed. Hoboken, NJ: Ktav & Yeshiva University Press, 1991.
5. Jakobovits I. *The Timely and the Timeless: Jews, Judaism and Society in a Storm-tossed Decade.* New York: Bloch, 1989, 128.
6. Steinberg A. Medical ethics: Secular and Jewish approaches. In: Rosner F (ed). *Medicine and Jewish Law.* Northvale, NY: Aronson, 1990, 19–39.
7. Pellegrino E, Thomasma DC. *For the Patient's Good.* New York: Oxford University Press, 1988.
8. Rosner F (transl). *Moses Maimonides' Treatise on Resurrection.* New York: Ktav, 1982.
9. Council on Ethical and Judicial Affairs, American Medical Association. The use of anencephalic neonates as organ donors. *JAMA* 1995;273:1614–18.
10. Arnold RM, Youngner SJ. The dead donor rule: Should we stretch it, bend it, or abandon it? *Kennedy Inst Ethics J* 1993;2:263–78.
11. Bleich JD. Establishing criteria of death. In: *Contemporary Halakhic Problems.* New York: Ktav & Yeshiva University Press, 1977, 372–93.
12. Rosner F, Tendler MD. Definition of death in Judaism. *J Halacha Contemp Soc* 1989;17(spring):14–31.
13. Maimonides M. *Mishneh Torah,* Laws of the Sabbath 2:19.
14. Karo J. *Shulchan Aruch, Orach Chayim* 329:4.
15. Tendler MD. Cessation of brain function: Ethical implications in terminal care and organ transplants. *Ann NY Acad Sci* 1978;315:394–497.
16. Karo J. *Shulchan Aruch, Yoreh Deah* 370:1.
17. Jakobovits Y. Brain death and heart transplants: The Israeli Chief Rabbinate's directives. *Tradition* 1989;24:1–14.
18. Ashkenazy T. Responsa *Chacham Tzvi* 77.
19. Sofer M. Responsa *Chatam Sofer, Yoreh Deah* 338.

V

International Perspectives

MANY COUNTRIES, including the United States, have legalized neurological criteria for determining death without engendering much public controversy. However, the issue has been a source of intense public debate in Denmark, Japan, and Germany. This section examines the experience in those countries. In each of them, the public has been widely engaged in the debate about brain death, and efforts to pass brain-death legislation have encountered serious opposition. The international experience illustrates how inseparable discussions of death are from the social and political environment in which they take place. At the same time, though, the debates in these countries hold some important lessons for the United States.

Bo Andreassen Rix explains that the newly formed Danish Council of Ethics responded to a draft bill to legalize brain death with a controversial report on the definition of death and related transplantation issues. The council's report distinguished between death as a medical or biological concept and the "everyday experience" of death. It concluded that a definition should stay close to the "everyday experience" and therefore advocated retaining cardiopulmonary criteria as the only basis for declaring death. However, not wanting to jeopardize organ transplantation, it offered for public and professional consideration an intriguing idea. The council said that brain death is the beginning of a certain "death process" and therefore organs can be taken from brain-dead patients without that action constituting killing, even though the patients are not yet dead. The proposition offers a departure from the seemingly sacrosanct dead-donor rule, which several authors in this volume (e.g., Fost, Brody, and Miles) also advocate broaching.

The Danish Council of Ethics presented their findings as part of a vast national public education campaign about brain death. The education efforts and the surveys monitoring Danish public attitudes and knowledge illustrate some of the challenges of bringing to the public the professional debate about the definition of death. For example, surveys show that the public continued to have difficulty distinguishing between persistent vegetative state and brain death despite the education campaign. And Rix suggests that a growing public awareness of the ambiguities surrounding the determination of death may have contributed to a decline in organ donations. In the end, the Danish Parliament passed brain-death legislation similar to that of other Western countries. The medical community's resistance to the idea of harvesting organs from patients prior to a declaration of death, for fear that it would constitute murder, probably contributed to that outcome.

Observers sometimes attribute Japan's longtime fierce resistance to brain death to uniquely Japanese spiritual beliefs and age-old traditions. Certainly, Margaret Lock notes in Chapter 14, these do figure in the debate. She calls the debate over brain death a microcosm of the Japanese tension between retaining its traditions and its participation in the modern world—a debate cloaked in the question of what is morally correct for Japan today. But her anthropological account is also striking in pointing out some of the issues that seem quite familiar to the Western world. The Japanese discomfort, for example, in calling someone dead whose body is still warm and who doesn't appear to be dead occurs at American bedsides as well. The Japanese call brain death "the death that cannot be seen" and worry that it relegates the determination of death to the world of medicine and technology rather than to the family. The fear of turning death over to the technologists is heightened in Japan because of the mistrust of medical professionals that has been engendered by apparent transplant scandals.

Growing pressure to facilitate transplants works against this resistance, however, especially as Japanese go abroad to receive organ transplants. Lock states that the effort to reconcile all these issues represents the most persistent search for a public consensus in Japan that has ever taken place on any subject. After years of heated debate, a brain-death statute was finally passed in October 1997, but its ambiguities reveal the country's continuing uneasiness with the subject.

In Germany the German Surgical Society issued a report on brain death in 1968, a few months before the Harvard committee, and came to similar conclusions. But, unlike in the United States, the issue remains a source of heated debate in Germany. In Chapter 15 Schöne-Seifert notes that, despite some ethical concerns raised in an early interdisciplinary debate, there was a de facto acceptance of brain death from 1968 until 1992. Medical scandals helped to shatter that fragile understanding, though, and today distrust of the medical profession is also a dominant feature of the German debate. As in Japan, Germany's debate is enmeshed in the country's struggles to define itself morally; the debate over brain death in Germany has become part of a wider antibioethics movement that is rooted in Germany's Nazi past.

The experience in these countries reveals several issues that have been skating beneath the surface in the United States: first, the feasibility of separating organ donation from a declaration of death; second, how public trust or mistrust of the medical profession hugely affects a debate about defining death and how a scandal undermining trust can quickly reshape the debate; and third, how much attention must be paid to the public's ordinary understanding of who is dead and who is not. These issues are central to the arguments presented by authors throughout this volume.

13

Brain Death, Ethics, and Politics in Denmark

Bo Andreassen Rix, M.D., M.A.

IN 1990, THE Danish Parliament passed a law defining the death of a human being as the diagnosis by a physician of death using either cardiorespiratory or neurological criteria. Thus, Denmark was the last country in Western Europe to accept brain death as the death of a human being.

Passage of the law (after several proposals from the government) followed a rather heated debate among the Danish public and in the media. Actually, the debate in Denmark about the definition of death and the feasibility of brain death as a criterion of death had begun in the early 1970s, when a group of physicians argued that Denmark should legalize brain death to increase the quality of cadaver kidneys for transplantation.

Before brain death was accepted in Denmark, the respirator was removed from the brain-dead organ donor and the surgeons had to wait for the heart to stop before the kidneys could be removed. To decrease warm ischemia of the kidneys, it was common to start resuscitating the dead donor immediately after asystole and to reestablish heart activity before organs were removed. The public was generally unaware of this practice, and physicians and nurses thought that it left them in a legal vacuum. The group of physicians who started the discussion in the 1970s provoked some public debate in the media, but the politicians were not ready to legislate for a new death criterion at that time.

In the 1980s, the Danish National Board of Health set up an expert committee to consider various aspects and possibilities of organ transplantation of hearts, lungs, and livers; Danish physicians had not yet performed these transplants because of the cardiac death criterion in force. In its report released in 1985, the committee naturally had to deal with the brain-death criterion, and the committee recommended that brain death should be regarded as a valid criterion of death. The committee based its recommendation on the argument that brain death is the irreversible cessation of all brain function and will unavoidably lead to heart death. It regarded organ transplantation and the brain-death criterion as interrelated.

In 1987, the Danish Secretary of Justice drafted a bill in which heart death remained a criterion of death and brain death was added as a second criterion of death. According to the Secretary of Justice, the bill had several purposes. It would make heart, lung, and liver transplants possible in Denmark because patients could be declared dead while still on a respirator, and the diagnosis of brain death would make it possible to terminate unnecessary treatment of the brain-dead body.

Somewhat to the surprise of the Ministry of Justice, the bill proved controversial as the media debated the consequences of the new death criterion. As a result of the debate, the bill received only a first reading in the Danish Parliament before being withdrawn. In the following 3 years, a more widespread public debate about brain death took place in Denmark, with members of the newly established Danish Council of Ethics as active participants. The bill was brought before Parliament several times and, when it finally passed in 1990, it had a 3–1 majority. The new law was more or less identical to the bill from 1987. It made cardiac death and brain death equally valid criteria of death and permitted organ donation only with the consent of the donor or relatives.

The Danish Council of Ethics Finds a Cause

The media had discussed the brain-death criterion, but it was the establishment of the Danish Council of Ethics in 1988 that made a more formalized and focused debate possible. The Danish Parliament established the council for the purpose of making recommendations to the Secretary of Interior on the ethical issues raised by new medical technology. The primary mandate for the council was ethical problems associated with genetics and assisted reproduction, but the council was a permanent body with authority to take up problems on its own initiative.

Nine members of the council were appointed by members of Parliament and 8 members by the Secretary of Interior, so the council had good political contacts and was considered an important national forum for the discussion of medical ethics. The 17 members had various backgrounds; 3 were medical doctors, 2 theologians, 2 lawyers, 3 teachers, 2 writers, 1 pharmacist, 1 social worker, 1 nurse, 1 biologist, and 1 dentist. Eight members were women in accordance with the statute of the council requiring gender equality, and the chairperson appointed by the Secretary of Interior was a woman who headed a teacher's college.

Although six members had a background in medicine or biology with special knowledge of genetics, the nonscientific members of the council signaled a political will to broaden the discussion of bioethics from the more technical to the social and philosophical aspects. However, the "lay" members were all well educated with middle or upper-class backgrounds, and the council thus represented traditional decision makers rather than the general public.

Several council members were skeptical about the brain-death bill and concluded that the primary purpose of the bill was to make heart and lung transplants legal without examining ethical aspects of a new criterion of death. The council decided to discuss the ethical issues involved and to prepare a report on the subject.

The Concept of Death in Everyday Life

In its report,[1] the council argued that a criterion of death should be discussed from an ethical and philosophical, rather than biological or medical, perspective. After some debate, all members agreed that a brain-death criterion could be valid and safe from a medical point of view. However, the majority of the council wanted a death criterion close to the "everyday life" experience of death shared by the people in the culture. These everyday experiences are different from scientific knowledge, and there is no direct connection between the concept of death in everyday experience and the medical definition of death.

For the majority of the council, the predominant argument was that, in everyday experience, the identity of a person comprises the integrity of a conscious mind and bodily function. The relatives and others will relate the identity of a person to both the body and mind. Therefore, the process of dying cannot be said to have come to an end when the brain is dead but respiration and heartbeat continue assisted by a respirator, as the body remains warm and has normal color.

According to the council, the death criterion closest to the concept of death in everyday experience is the cardiac death criterion. There was no doubt among the council members, however, that a brain-dead patient has reached the point of no return. Therefore, the council introduced the concept of a "death process" and argued that the diagnosis of the irreversible loss of all brain function should be followed by a cessation of all treatment so that the death process can continue and the relatives may witness the death process come to an end. For legal purposes, the time of death should be set when the death process has come to an end, that is, when the heart has stopped beating.

Despite the council's negative attitude toward a brain-death criterion, it generally did not oppose transplantation if informed consent had been obtained from the donor or the relatives. And it did not want to obstruct the possibility of organ transplantation from heart-beating donors. The council concluded:

1. A person is dead when all three functions—heart and circulatory, respiratory, and brain—have definitely ceased.

2. With the cessation of brain function, the person has entered the death process.

3. When a person is in the death process all treatment to prolong life functions artificially should be stopped. This cessation of treatment does not cause the person's death but ends the death process.

4. The time of death is given by the end—not the beginning—of the death process, i.e., the time when heart and respiratory function have irreversibly stopped.

5. The only purpose legitimating prolongation of the death process by treatment is transplantation from heartbeating donors. This is only permitted if the donor or his relatives have given their informed consent. The donation procedure will end the death process but will not constitute the cause of the donor's death.[2]

In the case of donation, treatment could be prolonged for 48 hours. When all brain function had ceased, two physicians with no stake in organ transplantation would make a report testifying to brain death and the course of death. The Council of Ethics also proposed legislation establishing a registry of persons who express a wish to donate organs and that organs could be transplanted only from those persons. This was not entirely consistent with their recommendation elsewhere in the report that organs could be removed with consent of the family.

In its final report, a majority of council members opposed to a brain-death criterion were joined by a minority of four members who favored legalization of brain death but accepted the council's report because it would permit treatment to be stopped on the brain-dead body and organ transplantation. Interestingly, the medical doctors in the council split on the issue; only one physician was in favor of the brain-death criterion.

Debate Activities Initiated by the Council of Ethics

The Council of Ethics sent its report to all members of Parliament and 14,000 free copies were distributed across the country. It argued that a change of the criteria of death was so important that the political decision should be postponed until more public debate on the ethical issues had taken place and all major political parties concurred. The council used its annual $300,000 campaign budget for a variety of education activities.

Council activities focused on such matters as informing the lay population about the technical and legal aspects of brain death (e.g., how brain death is diagnosed), how the brain-dead body is treated, when organs are used for donation, and aspects of information and consent. The council also wanted to bring forward ethical arguments both in favor of and against a brain-death criterion, so that the public was aware of all arguments. Some council members wanted to promote the views of the council.

Debate activities initiated by the council included public hearings in major cities and funding of more than 200 local debate meetings. The council also produced a film that was shown on national television and to more than 500 local groups ranging from boy scouts to retirees. The film described the dilemma of relatives who wanted a dignified death for their loved one but also felt an obligation to allow the organs to be used for recipients in need. The national television station also produced several debate programs and talk shows on the brain-death criteria and arguments for and against it.

The Council of Ethics also published several booklets and brochures to inform the general public. A brochure was distributed to all public libraries clarifying the difference between brain death and the permanent vegetative state because several public meetings had demonstrated that many people could not differentiate between the two. One special activity initiated by the Council of Ethics was a poetry and music contest for schoolchildren in which participants expressed their concept of death in modern society.

Public Debate in the Danish Media

The council's ability to initiate such a variety of activities probably contributed to the interest of all Danish newspapers in the ethical and medical questions raised by the brain-death criterion. In the 20 major Danish newspapers, more than 1,000 articles and comments on brain death and related subjects, such as organ transplantation and donor testaments, were published from 1987 to 1990. While most commentaries were from physicians, philosophers, theologians, lawyers, and politicians, several hundred letters from readers were published.

All leading Danish newspapers had editorials discussing the legislative proposals, and the report of the Danish Council of Ethics was also widely discussed. When the law establishing the brain-death criterion passed the Parliament in 1990, all national newspapers had editorials on the subject. The main concern in the editorials was the potential benefit of a brain-death criterion for potential recipients of donor hearts and other organs, and consequently most editorials in major papers favored a brain-death criterion. Many editorials also stressed the importance of informed consent from the donor or relatives before organs could be donated.

The council's intention was to facilitate transplants and still retain the cardiac criterion, but the newspapers, politicians, and medical establishment did not buy the argument. They argued that it was illogical and legally problematic to take organs from a person who is not legally dead. Although most editorials did not find the proposal from the Council of Ethics to be a good solution that cut the Gordian knot, most editorials congratulated the council for having started a public debate and for having brought more nuances into the discussion.

Contrary to the editorials and many of the professional comments, the majority of letters to the editor expressed views in line with the Council of Ethics. Many letters also expressed insecurity about the reliability of the diagnosis of brain death, and some found organ transplantations to be problematic when public health resources were scarce. However, these letters did not really express the general opinion of the Danish population. In a Gallup poll conducted by a major newspaper in the summer of 1989, 98 percent of the survey population knew of the debate on brain death and some 80 percent preferred the addition of a brain-death criterion.[3]

The Danish politicians could vote on the death criteria free from party ties, and up to the date of the vote many politicians made personal political comments in the newspapers and on television. Most politicians expressed mixed feelings about the brain-death criterion, but found that brain death was necessary for organ transplantation, which they favored. Although they politely commended the council for promoting a fine debate and for its report, in the end the politicians thought that they had to adopt legislation on brain death to make organ donation possible; they were under pressure from the media and patients to facilitate heart transplants. Some politicians suggested that the death criteria should be decided by a national referendum, but most politicians did not support the idea.

Physicians and the Debate over Brain Death

Most media comments by physicians strongly opposed the report from the Council of Ethics. Not surprisingly, the physicians could not accept the idea of organs being transplanted from brain-dead, heart-beating donors without brain death as the legal criterion of death. Most of them, including the Chief Medical Officer, argued that the removal of organs from heart-beating donors would technically be murder if a brain-death criterion was not legalized. A few physicians, though, among them a respected professor of neurosurgery, accepted the report from the Council of Ethics.

Unfortunately, most physicians did not really respond to the council's wish for a broader discussion of the concept of death in modern society. Rather, surgeons involved in organ transplantation focused on the urgent need for donor organs, noting that patients were dying on the waiting list. These arguments were supported by patients' associations such as the Kidney Association.

Until the law on brain death passed the Parliament in 1990, some Danish patients were sent abroad to have heart and lung transplants in other countries, paid for by Denmark's public health care service. The director of one German hospital involved in transplantation of hearts to Danish patients sent a letter to the Danish Ministry of Health stating that heart transplants to Danish patients could not continue if hearts from Danish donors were not available. Generally, Danish transplantation surgeons and those treating patients needing organs argued that it was unethical to refer Danish organ recipients to treatment in other countries if Danes would not donate to a common pool of organs.

A Population in Need of Knowledge

The Danish Council of Ethics sponsored two national surveys to assess public knowledge about brain death, one before the council initiated its debate activities in 1989 and one a year later. The surveys were conducted in collaboration with the Danish National Institute of Social Research.

A representative sample of some 2,000 Danish people age 16 years or older was surveyed, and some 80 percent responded. One question asked was: "When is a person declared brain dead?" Three possible answers were offered: "1. A person is declared brain dead when he is deeply unconscious but may wake up after a long period. 2. A person is declared brain dead when the brain has irreversibly lost all function. The body can keep functioning for months without treatment except nutrition. 3. A person is declared brain dead when the brain has irreversibly lost all function; the heart will stop beating shortly afterwards if respiration is not continued artificially." More than one answer could be marked.

Interestingly, about 10 percent of those interviewed in each survey marked Answer 1, whereas some 60 percent thought that the brain-dead body could live without a respirator for months (Answer 2). Thus, a majority of the Danish population had difficulty distinguishing between permanent vegetative state and brain death. However, 73 percent of respondents in the first survey and 78 percent in the last survey also marked Answer 3, which is the right answer. Although the results indicate continued confusion about brain death, public understanding was a little better after the media debate.

Shortly after passage of the brain-death law, a large national newspaper asked 1,300 people, representative of Danish society, if they felt well informed about the new law and its consequences. About 70 percent answered yes; only 4 percent felt they were very poorly informed. Nevertheless, 77 percent wanted more information about brain death. In 30 percent of families, organ donation had been discussed, and about 50 percent of those interviewed planned to discuss organ donation in their families.

In 1986, before the public debate, Denmark had one of the highest rates of kidney donations in the world, with 43 donations per 1 million residents. In 1990, after brain death had been legalized, the kidney donation rate fell by one-half. One reason was undoubtedly that the new law on brain death also regulated organ transplantation and required prior consent from the donor ("donor testament") or relatives. The old transplantation law allowed organs to be taken from the deceased without donor or family consent unless the relatives actively opposed donation. As relatives were not always aware that organ transplantation would take place if they did not oppose it and the hospital staff was not obliged to give that information, organ transplantation was a common practice based on presumed consent.

Another reason for the lower organ donation rate after the new law passed in 1990 may be insecurity about the brain-death diagnosis. Some physicians argued that the public debate about brain death created a negative attitude toward organ donation, and some surveys and letters to newspapers supported this view.

The national Board of Health started a campaign in 1991 to encourage people to carry a donor testament or to register as a donor. After the campaign, 73 percent of the population knew of the possibility of making a donor testament, but only a few percent carried one or had registered. In 1995, some 170,000 persons—about 3.5 percent of the Danish population—were registered in the national Donor Registry. According to the registry, interest is increasing, and registration had nearly doubled over the previous 3 years.

The Council of Ethics Reopens the Discussion of Brain Death

In its 1993 annual report, the Council of Ethics took up some of the old arguments about brain death.[4] A family had contacted the council concerning the death of their father. The father had been declared brain dead, and the family was asked for permission to transplant organs but wanted to wait for the arrival of a son who was coming from abroad. When the son arrived, he was happy to be "in time" for his father's death. The family found it an important experience to be by the father's bedside; to the family, the father seemed like he was in a deep sleep. The family decided not to donate organs, the respirator was switched off, and the family saw the father as he changed color and became pale.

When the family received the death certificate, they were surprised to learn that the date of their father's death was the day before the arrival of the son and before the day they felt the father had passed away. The family found they were under pressure to accept a concept of death different from their own and asked what date of death should be put on the gravestone. Although the priest said that they could use the date they wished, the family still felt it was wrong to have a date of death other than what was on the death certificate. The council, therefore, suggested that both the time of brain-death diagnosis and the time of heart death should be noted in the death certificate.

Some Lessons from the Danish Discussion of Brain Death

In most European countries a brain-death criterion was implemented without much debate among politicians or the public. In some countries brain death is not even defined by law; rather, it is a diagnosis introduced by the medical establishment without involvement by politicians, lawyers, or others. Then why was brain death debated in Denmark?

First, it is a Danish tradition to debate almost any subject of public interest, and educational programs for adults and public funding of small interest groups in Denmark make it possible to involve lay people in the discussion of complex issues such as brain death. The skepticism toward the medical establishment in some intellectual groups also fostered the debate, as these groups saw brain death as an attempt by physicians to pursue their professional interest in transplantation technology. Politicians could not ignore this skepticism.

Another important factor was the Danish Council of Ethics. The council was newly established and looking for a cause that could make it well known to the general public. The brain-death criterion was an obvious cause as the issue was rather clear-cut compared to gene technology or other complex matters. A bill was proposed shortly before the establishment of the council, and especially the very active theologians on the council opposed a new death criterion. Finally, the council had financial resources to initiate a variety of activities that made the perspectives of the council well known in Denmark.

Some bioethicists in Denmark believe that the Council of Ethics, in arguing for a particular outcome, did not play a positive role in the process that led to the Danish acceptance of brain death. They ask if a bioethical body should not merely be advisory, leaving it to elected representatives to make the final choices rather than advocating a particular legal or ethical approach. A committee of this kind is structured to elucidate both technology and ethics and to distinguish between facts and values for given issues, and it has been argued that this is the only democratic moral authority of such a group.[5]

The Danish Council of Ethics did not see its role as merely elucidating. In the comments to the bill that was later passed as the new law on death criteria and organ transplantation, the Secretary of Justice, disagreeing with the council's recommendations, stated that it would be legally unacceptable to remove organs from a person who is legally alive and that therefore brain death had to be a criterion of death. The council criticized the bill and argued for its own recommendations. In its comment, the council referred to the public debate; they argued that a large part of the population would consider a brain-death criterion to be against their philosophy of life and that a majority of the population found that donors themselves should be the only ones allowed to give consent to organ donation. These assessments were exaggerated. About 80 percent of the population were in favor of a brain-death criterion in surveys, and the brain-death criterion has caused very little debate since the law passed in 1990.

The public debate in Denmark made it clear that it was difficult to separate ethical aspects related to brain death per se from the fact that Danish patients were on the waiting list for donor organs. Although some politicians and the Council of Ethics wanted to focus on the ethical aspects of a new death criterion, most news media and most physicians participating in the discussions linked the two issues tightly together. Therefore, some debaters found that the physicians took advantage of patients' need for organs in their arguments.

The surveys by the Council of Ethics indicated some misunderstanding about the diagnosis of brain death, and brain death was to some extent mixed up with the permanent vegetative state. If a large part of the population is unsure whether someone who is brain dead could wake up, organ transplantations could cause distrust of the medical profession. In the Danish debate, misunderstandings about brain death among politicians, lay people, and even some health care professionals often misdirected the discussion of the principal ethical issues. Thus, the effort of the Council of Ethics to disseminate factual knowledge about brain death was an important contribution to the debate. Although a majority of Danes felt well informed, 77 percent still wanted more information, indicating that some insecurity about brain death still existed. However, it is expensive to educate whole populations, and perhaps information should primarily be distributed to certain target groups, such as young people applying for a driving license, hospital personnel, or others.

References

1. *The death criteria—a report.* Copenhagen: Danish Council of Ethics, 1989.

2. Rix BA. Danish ethics council rejects brain death as criterion of death. *J Med Ethics* 1990;16:5–7.

3. Cushman R, Holm S. Death, democracy and public ethical choice. *Bioethics* 1990;4:237–52.

4. Annual report 1993. Copenhagen: Danish Council of Ethics, 1994.

5. Cushman R, Holm S. Death, democracy and public ethical choice. *Bioethics* 1990;4:237–52.

14

The Problem of Brain Death

*Japanese Disputes about Bodies
and Modernity*

Margaret Lock, Ph.D.

TOMOKO ABE, a pediatrician employed for many years in a Japanese hospital that specializes in neurological disorders, has spent considerable energy during the past decade opposing acceptance of a diagnosis of brain death as significant in determining the end of human life. She is by no means alone: citizen groups, lawyers, members of the Japanese police force, and a good number of physicians have together managed to ensure that brain death has not been recognized as the end of life, and hence organ retrieval from brain-dead patients does not routinely take place in Japan. Only in October 1997 did Japan pass a law in which brain death can be recognized under certain clearly specified circumstances.

In discussing her objections with me, Dr. Abe emphasized that, in her opinion, the concept of brain death was created primarily to facilitate organ transplants. She is emphatic that when a dying person is understood as the focus of both a concerned family and a caring medical team, then it is difficult to interpret brain death as the demise of an individual. Dr. Abe's opinion is derived, she states, from reflection on her own subjective feelings as a pediatrician: "The point is not whether the patient is conscious or unconscious, but whether one intuitively understands that the patient is dead. Someone whose color is good, who is still warm, bleeds when cut, and urinates and defecates, is not dead as far as I am concerned. Of course I know that cardiac arrest will follow some hours later—but I think even more significant is the transformation of the warm body into something which is cold and hard—only then do the Japanese really accept death." Like most other Japanese physicians I have interviewed on this subject, whether or not they agree that brain death signifies the end of human life, Dr. Abe insists that the feelings of the dying patient's relatives must be put first and if, as is commonly believed, most Japanese do not recognize brain death as the end of life, then matters should rest at that. The respirator, without which cardiac arrest would quickly ensue, is not turned off until the family comes to terms with the idea that there will be no recovery—usually 4 or 5 days after brain death is medically established.

The "brain-death problem" *(nōshi no mondai)* has a history of nearly 30 years in Japan and remains the most contentious of bioethical issues. I believe that this debate, while it clearly voices a widely shared concern about the intrusion of biomedical technology into the process of dying, has also taken on both metaphorical and political meanings. What happens at the bedside of patients diagnosed as brain dead is a micro-cosm of an ongoing cultural debate about what is thought to be morally appropriate in contemporary society, together with a concern about Japan's position in the global economy. It is not surprising, there-fore, that a perusal of the well over 500 publications in Japanese on this subject since 1986 reveals a complex, often emotional discussion that leads to no conclusive answer as to why the country finds itself at this impasse.

Medical Experimentation under Fire

Shortly after the world's first heart transplant occurred in South Africa, attempts were made to repeat the procedure elsewhere. In 1968, just 1 year after the South Africa case, the 30th attempt was made in Sapporo, Hokkaido.[1] As elsewhere, the Sapporo procedure initially was heralded as a dramatic medical triumph. However, several months later, the physician in charge, Dr. Wada, was arraigned on a murder charge. He was acquitted only after 6 years of wrangling. Most Japanese believe, in retrospect, that the patient whose heart was removed was not brain dead and that the recipient, who died 2½ months after the operation, was not sufficiently in need of a new heart to have undergone the procedure.[2]

As part of the ongoing national debate about brain death, discussion of the case was formally reopened in 1991. The chairman of the Japanese Medical Association (JMA) testified before a government committee that the supposedly ineffective heart from the recipient patient had been tampered with after its removal, indicating that the involved physicians may have tried to exaggerate the degree of its deterioration.[3] The case is now regarded as a barbarous piece of medical experimentation carried out by a physician who received a good portion of his training in America, who now resides in Japan's "untamed hinterland" of Hokkaido, and who is, furthermore, described as self-aggrandizing, that is, un-Japanese.

In a good number of other organ transplant cases, the Japanese medical profession has not appeared in a good light. Together with the Wada case, physicians are extensively discussed and criticized in the media and have become iconic for the entire debate.

Contested Definitions of Death

In 1985 the Ministry of Health and Welfare set up a Brain Death Advisory Council whose final report contained the definition of brain death used in Japan until the 1997 law.[4] This report is explicit, however, that "death cannot be judged by brain death." Nevertheless, the diagnosis is frequently applied—not usually as a signal to turn off the respirator, but to prepare relatives for an impending death.[5] Relatives are usually informed that the patient is "almost brain dead" *(hobo nōshi no jotai)* and in a "hopeless" condition.

The ministry's report spurred other involved groups to articulate their positions. In January 1988, after a working group met over a 2-year period, the directors of the JMA voted unanimously to accept brain death as the end of human life. Nevertheless, deep divisions remain among the representatives of the various medical specialties and also among individual physicians. The politically outspoken Japan Association of Psychiatrists and Neurologists, for example (some of whose 6,900 members are responsible for making brain-death diagnoses), fear that equating brain death with death will lead to the slippery slope down which the handicapped, mentally impaired, and disadvantaged will be at risk for being diagnosed prematurely, in a greedy desire to get at their organs.[6] The society for specialists in emergency medicine, also directly involved in making brain-death diagnoses, took until 1994 to reach an agreement that brain death is the end of life.[7]

Some physicians and members of the public have formed the highly visible Patients' Rights Committee, whose interests range well beyond the question of brain death. Under the leadership of the flamboyant Dr. Honda from the prestigious department of internal medicine at Tokyo University, they filed several lawsuits charging murder when organs have been removed from brain-dead patients. The public prosecutor's office has not yet reached a decision on any of these cases, but threw two of them out of court, stating that there is no public consensus in Japan as to how to define death.[8]

As a result of the unresolved debate, copiously documented by the media, the government felt compelled in late 1989 to set up a Special Cabinet Committee on Brain Death and Organ Transplants in order to bring about closure. The group was so deeply divided that it appeared that it would never produce more than an interim report, but in January 1992 a final report was made public.[9] Although a consensus was not achieved, the majority position is that, from the medical perspective, brain death is equivalent to human death and can be accurately diagnosed using the Takeuchi Standard (virtually the same as criteria used in North America) already adopted by the Ministry of Health and Welfare. The majority report also asserts that it is "rational" to consider brain death as the end of life and therefore sensible to accept this as equivalent to social and legal death, a position that would coincide with the one believed to be dominant internationally.

Authors of the minority report called for the "social and cultural" aspects of the brain-death problem to be fully debated; they believed that the discussion had been largely confined to "scientific" information, which they considered inadequate.[9] The day after the announcement of the cabinet committee report, the Ministry of Justice, the National Police Agency, and the Public Prosecutor's Office all reiterated their continued resistance to a recognition of brain death as the end of individual life.[10]

Over the past 25 years, the Japan Federation of Bar Associations (Nichibenren) has continued to oppose the acceptance of brain death as death and has repeatedly expressed concern for the "sanctity of life" and about possible "medical experimentation." The federation has also pointed out possible unforeseen consequences in connection with inheritance claims and called a lack of public consensus on the issue a major stumbling block.[11]

The Patients' Rights Committee, lawyers, the police, several TV program producers, and many authors of newspaper articles and books on the subject of brain death, together with a good number of medical professionals, appear to be publicly contesting the authority of transplant surgeons. They believe that, in the rush to organ retrieval, the process of dying will be curtailed or even misdiagnosed. Most of these opponents are simultaneously pushing for informed consent and frank disclosure and discussion of diagnoses and prognoses with patients, neither of which is by any means routine in Japan. This contest, therefore, although at one level a debate about the accuracy and replicability of medical decision making, is also a challenge to the hegemony of invested authority, exerted in what several challengers characterize as a traditionally Japanese way, whereby subjects are rendered passive and expected to comply with medical regimen without question.

Reaching Public Consensus

The issue of brain death has provoked the most persistent search for a national consensus *(kokuminteki gōi)* among the Japanese public that has ever taken place. At least 15 national surveys about brain death and organ transplants were conducted between 1983 and 1995. Over those years the percentage of people who recognize brain death has increased from 29 percent to almost 55 percent.[12] All the surveys reveal a paradox, however, in that many people approve of organ transplants from brain-dead patients, although they themselves do not accept brain death as the end of life. It seems that Japanese people are willing to allow transplants to take place, even though they personally would not be comfortable with participating in such a procedure.

In the autumn of 1994, a private member's bill was submitted to the Diet to legalize brain death as the end of life and the removal of organs from brain-dead patients with the consent of family members.[13] The bill did not require that a patient's wishes be known, but that they should be "surmised" *(sontaku suru)* by close relatives. The bill was never discussed, parliament was dissolved, and a new government was elected. Those adamantly opposed to redefining death were quick to criticize this bill; family members are vulnerable in their grief, they argued, and if the will of the patient is not known, then there should be no question of either turning off the respirator or asking for a donation of organs.

In 1994, Soka Gakkai, Japan's largest lay Buddhist organization, with a membership of over 8.3 million and a powerful political wing, stated that transplant surgery is not in conflict with the teachings of their organization. They encourage donor registries, a donor card system, and the establishment of an information network.[14] Also in 1994, the former Minister of Health and Welfare announced that his ministry is not opposed to the institutionalization of transplant surgery that makes use of brain-dead donors.

Not surprisingly, the Japan Society for Transplantation concurs, but the actions of a team of physicians at Yokohama General Hospital have once again produced a strong current of criticism among dissenters both within the JMA and among the Japanese public. This team of surgeons reported that early in 1994 kidneys had been removed from four brain-dead patients before their hearts had stopped beating; the kidneys had been transplanted into eight waiting recipients. Yokohama General Hospital is a large urban tertiary care center, but has no ethics committee and does not meet the Health and Welfare Ministry requirements for an organ transplant center. Critics have pointed out that the transplant surgeons alone were involved with decision making in connection with this case and in obtaining family consent.

In October 1997, after 30 years of vituperative debate, a law was finally passed allowing organs to be retrieved from a patient diagnosed as brain dead, provided that the patient had previously given written consent to be a donor and that the family does not overrule the patient's wish. If no advance directives exist, then a brain-dead patient will continue to receive medical care after the diagnosis is made, until the family and medical team agree to terminate treatment. The law took effect in October 1997, after debate over such details as what constitutes the family. As drafted, brain death will constitute death only for those patients who wish to donate organs. The law has already been described as a "typically confusing Japanese compromise" by certain commentators.

A Dearth of Organs

The pressure on transplant surgeons exploded as a public scandal in 1996, when it was reported that the most prominent Tokyo surgeon advocating the legalization of brain death as the end of life had quietly imported and transplanted 13 kidneys from America. These organs had been rejected by UNOS, the American organ-sharing network; one of the donors had tested positive for hepatitis C, and another donor was 70 years old. Dr. Ota, head of the Japan Society for Transplantation, made a public apology, not simply because the organs were American rejects, but because he violated the guidelines of the newly founded Kidney Transplant Network and circumvented their system for equity in distribution of organs. Dr. Ota has resigned from his post as head of the national hemodialysis society.

A few desperate patients have gone abroad to receive transplants, most of them to the United States and Australia, but also to Korea, Taiwan, Thailand, and the Philippines. It is difficult to determine how many have done this, partly because a few of them received hate mail on their return to Japan and so, until recently, have not wanted to make their plight public. The government has not kept close track of these figures, but it is estimated that, as of 1995, a total of 15 patients had received a heart transplant abroad. Between 1989 and 1990, 62 patients had received a liver transplant abroad, and 17 others received kidneys.[15] The long-term outcomes of these patients are not known. In 1990 more than 100,000 patients were on renal dialysis in Japan, and a chronic shortage of donated cadaver organs means that this situation cannot be relieved.

In 1990 the number of non-heart-beating cadaver donors in Japan was estimated at 105, and the number of brain-dead donors at 3,115.[15] These figures are notoriously unreliable because hospitals involved with transplant surgery usually try to keep a low profile, but nevertheless they suggest an extraordinarily low rate of donation, especially since surveys indicate that approximately three-quarters of the Japanese public support the idea of organ transplants. My research reveals that very few families are actively approached about donation and that, unless the family raises the subject, it will be passed over in most intensive care units. Transplants from living, related donors do not cause public concern.

Public Commentary on the Problem of Brain Death

Numerous Japanese television programs, magazine articles, and books have repeatedly cast doubt on whether death can be understood as a clearly diagnosable event,[16] and many informants have given me an unsolicited comment to the effect that "the Japanese are not yet ready for brain death." It has also been argued in books and the media that irreversibility is difficult to establish conclusively, noting cases (outside of Japan) where mistakes have evidently been made.

Certain commentators question whether a lack of integrated brain function does indeed indicate death. One highly influential journalist, Takashi Tachibana, author of several books and coordinator of more than one television program on brain death and organ transplantation, emphasizes that brain cells continue to live even when the brain as a whole has no integrated function, as indicated by a flat electroencephalogram.[17] Mr. Tachibana dwells in all his media presentations on the "liveliness" of a brain-dead individual. A 1990 Saturday evening prime time program that he hosted, for example, opened with shots of a beautiful, active, 6-year-old child who was born, viewers were informed, from a brain-dead mother. "How can a brain dead body not be living," asked Mr. Tachibana rhetorically.[18] He and other writers, together with most of the more than 50 Japanese citizens I have interviewed on the subject, including both health care professionals and the public, point out that blood flows when the bodies of the brain dead are cut, hair and nails grow, basic metabolism continues, and live birth is possible from a brain-dead woman. The majority also emphasize that the brain dead remain warm and appear to be sleeping; they point out that nursing care and expressions of love and concern by the family of the dying involve touching, holding hands, and massaging. They agree that it goes against "basic human feelings" to assume that a warm body is dead, and many go on to assert that the average Japanese family could not in good conscience abandon a dying relative to a transplant team.

As the pediatrician Dr. Abe made clear, such arguments do not deny the presence of death, but explicitly suggest that the process of dying is arbitrarily transformed into a technologically determined point in time, as early as possible along the spectrum of biological demise. There is concern that family members cannot easily adjust to a medically determined diagnosis of irreversible brain function and that they are likely to assume that death is being declared before the process is completed.

Other writers, taking a slightly different tack, stress that, because brain death can be determined only by trained medical personnel—because it is *mienai shi* (death that cannot be seen)—it represents a radical departure from the usual situation, where the family participates fully in the dawning recognition of the process. Making integrated brain function the measure of death ensures that the family is pushed to the sidelines, rendered passive, and left entirely at the mercy of medical decision making.[19]

Recently, Kunio Yanagida, the son of Japan's most celebrated cultural historian of the same name who died some years ago, published two widely circulated articles and a book about his own son, who had tried to commit suicide. Yanagida had found his son hanging by a rope in his room, cut him down, and rushed him to a hospital. The patient's condition worsened over the next 3 days, and he was eventually diagnosed as brain dead. During those first days, Yanagida's eldest son asked the doctor if he could wipe away his brother's tears because "he seemed to be crying a lot." The doctor was sympathetic, but explained that this was purely a physical phenomenon and not an expression of emotion. "We don't know why this happens," he replied.

Yanagida started to think about organ donation while seated at the bedside because, when he and his son had watched a television program together on the subject, his son had expressed an interest in helping other people. His son's face was "bright and warm" as he sat holding his hand and whispering his name, and he "couldn't bear the idea of someone putting a knife into his son's body and taking out the heart." Yanagida became confused as to what brain death really signifies: Was his son indeed a corpse, or was he still suspended between life and death? His family experienced nothing but sympathetic support from the physician in charge of the case. Four days after the diagnosis of brain death, upon reading his son's diaries, in which he had expressed sadness at being of no use to anyone, Yanagida came to an understanding that it was his duty to "complete" his son's life. On the fifth day all treatment was stopped, and his son's kidneys and bone marrow were removed for transplantation.[20]

These articles clearly reveal the emotional struggle of someone thrust into grief over a sudden death, but they also thoughtfully capture the Japanese medical profession's dilemma over this technology, and they reveal a sensitivity to those waiting for organs. Nevertheless, there is little doubt that these publications will consolidate the majority opinion in Japan, namely, that families should not be rushed into accepting death the moment brain death is pronounced.

The Japanese media and various publications have also argued that brain death and a persistent vegetative state cannot be easily distinguished, often citing examples of patients who make partial, and occasionally complete, recoveries from a PVS. Three or four hospitals in Japan specialize in the treatment of PVS patients. One, where intensive nursing care is the prime treatment modality, has been the subject of a very moving national television program. This type of media coverage encourages extreme caution on the part of the public in moving toward an acceptance of brain death as the end of life, and it has been so widespread that it would be difficult for the average citizen to be unaware of the "brain-death problem."

In collections of essays and magazine articles written by a spectrum of Japanese intellectuals on the problem of brain death, sentiments such as *fushizen* (unnatural) appear repeatedly. Brain death is reported to be too unnatural to be equated with human death, for example, and the idea of "controlling" death is described as "going against nature."[21] The Kyoto philosopher Takeshi Umehara takes an extreme jingoistic position when he asserts that "we Japanese" have never accepted unnatural things, such as foot binding and the eunuch system, as did the Chinese. He adds for good measure that homosexuality and the use of drugs are not present in contemporary Japan. Umehara is not opposed to organ transplantation in principle, since he believes that Buddhism teaches people that they should be prepared to "sacrifice" themselves for others, but he insists that there is no "logical" proof that brain death is the end of life.

Several highly respected scientists have argued in widely circulated magazines that an individual—a person—is more than a collection of body parts. Yoshio Kawakita, a biologist who is also a Christian, has stated clearly that he cannot accept brain death as the end of life and opposes organ transplants. He states that it is "superficial" to argue that one can live on in another person as the result of a transplant, although people claim that this is a "humanistic" move. He calls that simply a rationalization to make way for technological intervention into the process of dying.[22]

The Culture of Technological Innovation in Japan

Contemporary Japanese attitudes toward scientific knowledge and technology are difficult to pin down because of their intimate connection to a widespread ambivalence about the process of Japanese modernization. Moreover, Japanese attitudes toward modernization cannot be understood in isolation from ever-changing interpretations, produced both inside and outside the country, about the relationship of Japan to the West. The form of the current debate about body technologies in Japan—the feasibility of tinkering with the margins between culture and nature and the very definition of those margins—reflects widespread general concerns about modernization, postmodernization, and "Westernization."

In Japan throughout the late nineteenth century, the eager quest for Western science and technology "was grounded in [a] sense of cultural certitude," an awareness that the "core" or the bass note *(koso)* of Japanese culture would remain unaffected. Technology, self-consciously aligned with the Other, was placed in opposition to culture in this discourse and epitomized by the platitudes *wakon yōsai* (Japanese spirit and Western technology) and *tōyō dōtoku, seiyō gijutsu* (Eastern morality, Western technology). Najita and others have shown how this confidence in the endurance of "traditional" culture was gradually eroded. Early this century and again, particularly after the Second World War, internal tension erupted over Japan's increasing technological sophistication and internationalization.[23] Fears about an immanent collapse of the nation's cultural heritage became commonplace, and one reaction was a reassertion of cultural essentialism.[24]

For many Japanese, the specter of Westernized individualism, utilitarianism, and superrationalism triggers emotional responses that push them toward a rhetoric of difference, even as they buck at its inherently nationalistic underpinnings. This is the discursive background against which the debate about brain death is taking place. Those who have doubts about the introduction of new technologies have to struggle very hard, therefore, to find a suitable language with which to articulate their discomfort. Criticizing a "Western," "scientific," interventionist approach to nature makes one vulnerable to accusations of Japanese essentialism and antirationalism. Equally difficult to voice is criticism of the epistemological grounds on which a scientific determination of death is constructed. Commenting on the unethical behavior of the Japanese press and on activities of Japanese physicians as being unscientific and untrustworthy is rather easily justified and, almost everyone agrees, is a valid position. Thus, the issue is politicized, but the possible contribution of culture to the argument is generally ignored or else explicitly rejected.[25] One exception has been the anthropologist Emiko Namihira, who asserts that Japanese attitudes of longstanding toward the dead body account for resistance to brain death and organ transplants. Her argument highlights the cultural construction of the "natural," but it is one to which most Japanese intellectuals with whom I have talked have reacted with a good deal of resistance.[26]

The Discourse on Social Death

In Japan, as we have seen, biological death is usually understood as a process and not as a point in time.[27] Moreover, a distinction is made by many commentators between biological death and social death, which is believed to take place some time after the demise of the physical body. Although few commentators talk explicitly about a Confucian-derived belief in the ancestors, their influence on the debate over brain death is apparent. Interviews I conducted with 50 adult Japanese informants, men and women, made it clear that concern about the fate of the body after biological death may well contribute to a reluctance to both donate and receive organs. Everyone I talked to stated that they no longer believe in the elaborate prewar ancestor system, integral to the extended family. Nevertheless, over half of the respondents indicated that they carry out regular, often daily rituals in their homes and at the graves of deceased parents and grandparents. Most pointed out that family and societal obligations require that the bodies and memory of deceased family members be treated with respect.

From an analysis of the very moving narratives provided by relatives of victims of the Japan Air Lines crash in the mountains of Gunma prefecture in 1985, Namihira concluded that the spirit of the deceased is often anthropomorphized and is believed to experience the same feelings as do the living. Hence, relatives have an obligation to make the spirit "happy" and "comfortable." People were in agreement that it is important for a dead body to be brought home and that a corpse should be complete (*gotai manzoku*), otherwise the spirit will suffer and may cause harm to the living. Namihira cites the results of a 1983 questionnaire given by a committee set up to encourage the donation of bodies for medical research: Of 690 respondents, 66 percent stated that cutting into dead bodies is repulsive or cruel and also shows a lack of respect for the dead.[28] Contrary to these figures, the number of people agreeing to autopsies has steadily increased in recent years,[29] as has the number of people willing to go abroad to obtain organ transplants, and there has been increasing public recognition of brain death as the end of life. Clearly, the population remains deeply divided in their attitudes toward the dying and the recently dead, and many would, in any case, probably state one thing in response to a survey and actually do another when confronted with personal suffering.

One other major facet to this dispute cannot be developed fully in this chapter—namely, that it is not simply attitudes toward the dying and dead that are of concern in Japan, but also attitudes about gift giving. As noted earlier, living related organ donation is not controversial, but a few commentators dwell on the question of the appropriateness of altruistic donation of organs by strangers. Japan has a remarkably refined system of gift giving, one that is in essence an obligatory system of on-going exchange of goods and services. Entering into any kind of for-malized relationship with people outside the family involves the giving and receiving of gifts of specified value on regular occasions. This system continues to be widely used informally, in the Japanese economy, and in the various institutions where professional services are made available. The result is that the "tyranny of the gift" noted by Fox and Swazey is ever-present in the minds of the majority of Japanese.[30] The idea of re-ceiving a gift as precious as a human organ is overwhelming to contem-plate for most people because the reciprocal obligations incurred to the family of the donor would be too hard to bear. Although anonymity in theory provides protection from fulfilling obligations, it does not relieve a recipient family of endless feelings of guilt.

This value system adds an additional burden for those seeking to break the impasse created by the problem of brain death. Not only does it make patients hesitant to seek out transplants, but it also raises darker concerns: Doctors, especially surgeons, routinely receive gifts, monetary and otherwise, for services to be rendered. Some commentators are con-cerned that organs may be donated to individual physicians as gifts or that money may be paid to doctors in order to become a favored poten-tial recipient. With the new law, it will be interesting to see whether attempts are made to control this custom.

A related point is that donated organs are believed to contain the essence of life present in the deceased person; organs remain animated even after transplantation. Patients I interviewed in Montreal often ex-hibit similar sentiments, but the traditional medical and philosophical system in Japan provides a convenient and widely accepted rationale to support such a belief system.[31]

Late Modernity, Cultural Identity, and the Other

The dilemma for progressive thinkers in Japan when considering ethical issues in connection with the problem of brain death is how to dispose of the remnants of patriarchal and patronage thinking—the reactionary part of the Confucian heritage—without drawing on a language that singlemindedly pursues a further entrenchment of the "Western" values of individual autonomy and rights. As one pediatrician has recently put it: "Why should we mindlessly imitate Westerners? We would only be turning ourselves into white Westerners with Asian faces."[32] Not surprisingly, to those of us who know Japan quite well, the debate is an overwhelmingly secular one in which representatives of religious organizations are, for the most part, absent.[33]

Although a certain amount of genuine passion is aroused over the fate of those individuals whose lives are directly involved, remarkably little has been heard from patients and their families, whether they be potential donors or receivers. Only since the beginning of 1994, the year in which an international conference on organ transplantation was deliberately staged in Japan by surgeons keen to break through the impasse, has the fate of those patients not able to receive transplants, together with those who have gone abroad to obtain organs, started to capture the attention of the media and the Japanese public.

Thus far, the problem of brain death has not been primarily about individual human suffering, but rather a manifestation of the struggle by citizens and activists from a whole range of political persuasions about what constitutes moral order in contemporary Japan. Those who recognize brain death as the end of life usually accept a modernist ideology of technologically driven progress in the relief of human suffering, while many of those against equating brain death with death embrace an argument about the essential difference of Japan and exhibit concerns about a perceived loss of moral order. Yet others try to seek out a less extreme position from where, rather slowly and painfully, a middle ground is emerging in which accounts of individual suffering have become more prominent. Nevertheless, extremists on both sides remain highly vocal and influential.

Lessons for the "West"

The Japanese debate about brain death raises several issues for outside observers. If the organ transplant industry is to flourish, and this ter all is the stimulus for most of the debate about death, then the Japanese experience would suggest very clearly that cultivation of public trust together with impeccable medical practice open to public scrutiny is indispensable. As we move into an era where the status of patients in a persistent vegetative state is increasingly brought up for discussion, inclusion of the public in this debate is without doubt advisable.

Second, I suggest, on the basis of this research, that the Japanese as a society are apparently more prepared than are we in North America to analyze what it is about death that disturbs them. The increasing attention given to euthanasia is forcing us to examine our consciousness with respect to attitudes toward death, but we still have a long way to go in allotting intellectually challenging media time and space equivalent to that devoted to this topic by the Japanese.

A fundamental issue highlighted by the problem of brain death in Japan is the status, legal and moral, given to death and the associated efforts to define and redefine it. It is argued increasingly by a good number of physicians, philosophers, and bioethicists who have followed the brain-death debate since its inception in the late 1960s that it is not appropriate to reduce our understanding of death to a biological definition.[34] The question of an irreversible lack of consciousness rather than an irreversible lack of brain function is now at the center of the argument, and for many commentators it is agreement on the demise of the person and not of the biological body that is at stake.[35] What we learn from Japan (and could equally well learn from a perusal of the value systems of many other cultures of the world) is that the person (*hito*) is not equated with individual consciousness, nor is the person located in the brain. Personhood is diffused throughout the mind and body and, moreover, is a condition that is fundamentally social and not individual in essence. An individual becomes a person only through maturation and participation in social life and ceases to be a person only after certain rituals are fulfilled. The law and daily life in Japan are grounded in the rights of and obligations toward primary social units, in particular the family, which usually overrides individual rights and interests. This is why the bill submitted to the previous Diet invested the family with the right to "surmise" the wishes of its deceased relative.

What this suggests, I believe, is that in this transnational world of increasingly pluralistic societies, we must begin to recognize a multiplicity of ways of comprehending and legalizing the process of dying and the management of the dead. Failure to do so may bring the transplant industry to a grinding halt, leaving sick and dying patients in the same situation as those whose plight is only just beginning to be recognized in Japan.

References

The research on which this chapter is based was funded by the Social Sciences and Humanities Research Council of Canada (SSHRC).

1. Ota K, Teraoka S, Kawai T. Transplantation in Asia: Organ transplantation in Japan. *Transplant Proc* 1995;27(February):1463–65.

2. Gotō M. Body and soul: Organ transplants. *Look Japan* 1992;38:32–33.

3. Kengi no kakata saisho no shinzō ishoku (Coverup suspected in first heart transplant). *Mainichi Shinbun,* March 31, 1991.

4. Kōseishō kenkyūhan ni yoru nōshi no hantei kijun (Brain-death determination criteria of the research division of the Ministry of Health and Welfare). *Kōseishō Tokyo,* 1985.

5. Lock M. Deadly disputes: The calculation of meaningful life. In: Lock M, Young A, Cambrosio A (eds). *Intersections: Living and Working with the New Medical Technologies.* Cambridge: Cambridge University Press. In press.

6. Yamauchi M. Transplantation in Japan. *Br Med J* 1990;301:507.

7. Nihon Kyūkyū igakukai rinji kai. Nōshi kanja e no taiō to nōshitai kara no zōki ishoku ni tsuite (Concerning the management of brain dead patients and organ transplants from brain-dead bodies). *Nichi kyūkyū ikai shi* 1994;5:314–16.

8. "Nōshi ishoku" michisuji nao futōmei ("Brain death, transplants," the path to follow is still unclear). *Nihon Keizai Shinbun,* January 23, 1992.

9. Kanto Chiku Kochokai, 1992, Rinji noshi oyobi zokiishoku chosa kai, Tokyo. "Nōshi ishoku yonin o saigo tōshin" (final report approves brain death, organ transplants). *Yomiuri Shinbun,* January 23, 1992.

10. "Nōshi wa hito no shi," tōshin (Brain death is death, says report). *Asahi Shinbun,* January 23, 1992.

11. "'Nōshi wa shi mitomeru': Nichibenren ikensho rincho o hihan jinken shigai no osore." ('Recognition of brain death as death': Fear of violation of human rights in the opinion of the Japanese Confederation of Lawyers). *Asahi Shinbun,* September 21, 1991.

12. 55% sansei o eta nōshi kara ishoku (55 percent approve of transplantation from brain-dead). *Mainichi Shinbun,* October 16, 1991.

13. The parliamentary system of many countries, including Japan, allows elected members to submit bills without party backing, for parliamentary debate.

14. Ross C. Towards acceptance of organ transplantation? *Lancet* 1995;346:41–42.

15. Ota K, Teraoka S, Kawai T. Donor difficulties in Japan and Asian countries. *Transplant Proc* 1995;27(February):83–86.

16. Uozumi T. Nōshi mondai ni kansuru shikkan to teian (My opinion and proposals on the brain-death issue). In: Umehara T (ed). *Nōshi to zōkiishoku (Brain Death and Organ Transplants).* Tokyo: Asahi Shinbunsha, 1992; Hirosawa K. Tachiba kara mita nōshi to shinzō ishoku (Brain death and heart transplants

from the point of view of a circulatory system specialist). In: Umehara T (ed). *Nōshi to zōkiishoku (Brain Death and Organ Transplants)*. Tokyo: Asahi Shinbunsha, 1992; Komatsu Y. Sentaku gijutsu to nōshironsō no shikaku (The blind spot in advanced technology and brain death debates). *Gendai Shisō* 1993;21:198–212.

17. Tachibana T. *Nōshi (Brain Death)*. Tokyo: Nihon Hōsō Shuppan Kyōkai, 1991.

18. Program produced by NHK television, 1990.

19. Nakajima M. *Mienai shi: Nōshi to zōki ishoku (Invisible Death: Brain Death and Organ Transplants)*. Tokyo: Bungei Shunju, 1985.

20. Yanagida K. Gisei waga musuko, nōshi no jūichi nichi (Sacrifice our son and eleven days with brain death). *Bungeishunju* 1994;72:144–62; Nōshi, watakushi no teigen (Brain death, my proposal). *Bungeishunju* 1995;73:164–79.

21. Hirosawa K. Junkanki senmoni tachiba kara mita nōshi to shinzō ishoku (Brain death and heart transplants from the point of view of a circulatory system specialist). In: Umehara T (ed). *Nōshi to zōkiishoku (Brain Death and Organ Transplants)*. Tokyo: Asahi Shinbunsha, 1992; Watanabe T. *Ima naze shi ka (Why death now?)*. Tokyo: Niki Shuppan, 1988; Umehara T. Hajime ni (Introduction). In: *Nōshi to zōkiishoku (Brain Death and Organ Transplants)*. Tokyo: Asahi Shinbunsha, 1992, 17.

22. Kawakita Y, Sasaki C. *Dialogue between History of Medicine and History of Science*. Tokyo: Chūōkōron, 1992.

23. Najita T. On culture and technology in postmodern Japan. In: Miyoshi M, Harootunian HD (eds). *Postmodernism and Japan*. Durham: Duke University Press, 1989.

24. Harootunian HD. Visible discourses/invisible ideologies. In: Miyoshi M, Harootunian HD (eds). *Postmodernism and Japan*. Durham: Duke University Press, 1989, 63–92.

25. Nakajima M. *Mienai shi: Nōshi to zōki ishoku (Invisible death: Brain death and organ transplants)*. Tokyo: Bungei Shunju, 1985; Nudeshima J. *Nōshi, zōkiishoku to nihon shakai*. Tokyo: Kōbundō, 1991.

26. Namihira E. *Nōshi, Zōki ishoku, Gan Kokuchi (Brain Death, Organ Transplants, Revealing a Diagnosis of Cancer)*. Tokyo: Fukumu Shoten, 1988.

27. Uozumi T. Nōshi mondai ni kansuru shikkan to teian (My opinion and proposals on the brain-death issue). In: Umehara T (ed). *Nōshi to zōkiishoku (Brain Death and Organ Transplants)*. Tokyo, Asahi Shinbunsha, 1992; Hirosawa K. Tachiba kara mita nōshi to shinzō ishoku (Brain death and heart transplants from the point of view of a circulatory system specialist). In: Umehara T (ed). *Nōshi to zōkiishoku (Brain Death and Organ Transplants)*. Tokyo: Asahi Shinbunsha, 1992; Komatsu Y. Sentaku gijutsu to nōshironsō no shikaku (The blind spot in advanced technology and brain death debates). *Gendai Shisō* 1993;21:198–212.

28. Namihira E. *Nōshi, Zōki ishoku, Gan Kokuchi (Brain Death, Organ Transplants, Revealing a Diagnosis of Cancer)*. Tokyo: Fukumu Shoten, 1988.

29. Monbushō. Kaibōtai shūshū sū to kontai hiritsu (Numbers of bodies do-

nated for autopsy and percentage). Tokyo: Monbushō Igaku Kyōikuta Shirabe, 1993.

30. Fox R, Swazey J. *The Courage to Fail: A Social View of Organ Transplants and Dialysis.* Chicago: University of Chicago Press, 1978.

31. Lock M. *East Asian Medicine in Urban Japan: Varieties of Medical Experience.* Berkeley and Los Angeles: University of California Press, 1980.

32. Zōki ishoku no saizensen (The frontline in transplants). *Newsweek Nihon Han Japanese Edition*, February 25, 1993.

33. Becker C. *Breaking the Circle: Death and the Afterlife in Buddhism.* Carbondale: Southern Illinois University Press, 1993; Hardacre H. Response of Buddhism and Shintō to the issue of brain death and organ transplant. *Cambridge Q Healthcare Ethics* 1994;3:585–601.

34. Truog RD. Is it time to abandon brain death? *Hastings Cent Rep* 1997; 27(January–February):29–37.

35. Green M, Wikler D. Brain death and personal identity. *Philos Public Affairs* 1980;9(2):105–33.

15

Defining Death in Germany

Brain Death and Its Discontents

Bettina Schöne-Seifert, M.D.

BRAIN DEATH HAS been a source of heated debate in Germany. Although some issues are akin to those that have surfaced in the United States, some features of the debate are distinctly German. This chapter examines the German experience. It consists of three parts: (1) a review and analysis of the German brain-death debate of the 1960s, (2) a brief description of the widespread acceptance and use of brain-death criteria in clinical practice for many years prior to legislation, and (3) a discussion of the ongoing campaign against brain death, including some thoughts on how it relates to today's German bioethics controversies.

The Early Debate about Brain Death

The earliest published treatment of ethical aspects of brain death that I found was in 1962 in the widely read journal of the German Medical Association. It is (in translation) a detailed paper by French neurologist Mollaret,[1] who 3 years earlier had classified as *coma dépassé* ("beyond coma") the biological, or rather pathological, status of being that we now call *brain dead*.

In April 1967, at the annual meeting of the German Society for Surgery, then-President Werner Wachsmut identified problems in determining death as a new challenge resulting from progress in both resuscitation medicine and organ transplantation. He recommended appointing a committee to analyze these problems. About a year later, this committee (of two surgeons, one neurosurgeon, two anesthesiologists, and one professor of law) presented their results and published them a short time later[2]—2½ months before publication of the well-known report of the Harvard committee.

The two committees' recommendations were, not surprisingly, quite similar. The German Surgical Society's recommendations, titled "Criteria of Death," explicitly and exclusively used the term *Gehirntod* (brain death) rather than Harvard's unfortunate *irreversible coma*. The German requirements for diagnostic tests met some of the criticisms that would later be leveled against the Harvard guidelines.[3] Thus, in contrast to the Harvard guidelines, the German ones did not confuse (irrelevant) spinal reflexes with brainstem reflexes; they explicitly asked for a positive apnea test; they required "loss of consciousness" instead of Harvard's "unreceptivity and unresponsivity"; they asked for a 12-hour (rather than 24-hour) observation period; and, finally, they saw a flat EEG (of 30 minutes, to be repeated after 12 hours) as a necessary rather than a desirable confirmatory test. However, like the Harvard report, the German report restricted itself to spelling out criteria and tests of whole-brain death, without wasting a word on the underlying definition of death and the problems of its justification.

The temporal coincidence of these two publications is, of course, due to the strong interest Western medical communities shared in these issues. In 1967, at the first World Meeting on Medical Law in Ghent, Belgium, a similar list of criteria had already been proposed. A brain-death formulation was also adopted by the World Medical Association at its meeting in Sydney in August 1968 (the very week of the Harvard publication), as part of the "Declaration of Sydney."[4] The issue, no doubt, was in the air.[5] What is somewhat puzzling, though, is the consistent failure to address explicitly the conception and definition of death taken to underlie brain-death criteria. To my knowledge, in the United States this debate did not begin until the second half of the 1970s, peaking at the time of the President's commission, and the debate still continues, though less intensely.

In Germany, however, an impressive ethical debate began earlier among a few theologians, lawyers, and physicians in neurology, surgery, pathology, and forensic medicine. From the published material, it appears to have included some two dozen participants who seemed to anticipate almost all aspects of the contemporary debate. But the debate seems not to have had much influence on policy. Two weeks after publication of the German Surgical Society's guidelines, an editorial in the same journal,[6] supporting brain death and consent for organ donation by donor or proxy, noted that "physicians in the Federal Republic of Germany currently differ on nuances of the professional ethical aspects of organ transplantations." But, it continued, "even if some prominent German doctors argue especially carefully and cautiously, it can be noted that, overall, considering the legal and ethical aspects sketched above, no overriding doubts result." Thus, neither physicians using the brain-death criteria nor the public seem to have cared much about the doubts and problems that had been expressed in that small-scale interprofessional debate. Remember that acceptance of medical authority and paternalism still prevailed.

Not until Christian Barnard's first human heart transplant in Capetown in December 1967 did the public debate about brain death begin. The liberal weekly magazine *Der Spiegel* published a lengthy essay on April 1, 1968, titled (in translation) "Death—Uncertain Frontier." It reported that, after Barnard's pioneer intervention, "not without shivers of horror, drinking rounds and coffee klatsches, tradesmen and intellectuals, journalists and starlets were unexpectedly involved in a dispute that had raged among scholars—physicians, lawyers, and theologians—for years."[7] The concept of death was also said to have become "a dominant topic of physicians' conferences and in the scientific press."

To be sure, the problem of choosing to classify the brain dead as either dead or alive is not specific to heart transplantation, but heart transplants imposed the problem on the public mind more clearly than had kidney transplants. Kidney transplantation was on its way to becoming an established procedure at the time of the first heart transplant; the first kidney transplant in Germany was in 1963, 11 were performed in 1967, and 27 in 1968.[8] The official understanding was that the transplants used postmortem organs. Numerous contemporary commentators referred to the controversial status of the donors as those who had been or would be "merely" brain dead.[7,9]

The richness of that early discussion is apparent in some of the positions held and the distinctions that were already being made. It was already emphasized that "determining death to have occurred presupposes, of course, determining the value of the *concept* of death—something to be missed in most elaborations on the determination of death."[10] Moreover, various authors acknowledged that the motivation for changing the criteria of death (from heart to brain) was to make decision making about withdrawing life-sustaining treatment and organ removal from brain-dead patients consistent with other norms regarding life and death.[7,9,11] As to the status of a definition of human death, some authors thought that, "from a biological point of view, determining the time of death must—within certain limits—be arbitrary . . . being a value judgment" that results not "from biological but from a societal need."[12] Others, opposed to any change in criteria, insisted on a strictly "biological" definition of death.[13]

A justification frequently put forward for the adoption of a whole-brain criterion of death—one of the two core arguments used to justify brain-based definitions of death—is the total loss of consciousness, known to have occurred in brain-dead patients.[14] The irreversible loss of "mind," or some would say "soul," which occurs with the total loss of consciousness was thus considered crucial. This argument was, for example, heartily endorsed by the well-known Protestant theologian Helmut Thielicke:

> If we speak of the physician's duty to preserve life, then this cannot mean simply biological life, but only "human" life. Characterizing this human life demands other criteria than those manifested in cardio- and encephalograms. From the early history of the Bible to Martin Heidegger—to describe a somewhat adventurously broad arc of over-view—the definitive criterion for differentiating between animal and human life is the fact that human existence is characterized by self-awareness . . . If we take self-awareness seriously as the true signature of human existence, then the complete and irreparable cessation of self-awareness would be the criterion for the end of human existence. Man without a trace of any self-awareness would be like a merely bio-logical preparation, which it might be desirable to keep alive in order to have a reservoir for organ transplantations . . . but not as a matter of [patient-oriented] medical ethics.[15] (36–37)

Thielicke explicitly distinguished between the life of an "organism as a whole" and the "vital conservation" of single organs by keeping a brain-dead patient on artificial respiration.[15] This distinction is often attributed to Hans Jonas,[16] who would later endorse it, although he understood it differently, in that he viewed a brain-dead body as a whole organism. The renowned Catholic theologian Franz Böckle argued similarly,[17] introducing the distinction between life as a "person" and merely "biological human life."

In a 1968 overview article by a professor of forensic medicine,[5] the loss-of-mental-life argument is said to predominate among both religious and secular proponents of brain death. This is remarkable because it is just this argument that is so discredited in the current (theologian-driven) German opposition to the concept of brain death (see below). However, proponents no less than opponents of this argument perceived a danger of "determining death no longer according to mainly objective aspects, but as a now teleological concept primarily according to subjective aspects"[9] and of "the danger of perverting the concept of the 'human' to suit practical considerations."[5]

For some of those who nevertheless favored the brain-death criterion, this was reason enough to urge standards for determining death to be regulated by statute.[9] Others preferred merely legalizing freedom for physicians to decide, without specifying substantive criteria or tests.[5] There was wide agreement—in line with a requirement that is now universal—that at least two independent physicians must make any such determination.[9,11]

The second argument supporting whole-brain death is based on loss of integrative functioning or self-governance (very familiar to participants in today's debate). It also was put forward in that early German debate.[9]

Turning now to early opposition to the brain-death criterion, one finds again that almost the entire spectrum of current arguments had already been voiced. The integration argument was considered incoherent:

> The mutual interactions of the parts of the organism in the human and in all chordates are maintained by the circulatory organs as well as by the nervous system. The functional unity is not completely ended until the functions of both systems are completely ended. The nervous system's integration of the parts of the organism is complex and the brain cannot, in this respect, be considered in toto or without the spinal cord . . . Hence, the principle of disintegration and of the dissolution of the biological functionary unit is no suitable criterion to define death and its determination.[13]

Related and again now familiar concerns were that the loss-of-mental-life argument is based on a reductionist concept of human beings and that it implies the acceptance of a *higher* brain definition of death (considered highly objectionable), that it would require a conclusion that embryos (with a still undeveloped brain) lack (full) living status, and that any plausible conception of death has to be applicable to any species, hence also to those without a mental life.[13]

Notably, secular and religious opponents of brain-death criteria nevertheless considered organ salvaging from the "dying" brain-dead patient to be permissible. They were ready to grant this exemption from the prohibition to kill[10,11,13]—basically, because they acknowledged brain death to be "a point of no return" in dying.

Looking back, the arguments for and against a brain-based definition of death already were remarkably complete, though not the specter of conclusions finally to be drawn from them. Like today, whole-brain criteria were advocated based on the loss of mental life or of self-governance. Those who opted for the classic heartbeat criterion did so out of opposition to both of those arguments or from fear of general "inhumane consequences."[13]

In particular, two minority positions found among those who advocate the loss-of-mental-life argument today were not articulated in the 1960s. The problem of patients in a persistent vegetative state was not much in the air then, and that probably explains why nobody adopted an explicit higher-brain definition of death and the associated criteria (which are the coherent consequences of the pure loss-of-mental-life argument). Nor did anybody argue for the hybrid position that is now sometimes called the "tutioristic" position. According to this position (which I personally find most convincing), the only coherent, plausible, and indeed sufficient justification for accepting a brain-death criterion is the argument from total loss of any mental capacities, that is, loss of mind and thereby of the mind-body integration due to the loss of one integration component. However, for this loss to be certain, complete, distinct, and immediately diagnosable (an aspect considered psychologically important), one has to, according to this intermediate position, play it safe—by adopting a whole-brain rather than a higher-brain criterion. This partially pragmatic position is, to be sure, held only by a small minority of today's participants in the brain-death controversy in Germany.

The apparently unresolved dispute did not, however, prevent the application of brain-death criteria in clinical practice. Shortly before the German Surgical Society published its purely descriptive guidelines for diagnosing whole-brain death in 1968, *Der Spiegel* had wisely noted:

Physicians by themselves will hardly be able to answer the question . . . , whether those who, being brain dead, can be kept functioning are still humans, person-like beings . . . For the physician's everyday practice, this question [as to the status of brain death] is decided without official backing. Not when they are in doubt [whether brain-death criteria are met], but when they consider themselves on the "certain side," they stop the respirator as soon as brain death has occurred. Nonetheless, without question, this does not eliminate the moral doubts.[7]

Undisputed Brain-Death Practice, 1968–1992

For 14 years after the publication of the German Surgical Society's guidelines, brain death was more or less routinely accepted without question in German intensive care units. Finally in 1982 the German Medical Association published brain-death testing guidelines—again without providing a supporting definition of death. These guidelines have been supplemented twice.[18]

The guidelines represent a middle position with regard to test requirements: For patients with known primarily supratentorial brain damage, clinical examination over 12 hours in adults, 24 hours in infants, and 72 hours in newborns is considered sufficient without additional technical testing. Obviously, the underlying justification is that in these patients the cerebrum had already been damaged before the brainstem ceased functioning. In contrast, in patients with primary brainstem damage, a flat EEG over 30 minutes has been required as a confirmatory test—though only since 1986.

Skepticism as to whether the brain dead are "really dead" was expressed from time to time in the media, mainly fueled by the fact that many people do not think brain-dead patients look dead. Although I know of no data indicating how widespread this skepticism was, it did not prevent the vast majority—in 1990, 90 percent of relatives[8]—from giving substitute consent for organ donation. (This high figure reflects a very selective practice of approaching relatives, leading to a low overall donation rate.) In 1990, the Catholic and Protestant Church published a common statement on the ethical acceptability of organ donation and on accepting brain death as the death of human beings.[19] I know of only one group of German authors to publish critical analyses on the definition underlying brain death between 1970 and 1992.[20]

In 1978, a first legislative attempt to regulate organ transplantation would, as a side effect, have legalized whole-brain death, and it did not attract much attention at the time. The bill was defeated because of unresolvable differences over explicit versus presumed consent requirements. (Until October 1994, when a constitutional change granting federal jurisdiction took effect, legislative authority for administrative aspects of transplantation resided with the states; to achieve uniform policy throughout the country, each state would have to adopt a model draft or consent to a states' contract authorizing federal legislation.)

Discontents since 1992

In the fall of 1992, problems with brain death gained widespread public attention mainly as a result of the Erlanger case. The case involved a young, brain-dead woman whose physicians tried unsuccessfully to maintain her pregnancy until fetal viability. While criticism focused on the perceived instrumental use of the young woman by decidedly pro-life physicians, others—whose views on sustaining her pregnancy varied—questioned whether she was dead.

Since then, opposition to brain death has intensified. It started with critical publications by single authors from various disciplines,[21] and this opposition became a real campaign in the spring of 1995 in response to the drafting of transplant legislation that would legalize the longtime de facto practice of accepting whole-brain death criteria. Passage of this legislation in the fall of 1997, despite the harsh public opposition, surprised many observers. The opposition included a group of more than 170 academic theologians, 100 physicians, and 5,000 other citizens who formed the Berliner Initiative against brain death. The public had already reacted to the Erlanger case and presumably other scandals in organ procurement (involving instances of illegal sale of corneas, transfers of dying donors, and unfair preferential organ allocation) with a considerable cutback in organ donation—from a 90% consent rate by relatives in 1990 to a 69% rate in 1994.[8]

Both the German Medical Association's Scientific Board and the German Scientific Societies reacted to the growing skepticism on brain death by publishing, for the first time, a justification of brain-death criteria.[22,23] The board insisted, without much argument, that a higher-brain definition of death was both intellectually implausible and morally problematic. Such a definition would be "value-laden" rather than based solely on "biological fact" (implying that this is not the case with a whole-brain definition) and, hence, would be subject to "dangers of abuse." The board also considered it problematic because it ignored the fact that "self-governance" was still intact when the higher brain was destroyed. The German Scientific Societies, in contrast, seems to adopt only the loss-of-mental-life argument, although this seems open to interpretation. The numerous theologians opposing brain death have not (yet) made the churches officially retract their approval of brain death, although support has been less forthcoming in recent formulations by church representatives.

With few exceptions,[24,25] those who write and talk in favor of brain death adopt the "official" argument of loss of both mental life and self-governance. Nobody argues for a higher-brain definition. And those few who consider whole-brain death justified by the pragmatic hybrid position described above might well spoil the political terrain for any brain-death criteria for the price of what they consider intellectual coherence. Those opposing whole-brain death advance an array of arguments for returning to traditional heart-lung criteria.

This seems to be notably different from the Anglo-American situation, where a return to heart-lung criteria is very rarely endorsed,[26] and where proponents of higher-brain definitions see their impact as keeping options open or as stabilizing the acceptance of whole-brain death by enhancing its intellectual coherence. For most German authors, there is no need even to explain why classifying permanently unconscious patients (or a subgroup of them) as dead is implausible and unacceptable. Thus, only when a brain-based definition of death safely excludes a shift to a higher-brain definition does it seem potentially acceptable to the public.

In June 1995 and September 1996, federal health officials held public hearings on brain death and the closely related question of consent for organ donation. These issues are related because opponents of brain-death criteria, claiming that the brain dead are dying donors, do not accept proxy consent to organ procurement. Twenty "experts," invited by the political parties in Parliament according to whether their positions on brain death seemed acceptable to the invitors, testified. Almost certainly unrepresentative of public opinion, exactly half of them—from medical, theological, philosophical, or professional care-giving backgrounds—criticized the definition underlying brain death as erroneous and dangerous. Opting for a return to the traditional cardiac criteria, most of these opponents nevertheless considered organ salvaging from the "dying brain dead" permissible by personal consent. Notably, quite a number of them claimed that removal even of unpaired organs would not constitute killing because the process of salvaging the organ (e.g., maintaining the patient on a respirator) prolongs the donor's life.[27] I need not comment on the implausibility of this argument.

Among the arguments against brain death currently and repeatedly endorsed in German writing, many are familiar from both the early German and the current American debate. I consider some convincing: (1) that despite repeated claims to the contrary,[28] brain death cannot be said to be simply another criterion for death as it had always been understood and defined; (2) that the argument from self-governance (in the German debate most diligently favored by Birnbacher)[29] is incoherent because it grants brain-based vegetative governance an unjustified primacy over both heart-lung and spinal cord;[30,31] (3) that brain death, as commonly tested, does not necessarily imply complete loss of brain functioning,[32,33] which represents yet another challenge to the self-governance argument.

Other arguments seem especially prominent in Germany:

1. Some argue that we know too little about the mechanisms of dying and should thus refrain from adopting, or at least legalizing, brain death.[34-36] This is implausible because it assumes that something factual remains to be detected in the process of dying that might be relevant to the dispute. Moreover, the concern falsely presupposes the existence of some objective "real" dividing line between life and death. This same premise, by the way, is also held by some proponents of brain death, who refer to "the insights of medicine, that man is dead after the functioning of the entire brain has irreversibly ceased."[37]

2. Several opponents make claims along the lines of the statement "whether and what man (in a coma) senses cannot be answered objectively, because it asks for his subjective experience . . . Any identification of the limits of what can be described scientifically with the limits of reality is dubious."[27] What is surprising and implausible here is not the skepticism, as such, but its specificity. If one questions the brain-basedness of the mental, why not question its body-basedness altogether? It seems, moreover, to be a strategy of the opponents of brain death to blur the distinction between brain death and irreversible coma or the vegetative state by subsuming them all under "coma"—intentionally repeating the Harvard committee's early mistake.

3. A minority of those favoring a cardiopulmonary criterion of death emphasize that brain-dead patients appear to be alive and cite the French

philosopher Lévinas when they argue that all of ethics is derived from the bodily *experience* of the other person.[30]

4. A core objection is the claim that brain death supports a reductionist view of human beings, even if one grants the concomitant loss of mental functions. As stated by the Lutheran Bishop Huber, a brain-death opponent: "The brain death definition, too, takes part in the anthropological tradition that defines man essentially as *res cogitans*. A certain conception of human consciousness and related self-governance becomes the decisive criterion of life."[38] However, supporters of brain death actually hold a holistic view because they conceive of human life as requiring both the mind and body components and leave open whether death requires the loss of one or both. Brain-death opponents, on the other hand, might be said to have a holistic view only of *death,* for which they require a loss of both components.

Nevertheless, this reductionist claim is at the heart of most current secular and religious opposition to brain death. Brain death is seen as supporting modern medicine's tendency to instrumentalize humans. And here, I think, lies one key to understanding the content, moral impetus, and surprisingly great public impact of the campaign against brain death. I regard it as yet another chapter in the unfortunate story of contemporary German "anti-bioethics."[39] Many people have extended their hostility against specific positions—for example, permissiveness on voluntary euthanasia, abortion, euthanasia for severely handicapped newborns—to bioethics in general.

This phenomenon, which is both unjustified and counterproductive in terms of tackling bioethics' many urgent problems, results from several factors specific to Germany.

1. The recent history of atrocities by the Nazis and their abettors, including the mass murder of mentally handicapped patients (mislabeled "euthanasia") and the Nazi eugenics program.
2. The subsequent sensitivity to slippery-slope risks, resulting in opposition among some parties to even the discussion of euthanasia. As one example, the Australian philosopher Peter Singer was prohibited from lecturing in the country because of his permissive views on euthanasia of disabled neonates.[40]
3. Academic philosophers' late interest in "applied" issues and their relative lack of familiarity with modern pragmatist and utilitarian or other consequentialist ethical theories. This has fostered both

professional and public misconceptions of those approaches and positions. Hence, pragmatic concerns tend to be seen as ethically irrelevant. Not uncommonly, *utilitarian* is used as a synonym for inhumane and discriminatory.

4. The absence of a patients' rights movement challenging medical paternalism, as existed in the United States in the 1970s. A tension exists between, on the one hand, medical law and bioethics whenever it is autonomy-oriented and, on the other hand, the physicians' role as it is conceived and actually experienced by many. Mistrust and confusion in both directions seem to be the inevitable result.

5. A lack of public debate and systematic education on bioethics issues, for reasons indicated above. Therefore, one-sided media coverage or problematic slippery-slope prophecies enjoy undeserved resonance with the public.

I believe that opposition to brain death reflects these German realities. To be sure, brain death deserves critical analysis and public concern. Any definition of death is, within biological constraints, shaped by varying social, psychological, and anthropological concerns. However, in Germany, the controversy about brain death is to a considerable extent misconceived as yet another utilitarian, technocratic (here: pro-transplantation) discrimination against the weak (here: of the "dying"). One example is the recent expert statement of Lutheran Bishop Wolfgang Huber, who finds an (evil) "ethics of interests" rather than an "ethics of dignity" underlying the acceptance of brain death: "Within an ethics of interests, disclaiming rights to life need not be justified; rather their recognition needs justification. It can be justified only if an individual has subjective interests in living and can articulate them. Thus self-consciousness and communicability are presupposed ... Ethicists who argue like that ... submit man to the disposition of other men. It is precisely this claim to power that an 'ethics of dignity' opposes."[38] Another telling example is the statement of theologian Grewel in a widely published legal journal:

> By starting to legitimize organ transplantations via the concept of brain death, medicine ... has subscribed to a system that, under the name of "bioethics," propagates a utilitarian view of man ... Not everyone with a human face is a recognized and respected human anymore, instead, respect for his human dignity and his right to life is tied to

the precondition that he can prove certain minimum levels of functional ability and intactness, especially brain function (consciousness!), as an entrance ticket.[35]

The false assumptions common to these voices and to many more are that acceptance of brain death (1) relies on "wrong" factual or anthropological premises and (2) is to be seen in continuity with other forms of patient discrimination. I wonder whether, with regard to these positions, there is much to be learned from Germany. Fortunately, an unexpected majority of German parliamentarians finally voted in favor of the German Transplantation Act. This new law, which took effect in December 1997, legalizes what had been clinical practice regarding brain death.[41] It remains to be seen whether and how the debate about brain death has changed public attitudes.

References

Work on this chapter was done primarily during a fellowship at the Wissenschaftskolleg zu Berlin, for which I am most grateful. I also thank Mitch Cohen for assistance in translation and Robert Arnold, Renie Schapiro, Stuart Youngner, and William W. Winslade for their helpful comments and critique.

1. Mollaret P. Über die äussersten Möglichkeiten der Wiederbelebung: Die Grenzen zwischen Leben und Tod. *Münch Med Wochenschr* 1962;34:1539–45.

2. Deutsche Gesellschaft für Chirurgie. Kriterium des Todes. *Deutsch Ärzteblatt* 1968;19(May 11):1113–14.

3. President's Commission for the Study of Ethical Problems in Medicine and Biomedical and Behavioral Research. *Defining Death: Medical, Ethical, and Legal Issues in the Determination of Death*. Washington, DC: Government Printing Office, 1981.

4. World Medical Association. Declaration of Sydney (in German translation). *Deutsch Ärzteblatt* 1968;35:1865–67.

5. Pribilla O. Juristische, ärztliche und ethische Fragen zur Todesfeststellung. *Deutsch Ärzteblatt* 1968;41:2256–59,2318–22,2396–98.

6. Editorial: Organtransplantationen—Feststellung des Todes. *Deutsch Ärzteblatt* 1968;21:1234.

7. Report: Tod—ungewisse Grenze. *Der Spiegel* 1968(April 1):152–77.

8. Deutsche Stiftung Organtransplantation, Neu-Isenburg.

9. Schönig R. Zur Feststellung des Todeszeitpunktes. *Neur Jur Wochenschr* 1968:189–90.

10. Gerlach J. Die Definition des Todes in ihrer heutigen Problematik für Medizin und Rechtslehre. *Arztrecht* 1968;6:183–86.

11. Pompey H. Gehirntod und totaler Tod—Moraltheologische Erwägungen zur Herztransplantation. *Münch Med Wochenschr* 1969;13:736–41.

12. Liebhardt EW, Wuermeling HB. Juristische und medizinisch-naturwissenschaftliche Begriffsbildung und die Feststellung des Todeszeitpunktes. *Münch Med Wochenschr* 1968;110:1661–65.

13. Gerlach J. Gehirntod und totaler Tod. *Münch Med Wochenschr* 1969;13:732–36.

14. Spann W, Liebhardt E. Reanimation und Feststellung des Todeszeitpunktes. *Münch Med Wochenschr* 1967;27:1410–14.

15. Thielicke H. *Wer darf leben? Der Arzt als Richter.* Tübingen: Rainer Wunderlich Verlag, 1968.

16. Jonas H. Against the stream: Comments on the definition and redefinition of death. In: *Philosophical Essays.* Englewood Cliffs, NJ: Prentice-Hall, 1974, 132–40; Gehirntod und menschliche Organbank: Zur pragmatischen Umdefinierung des Todes. In: Jonas H. *Technik, Medizin und Ethik: Zur Praxis des Prinzips Verantwortung.* Frankfurt: Inselverlag, 1985.

17. Böckle F. Probleme der Organtransplantation in theologisch-ethischer Sicht. In: Toellner R. *Organtransplantation: Beiträge zu ethischen und juristischen Fragen.* Stuttgart: Gustav Fischer Verlag, 1991, 89–96.

18. Bundesärztekammer: Kriterien des Hirntods: Entscheidungshilfen zur Feststellung des Hirntods. *Deutsch Ärzteblatt* 1982;79:45–55, 1986;83:2940–42, 1991;49:2417–22.

19. Kirchenamt der Evangel. Kirche in Deutschland und Sekretariat der Deutschen Bischofskonferenz (ed). *Erklärung der Deutschen Bischofskonferenz und des Rates der Evangelischen Kirche in Deutschland.* Hannover, 1990.

20. Kurthen M, Linke DB, Moskopp D. Teilhirntod und Ethik. *Z Ethik Med* 1989;1:134–42.

21. Hoff J, In der Schmitten J (eds). *Wann ist der Mensch tot? Organverpflanzung und Hirntodkriterium.* 2d ed. Reinbek: Rowohlt Verlag, 1995.

22. Wissenschaftlicher Beirat der Bundesärztekammer: Der endgültige Ausfall der gesamten Hirnfunktion ("Hirntod") als sicheres Todeszeichen. *Deutsch Ärzteblatt* 1993;90:1975–78.

23. Erklärung Deutscher Wissenschaftlicher Gesellschaften zum Tod durch völligen und endgültigen Hirnausfall—Hirntod (1994). *Frankfurt Allgem Z* 1994(September):N3.

24. Spittler JF. Der Hirntod ist der Tod des Menschen. *Universitas* 1995;50:313–27.

25. Steigleder K. Die Unterscheidung zwischen dem "Tod der Person" und dem "Tod des Organismus" und ihre Relevanz für die Frage nach dem Tod eines Menschen. In: Hoff J, In der Schmitten J (eds). *Wann ist der Mensch tot? Organverpflanzung und Hirntodkriterium.* 2d ed. Reinbek: Rowohlt Verlag, 1995, 95–118.

26. Evans M. A plea for the heart. *Bioethics* 1990;4:228–31.

27. Gallwas HU, Geilen G, Geisler L, et al. Wissenschaftler für ein verfas-

sungsgemässes Transplantationsgesetz: Gegen die Gleichsetzung hirntoter Patienten mit Leichen. In: Hoff J, In der Schmitten J (eds). *Wann ist der Mensch tot? Organverpflanzung und Hirntodkriterium.* 2d ed. Reinbek: Rowohlt Verlag, 1995, 513–22.

28. Wissenschaftlicher Beirat der Bundesärztekammer. Der vollständige und endgültige Ausfall der Hirntätigkeit als Todeszeichen des Menschen—Anthropologischer Hintergrund. *Deutsch Ärzteblatt* 1993;90:2926–29.

29. Birnbacher D. Definitionen, Kriterien, Desiderate. *Universitas* 1995;50: 343–56.

30. Hoff J. Von der Herrschaft über das Leben: Zur Kritik der medizinischen Vernunft. In: Hoff J, In der Schmitten J (ed). *Wann ist der Mensch tot? Organverpflanzung und Hirntodkriterium.* 2d ed. Reinbek: Rowohlt Verlag, 1995, 270–331.

31. Kurthen M, Linke DB. Vom Hirntod zum Teilhirntod. In: Hoff J, In der Schmitten J (ed). *Wann ist der Mensch tot? Organverpflanzung und Hirntodkriterium.* 2d ed. Reinbek: Rowohlt Verlag, 1995, 82–94.

32. Klein M. Hirntod: Vollständiger und irreversibler Verlust aller Hirnfunktionen? *Z Ethik Med* 1995;7:6–15.

33. Wiesemann C. Hirntod und Gesellschaft: Argumente für einen pragmatischen Skeptizismus. *Z Ethik Med* 1995;7:16–28; Däubler-Gmelin H. Entmündigt die Sterbenden nicht. *Die Zeit* 1995 (June 2):42.

34. Deutscher Berufsverband für Pflegeberufe: Zum Entwurf eines zukünftigen Transplantationsgesetzes. *Ausschussdrucksache Deutscher Bundestag* 1995; 13(116):34–39.

35. Grewel H. Zwischen Lebensrettung und Euthanasie: Das tödliche Dilemma der Transplantationsmedizin. *Z Rechtspraxis* 1995;217–20.

36. Höfling W. Plädoyer für eine enge Zustimmungslösung. *Universitas* 1995; 50:357–64.

37. Wolfslast G. Organtransplantation: Gegenwärtige Rechtslage und Gesetzentwürfe. *Deutsch Ärzteblatt* 1995;92:24–27.

38. Huber W. Organtransplantation, Hirntod und Menschenbild. In: Hoff J, In der Schmitten J (eds). *Wann ist der Mensch tot? Organverpflanzung und Hirntodkriterium.* 2d ed. Reinbek: Rowohlt Verlag, 1995, 462–76.

39. Schöne-Seifert B, Sass HM, Bishop LJ, et al. Contemporary bioethics in the German-speaking countries. In: Reich W (ed). *Encyclopedia of Bioethics.* 2d ed. New York: Macmillan, 1995, 1579–89.

40. Schöne-Seifert B, Rippe KP. Silencing the singer: Antibioethics in Germany. *Hastings Cent Rep* 1991;21:20–27.

41. Gesetz über die Spende, Entnahme und Übertragung von Organen (Transplantationsgesetz-TGP). *Bundesgesetzblatt* 1997;74:2631–39.

VI

Public Policy Considerations

In this part, Alta Charo and Dan Brock consider the possibilities and problems of translating what has been a largely academic debate about defining death into a public policy issue. Both consider how the public might respond to the idea that death may not be an unambiguous biological category. Charo's emphasis is on how the law and public policy have dealt with other so-called biological facts such as gender, race, and parenthood; she describes their relevance to attempts to redefine death. Brock focuses on what the public would want to know or should know about the ambiguities surrounding the determination of death.

Charo raises three critical points. First, in the world of public policy, scientific "reality" is not as important as public perception. For example, the law justifies distinctions based on the "enduring myth of a biological basis for race," although it lacks a sound biological justification.

Second, Charo argues that, while "biological facts" constrain legal options, they do not determine the law. The public is willing to accept law that "ignores or misconstrues biological facts in order to achieve some public purpose." She points out, for example, that laws treating adoptive parents as if they were the biological parents are accepted because the public is willing to ignore biology if the law promotes an important public value that has few negative consequences and cannot be promoted in other ways. It is unclear whether attempts to redefine death meet this description.

Finally, Charo shows the limited applicability of sophisticated academic analysis to public policy. After examining the current public pol-

274 · Public Policy Considerations

icy regarding reproductive technology and the definition of the beginning of human life, she concludes that public acceptance is more closely tied to common sense and experience than to academic rigor.

Brock addresses a related issue: How much can and should the public be involved in determining the definition of death? He argues that the public should be informed about the social implications of various definitions of death and their relevant consequences. This requirement mirrors the "reasonable person" standard of informed consent—while all information should be provided, if asked, the initial conversation should concentrate on those topics a reasonable person (public) would want to know. Brock believes this includes information about irreversibility, the topic addressed by Lynn and Cranford in Chapter 6, but not whether "pockets of cellular activity" are inconsistent with death, as raised by Brody, Pallis, and Bernat in Part II.

Unfortunately, Brock's conclusion, however reasonable, is based merely upon intuition. As is revealed by Siminoff and Bloch in Chapter 10, there is little information about what the American public knows or wants to know about defining death. Rix's review of the public education campagn in Denmark (Chap. 13) suggests that Danish citizens were insecure about the diagnosis of death, confused about the difference between persistent vegetative state and brain death, and unsure of how long a heart could beat once the patient is declared brain dead.

Brock also claims that "public policy should be guided by the aim of promoting the well-being and respecting the rights of the citizens subject to that policy." Although both democracy and moral theory lead to a strong presumption in favor of the truth, one may sometimes be justified in hiding nuances and disagreements regarding the definition of death to avoid adverse effects on public policy. For example, Brock raises the question of whether an open debate regarding the whole-brain versus higher-brain definitions of death would have a negative effect on organ donation by destroying the useful "fiction" that death is an "objective, scientific determination in which there is no role for values."

Even if we had data regarding this question, deciding when the consequences are severe enough to preclude open discussion is likely to be extremely difficult, if not impossible. First, while we blithely talk of "the public" as an entity, it is unclear whether this is feasible in our diverse, multicultural society. Second, imagine trying to determine when the consequences are severe enough to justify "hiding or sidestepping the complexities, ambiguities, uncertainties, and controversies in policy debates about the definition of death." How confident would one have to be that an open discussion would decrease public confidence? How can one measure the effect of decreasing confidence, and how severe must the consequences have to be to decide not to discuss this debate? Alternatively, how does one assess the positive consequences of open discussion or of deflating "fictions."

Moreover, who decides whether to tell the truth or try to optimize consequences? Academicians? Health care providers? Elected officials? Can the decision whether or not and how to have a public discussion predetermine the outcome? For example, proponents of the status quo may discourage public debate while opponents push it. Charo and Brock remind us that in this debate, unlike academic debates, cultural beliefs and values may be more important than intellectual coherence and truth.

16

Dusk, Dawn, and Defining Death
Legal Classifications and Biological Categories

R. Alta Charo, J.D.

THOSE WHO STRUGGLE with a definition of death or with identifying a set of criteria for declaring death often feel compelled to make their work consistent with known biological facts. Certainly, biology is a strong determinant of legal classification schemes. Consistency between a law and an underlying reality seems not only intellectually honest but also necessary to ensure public acceptance of the new rules. But this is not necessarily the case.

In many instances, the public has become comfortable with rules based on treating people or things *as if* they tracked an underlying biological reality—what might be called *legal fictions*. This chapter reviews legal categories that purport to represent biological phenomena, such as life and death, kinship, race, and gender and briefly explains how the law often ignores or misconstrues biological facts to achieve some public purpose, such as administrative simplicity. Since choosing a legal definition of death entails deciding whether legal death should coincide with biological death and since the biological definition of death is, like many biological phenomena, inherently ambiguous, the effort to define death would benefit from taking advantage of our experience in these other public policy areas.

Legal Fictions That Invoke a False
Biological Reality

The normative power of what is perceived to be an unshakeable biological reality is brought home most forcefully when examining classification systems that are actually political and cultural constructs but attain persistent, unchallenged credibility because they are thought to be based instead on physical reality. The biological determinism that underlay many nineteenth-century notions of women's capabilities and roles is one example. Racial classifications are another.

Interestingly, racial classifications were first proposed by Carolus Linnaeus, author of the 1758 founding document of taxonomy, the *Systema Naturae*, as terms that reflected not biological difference, but merely geographic clustering. It was Johann Friedrich Blumenbach (1752–1840), a German anatomist and naturalist, who proposed a human taxonomy in which, while all peoples originated from a single common man, some groups—"races"—differed in characteristic ways from the original aesthetic ideal. These races conveniently clustered geographically, which was explained by noting that the differences undoubtedly arose due to adaptation to climate and diet as humans spread over the globe. In this pregenetic era, it was believed that changes occurring in one's lifetime, such as darkening of skin in response to sunlight, could eventually be passed on to children.[1]

Modern geneticists thought that examining the frequency of genetic markers would yield a more precise accounting of these races; it did not. On average, there is only 0.2 percent difference in genetic material between any two randomly chosen people. Further, when two random individuals are chosen and one examines only the material that differs between them, on average only 6 percent of it will be associated with the "race" to which the two people have been assigned. Another 9 percent will be associated with the individuals' respective nationalities (as a rough proxy for geographically based reproductive clustering), and 85 percent will not be associated with any variable in particular. In other words, to the degree that individuals do differ genetically, racial classification will correlate with only one-twelfth of the difference.[2]

Furthermore, the choice to classify people by color of eye, hair, and skin, along with teeth, eye shape, and hair texture, was in part tautological—these were the features that appeared to vary most in association with geography—and responds primarily to the instinct to classify by what can be seen. Classifications could as easily, and more cleanly, be made by blood type, antigen type, or fingerprint. Fingerprints tend to feature loops, or whorls, or arches. Classifying humans this way would yield a "loops" race consisting of most Europeans, sub-Saharan Africans, and east Asians; a "whorls" race of Mongolians and Australian aborigines; and an "arches" race of Khoisans, central Europeans, and others.[3] But these groupings would not have coincided with the original geopolitical bases for making racial classifications at all, and they would have undermined the notion of race by failing to accord with the pattern of trait differentiation in facial features.

Nonetheless, there is an enduring myth of a biological basis for racial classifications, and it is this myth that has strengthened the arguments for a "natural" or "god-given" separation of humans. This has been the basis for religious teachings and social policy for so long that it is nearly impossible to penetrate pervasive misunderstanding with actual facts. Indeed, even when we seem to be breaking through the myth (e.g., by offering a box labeled "multiracial" for those who view themselves or are viewed by others as having "mixed" parentage), we nonetheless reinforce the notion that the parents, or grandparents, were a "pure" white, or black, or yellow, or red. No such phenomenon exists.

Although race undoubtedly exists as a social classification, sometimes welcomed, more often resented, it is hardly a biological distinction. Nonetheless, the race-based social classifications, which might otherwise break down under the pressure of competing classifications based on geography, language, religion, wealth, or system of moral philosophy, have endured by pointing to this faux-biology and proclaiming an objectivity and inevitability to eye/hair/skin color categorizations.

The lesson for those tampering with culturally ingrained notions of death is clear: the mere belief that there is a clear, unshakeable biological definition can defeat generations of scholars who write about why there is little that is clear, unshakeable, or unrelated to political or social goals. Since biological realities are often mistaken for a divine or natural blueprint of the social world, challenging what appears to be writ in physiology will often be received with outrage, humor, incredulity, or dismissiveness; rarely will it be received with comprehension and acceptance.

Legal Fictions That Ignore Known Biological Reality

Despite the normative power of biology, however, there are times when law succeeds in creating rules that deliberately ignore that normative power or even pretend that the underlying biological reality does not exist at all. The blood ties between parent and child have almost mythological significance in every culture, resulting in the creation of a grand presumption, to wit, that all "real" families have one father and one mother, each biologically related to the child. Indeed, the law—which presumes that biological parents are entitled to be the rearing parents of their offspring—reflects an often unexamined assumption that the biological (i.e., natural) definition of family is one that is presumptively better than any competing definition.[4] At times, however, substitute parents are needed when biological linkages are missing or inconvenient. Modern adoption is evidence of a strong social tradition that recognizes the purely social and psychological dimensions of parenting.[5]

More importantly, adoption is an example of a global change in a child's status. Unlike the case of foster parenting, in which the original parents retain a legally recognized tie to the child, although the foster parents may now have some specific guardianship rights, in adoption the law pretends that the original parents never existed. A new birth certificate is issued, and the adoptee is legally treated for all purposes as equivalent to the biological child. Some people may know that the adoptee is not related and may in their own minds make psychological distinctions between adoptees and biological offspring, but as far as the law is concerned, this adoptee is indistinguishable from a related child. In a sense, this is a legal fiction because it ignores an unambiguous biological phenomenon—unrelatedness—to serve a public purpose.

What makes this interesting is that the phenomenon of giving parental rights and duties exclusively to one man and one woman is based on the notion, mentioned above, that the biological family is not only the norm, but normatively the best. By granting adoptive parents the same rights and duties as biological families, the law extends to adoptive families—permitted for purely social purposes—the same credibility that it extends to biological families, even though the justification of their "naturalness" is entirely missing.[6]

This kind of legal fiction is well tolerated provided that it is necessary to achieve a fairly compelling purpose, such as assuring that a child's best interests are considered. To sustain this tolerance, however, that public purpose may not be achieved at the expense of those whom biology would have indicated are entitled to parental status. The well-publicized case of Baby Jessica illuminates this point.[7] Although adopted as an infant, she was removed from her home at age four and returned to her biological parents. Irregularities in the initial adoption had unfairly denied her biological mother the opportunity to revoke her consent to the adoption and her genetic father the opportunity to rear her. Despite widespread belief that it was in Jessica's best interests to remain with her adoptive family, the courts favored the biological parents because legal fictions cannot trump an unfair disregard for the entitlements that law says nature endows to biological parents.

In the context of defining or declaring death, the adoption experience would seem to indicate that the public *could* tolerate definitions and criteria clearly at odds with some underlying biological truth, provided that the purpose of denying reality is compelling; the fiction actually achieves this purpose; and affected parties are adequately protected from gross unfairness. One possible application of this lesson is in the area of anencephalics; while neither defining such infants as dead nor denying that most people and most biological definitions of death would consider them alive, the law could treat them as if they were dead, just as it treats adoptees as if they were born into their families, so long as there is good cause and no perceived harm to the infant or others.

Legal Fictions That Ignore Unknown Biological Reality

Law has historically viewed the definition of death as entirely a matter of medical judgment beyond the purview of lawmakers. Instead, law has concerned itself with using legal fictions to overcome the inability of physicians to ascertain whether someone actually has died or, if he did, at what time. The purpose of these efforts was not to determine whether technologies should be employed to maintain some aspect of physiological function, but rather to clear the administrative confusion created by this indeterminacy.

One longstanding fiction concerns those who have disappeared for many years. Such an absentee is either dead or alive, but no one knows which. The number of these "living dead" in the United States has been estimated at between 60,000 and 100,000,[8] and they create a morass of legal problems. May their spouses remarry? Should their heirs collect their estates? Should insurance claims be paid? In the past, those left behind found their lives on indefinite hold as long as no proof of death could be found, because common law had a presumption of continued life. But common law evolved by changing that presumption. Thus, nearly all U.S. states now presume a person dead after roughly 7 years of absence and allow the survivors to move on with their lives, unless someone makes a persuasive case that it is nonetheless likely the absentee is alive.[9]

This presumption of death operates differently than do fictions employed in adoptions, where law ignores known biological reality to achieve a compelling public purpose. Presumptions of death merely allow the law to infer from a particular kind of evidence—long absence—that someone is dead. Having made that inference, the law then treats the person as certainly, rather than only probably, dead. In a world of odds, a presumption of fact allows law to achieve the kind of binary clarity—alive versus dead—that it needs for the purposes of existing rules. Knowing someone has a 60 percent chance of being dead is of no use to the surviving spouse, who cannot get only 60 percent remarried. In a world of odds, law accepts imperfect proof of a biological fact to substitute for actual knowledge of the fact. Although this is just one aspect of the generic problem of proof in law, it is also a form of fiction, in that the law will now proceed as if there is no underlying doubt about the accuracy of the declaration of death.

Like adoption fictions, however, public tolerance wears thin when the presumption creates gross unfairness. In this setting, an erroneous declaration of death would strip an absentee of his property, marital and parental status, and citizenship. Thus, some civil law jurisdictions were unwilling to adopt the common-law approach of "missing and presumed dead," even though—except in times of war[9]—absentees return more frequently in fiction than in fact.[10,11] Statutory rules that codified the common law, however, balanced the admittedly devastating injury to a wrongly declared absentee against the frequent and significant harm to an absentee's survivors and found that some reasonable provision for reimbursing infrequently returning absentees for their lost property and civil status would be an imperfect but nonetheless adequate response overall.

Similarly, debates over the criteria for declaring death could acknowledge the impossibility of perfect proof. Where reasonable criteria are developed, akin to an absence of 7 years, then law could infer actual death from criteria indicating highly probable death. Those meeting these criteria, like missing persons, would then be treated as if no doubt exists as to their death. The challenge to this approach lies in the injury caused by an erroneous declaration. Unlike the returning absentee, who can at least be substantially compensated for the loss of property, the person erroneously declared dead and then treated in such a manner as to actually cause death will have no recourse. The policy debate for this scenario, then, revolves around accurately identifying who is at risk of an erroneous declaration (e.g., non-heart-beating organ donors who are declared dead after 2 minutes of asystole), how many such persons are likely to exist, what actual harm they would suffer if killed rather than maintained in that condition, and the costs to the many people whose interests will be indefinitely ignored should society opt to define all such persons with marginal life signs as fully "alive."

A second area in which law creates presumptions of death concerns the official time to be recorded as the moment of death. The issue takes on importance in the case of accidents in which two people die so close in time that it is impossible to tell which person died first. Should there be an issue of inheritance between them, it is important to know which person survived longer; if the survivor was an heir to the first person to die, then property would flow from the first person to die to the survivor, and thence to the survivor's heirs. Since the two people may have had different residuary heirs, figuring out which person died first would determine which residuary heirs to the respective decedents would stand to inherit the estates. In the absence of evidence of survivorship, however, the lack of certainty could lead to interminable delays in probating the estates.

To facilitate the orderly transfer of property from owner to heir in these cases, many states have enacted a simultaneous death statute. As with absentees, the law creates a new presumption—here, that the people died in the same instant—which will be the basis for distributing property unless someone can prove that one of them probably survived the other.[12] Unlike the absentee presumption, however, this presumption does not operate by taking a particular fact, such as absence of 7 years, and then declaring that this fact alone is enough to constitute proof that a person is probably dead. Here, no best guess of the order of deaths is made. Instead, a wholly new, and quite unlikely, version of biological reality is adopted as presumptively true absent good evidence to the contrary. In this sense, the simultaneous death statutes are creating presumptions of law, not simply setting forth permissible inferences of fact from clues like extended absence.

That these statutes represent presumptions of law rather than inferences (or presumptions) of fact is made abundantly clear by the Uniform Probate Code (UPC), which introduced a revised rule, in which persons killed in a common accident are presumed to have died at the same instant unless someone proves that one of them probably survived at least 120 hours longer than the other.[13] Thus, under the UPC, where one person is declared dead at the scene and the other arrives alive at the emergency room but dies soon thereafter, property from the person dead on the scene does not go to the person dead in the emergency room and thence to the heirs of the person in the emergency room. Instead, the heirs of both share the estates, as they would had these two actually died simultaneously.

One reason such a presumption of law is tolerated is that the competing interests are both socially constructed. The purpose for noting the order of deaths is to facilitate invoking inheritance laws. Where determining this fact is too unwieldy or where facilitating probate seems substantively pointless, as between two persons who died so close in time that no real use of property could be made by the survivor, the law simply declines to use the general rule.

Indeed, the law need not have used the fiction of simultaneous death at all—it could have been written simply to say that the order of deaths does not apply when it cannot be determined or when to do so does not further the purposes of probate law. But by pretending that the deaths really were biologically simultaneous, there is no need to write myriad special provisions throughout federal and state codes. Instead, existing codes can be used, and the simultaneous times of death neatly plugged into existing formulae. This is very much like adoption, where the legal (albeit not psychological) fiction of kinship permits a global change in the adoptee's civil status, with no real harm to anyone caused by the legal fiction.

For situations of persistent vegetative state (PVS), such presumptions of law could be used to treat such patients as if they were dead. Whether globally or simply for large areas of law, such as property ownership and family, presumptions could be used where the PVS patient's persistent ownership and marital status can wreak havoc on others while bringing no personal satisfaction. Using such presumptions only for certain areas of law, like property and family law, is one tool for avoiding the most controversial aspects of a general redefinition of death in the direction of a higher-brain death model; since only family and property status are at issue, the presumption would not affect decisions concerning maintenance of physiological support, such as assisted nutrition and hydration, or organ removal.

Legal Fictions That Oversimplify Biological Reality

Transitional states or intercategory states pose a perennial problem for a legal system built around mutually exclusive categories. A person is treated in law as male or female, for example, not both. But gender, though a largely binary category, is not clear-cut. Many people exist in a state dubbed *intersex,* and the law responds poorly to such outliers. Other classifications, such as life and death, also appear binary but have very fuzzy margins. The challenge for law, which is built around notions of night and day, is to set rules for dusk and dawn.

Sex as a Nonexclusive Biological Category

Classifying people in law as male or female is undermined by a genuine ambiguity in the biological definitions of sex. If someone exhibits breasts and a vagina, does that make this person female? It does for most casual observers, and biologists would certainly agree that these are the species-typical characteristics of a female. But if she (he?) also has a Y chromosome, geneticists would call him (her?) male. How should the law classify such a person?

The answer, not surprisingly, varies. The characterization of such a person will depend on the purpose for which the characterization is sought. For kinship, such a person will be characterized in accordance with genetic make-up; thus, although a man undergoing a sex change operation may be reclassified as "female" for the next census, he will not go from "father" to "mother" of any genetic offspring. Provided that there is a sensible relationship between the reason the information is being sought, such as tracing biological lineage, and the choice of definitional criteria, such as chromosomal composition, these unusual cases can be handled adequately, albeit awkwardly, by the law.

Where the interaction between purpose and classification is less clear, however, a struggle can develop over how law ought to choose among competing or blurred classification schemes. One example of this is the classification of athletes as men and women for the purpose of eligibility in sex-segregated sports competitions, regardless of whether these athletes have been raised to think of themselves as male or female.

Because of the obvious advantages in strength and size of most men as compared to most women, it has long been accepted that the two sexes should compete separately. But during the 1960s, women athletes began harder physical training and, in some cases, the use of anabolic steroids. Their increased strength and musculature led some to wonder whether they were men masquerading as women. The concerns came to a head when two Soviet sisters, Irina and Tamara Press, won six gold and silver track and field medals in the 1960 and 1964 Olympics. Major sporting organizations decided soon thereafter that all women should undergo "gender verification" to prove their femininity.

Although techniques for gender testing have evolved over time to take advantage of new technologies, athletic federations, as well as some physicians, say the testing is unreliable, unnecessary, and unfair to women, who may be wrongly disqualified and ridiculed because of the results. The first attempt at sex testing was in 1966, by the International Amateur Athletic Federation (IAAF), which performed phenotypic testing by parading naked female athletes before a panel of male physicians. Criticized as degrading, this was soon replaced by the International Olympic Committee with the buccal smear test for the Barr body (X chromatin). The buccal smear is minimally invasive, is inoffensive, and gives rapid results. It does not, however, detect women atypically virilized by such conditions as congenital adrenal hyperplasia, although it does show the chromosomal aberration (XY) of phenotypic women with testicular feminization.[14]

At the Barcelona Games in 1992, the Barr test itself was replaced by the polymerase chain reaction (PCR) test, which detects the presence of the Y chromosome. The introduction of buccal sampling and PCR was considered the crowning achievement in subtle, relatively noninvasive testing.[15] Unfortunately, Barr body testing is subject to error, and PCR is *so* sensitive that even a small number of a male technician's own shedding skin cells can contaminate the sample; since 1968, 50 to 70 Olympic athletes have been disqualified or have dropped out because of genetic tests, though only 7 cases of "justifiable" exclusion were ever confirmed. Although the IAAF stopped testing female athletes in 1992, after they concluded that chromosome testing was inconclusive and scientifically inaccurate in determining the sex of an athlete, it continues in other sporting federations.[16] The International Olympic Committee, reluctant to drop sex testing altogether, decided that the 1996 Atlanta summer games would feature only limited sex testing, using the original technique of genital examination, which is now viewed as less problematic than either chromosome or PCR testing.[17]

Sex testing, as flawed as it is, might be acceptable if it actually furthered a clear and compelling policy goal. Unfortunately, it does not. Its purported purpose, to level the playing field for women by having them compete only against women, ignores the very real variation in genetic coding for body type among ordinary women. Those who are born with a strong predisposition to greater than average height, for example, will have an advantage in some track and field events. And, undoubtedly, some of these women will be at a physical advantage comparable to that enjoyed by many men. Without clarity about the purpose of the sports spectacle, the credibility of humiliating and often erroneous sex testing will be undone, as little purpose seems to be served by resorting to such a problematic practice.

Like those for declaring the sex of a person, criteria for declaring death could be constructed to differ on a situation-specific basis. For example, death could be defined as irreversible loss of higher-brain function for those purposes that can be substantively fulfilled only when a person is sentient, such as marital status, but as loss of all brain function for questions of medical maintenance of body functions. But such varying criteria will only be tolerated if there is agreement that important purposes are served by adopting criteria at all in a particular situation and that the criteria chosen are neither too broad nor too narrow when applied.

Life as a Transitional Category

It is perhaps no surprise that the field of reproductive law and policy is drowning in several fundamental misconceptions: (1) that there *is* a single, accepted biological answer to the question "When does human life begin?" (2) that moral philosophy universally holds that human rights attach to any human life; and (3) that law is obligated to hold that legal rights attach to any entity that is biologically human and alive or that is accepted by moral philosophy as the possessor of human rights.

Like the process of dying, the process of conception and birth has no single demarcation between life and nonlife. Rather, living cells with human genetic material begin multiplying and differentiating and finally become physiological systems capable of sustained existence outside the uterine environment. This process of development offers many developmental markers, but none, in and of itself, satisfies the philosophical and legal question of when society must (or even ought to) embrace the entity as a full member of its community. Different cultures feel bound to recognize the full range of human rights in such entities at times as different as fertilization or 30 days after birth.

Nonetheless, American law has historically looked to biology to determine the time at which to initiate legal standing. Live birth was long the initial prerequisite for conferral of legal standing,[18] since it provided the simplest bright line rule and the most obvious time at which to recognize the existence of a new entity as a legal person.[19]

As technology advanced, medical practitioners discovered that fetuses became capable of independent integrated functioning in utero at the so-called moment of viability. Consistent with a position that all human bodies capable of independent integrated functioning (even if they currently were not, in fact, independent of the mother's womb) receive legal standing, the courts were forced to abandon the live birth rule because the point at which the criteria for legal standing were satisfied preceded birth. Starting with *Bonbrest v. Kotz*,[20] a flurry of cases were decided applying the new biological bright line, most often to confer legal standing upon viable fetuses to sue (after birth) for prenatal injuries inflicted after viability.[21]

Justice Blackmun's opinion in *Roe v. Wade* appeared to settle the remaining issues concerning the legal standing of fetuses,[22] but closer examination reveals that it merely settled the status of a fetus vis-à-vis a competing interest on the part of a woman to terminate her pregnancy. The Court simplified this balancing process considerably when it declared that, based on historical analysis, the Constitution and its amendments were drafted without any thought that the word *person* would encompass fetuses.

The word *person* is used as a term of art in law to signify an entity granted equal protection of the law. The term is *not* co-extensive with the biological concept of "a live human"; corporations can be persons while fetuses or antebellum slaves are not. But the intuition that legal persons *ought* to be co-extensive with biological persons stems from the larger intuition that the legal system ought to be co-extensive with physical reality.

Unfortunately, as with the case of gender, biology cannot neatly define the term *person*. Although biology can define *human* or *alive*, it cannot define personhood solely in terms of physical characteristics. For example, to define all living cells with a human genome—such as a fertilized egg—as a person would also define every living cell in our skin, kidneys, and other organs as a person as well. Thus, some philosophical inquiry into the purpose for dividing live human cells as "persons" or "nonpersons" is required in order to use available biological information.

Applied to the area of death, the never-ending struggles over reproductive policy demonstrate that public acceptance does not necessarily follow from subtle solutions based on nuanced philosophical or legal thinking. Indeed, the political strategies followed by the major camps in the abortion wars are based on this observation. Public acceptance is far easier to gain by urging people to focus on a single, simple, seemingly self-evident truth: fetuses are human and alive, just like us, and therefore should be treated just like us; or, if there is anything you own, it is your own body, and no one's body is available for others' use, as if slavery had not been abolished.

The fact that neither statement, in such bald terms, could withstand the rigor of philosophical analysis is less important to public debate and public acceptance than the fact that both statements are accessible to common sense and common experience. When questioned closely, most people in either camp would concede that there are exceptions and gradations in the application of such views. But the point, for them, is that these statements embody a strong presumption about the hierarchy of values to be upheld in any particular situation where they are implicated.[23,24]

For policymakers working on rules governing death, therefore, it is essential to both acknowledge and discard the fact of the biological ambiguity underlying the debates. This ambiguity, in practice, will be of far less consequence than the identification of any simple rules that are accessible to common sense and common experience.

Conclusion

Death is a phenomenon that is widely perceived as a physical event, determined by biology and diagnosed by physicians or physiologists. Any law that attempts to redefine death purely as a social construct is likely to be rejected unless it follows one of two paths.

First, the law could remain grounded in biological and medical realities, however imperfectly discovered, by matching legal categories to more refined physical categories, such as "psychologically dead," "bodily dead," or "totally dead." Legal rules governing situations ranging from property transfer to withdrawal of entitlements to medical services could then be written with reference to the particular aspect of death most pertinent to the purpose of the rule. This has the advantage of using all of the credibility that comes with adoption of classification schemes that seem to be unchangeable and ordained. It renders law vulnerable, however, to poor fit between purpose and category should scientists discover new ways to describe the various aspects of death.

A second path leads toward an open rejection of biological reality and the use of a legal fiction. In this regime, certain kinds of deteriorating states would be acknowledged as phases of life, but individuals in those states would be treated as if they were dead. Accomplishing this requires strong justification and detailed attention to both the benefit/burden ratio and the procedures by which errors will be avoided or redressed. A key advantage to this approach is its independence from evolution in scientific thinking. A significant drawback, however, is that these fictions are not likely to work on a categorical basis (e.g., pretending all PVS patients are dead for all situations), since the benefits, burdens, and errors will be situational. Instead, this approach will lead to a steady stream of debates over which situations are worthy of such fictions and why.

The present adoption of brain death into state law straddles these two approaches and has an element of legal declaration of the "winning" scientific theory. While this approach has succeeded at the legislative level and has made organ procurement possible, it has failed to succeed completely at the emotional level. This failure, in part, accounts for the resistance encountered to expansion of the legal definition of death to encompass other nonsentient states. If one's goal is to expand the notion of death, further tinkering with the law's choice of definitions from among competing scientific theories may not be successful.

References

The author acknowledges the helpful comments on the outline of this draft made by the participants of the November "Law and Equality Brown Bags" series at the University of Wisconsin: Pamela Bridgewater, Evan Gerstemann, John Kidwell, Neal Komesar, Marc Galanter, Krista Ralston, Jane Schacter, Alan Weisbard, and Daniel Wikler.

1. Gould SJ. The geometer of race. *Discover* 1994;15(2):65–69.

2. Hoffman P. The science of race. *Discover* 1994;15(2):4.

3. Diamond J. Race without color. *Discover* 1994;15(2):83–89.

4. Charo RA. Biological determinism in legal decisionmaking: The parent trap. *Texas J Women Law* 1994;3:265–307. See also Strathern M. *Reproducing the Future: Essays on Anthropology, Kinship and the New Reproductive Technologies.* London: Foutledge, 1992; Chodorow N. *The Reproduction of Mothering: Psychoanalysis and the Sociology of Gender.* Berkeley and Los Angeles: University of California Press, 1978; Sorosky AD, Baran A, Pannor R. *The Adoption Triangle.* Fall River, Mass.: Anchor Press, 1978.

5. Presser SB. The historical background of the American law of adoption. *J Fam Law* 1971;443:11; Sloan IJ. *The Law of Adoption and Surrogate Parenting,* 1988, 5–11; Huard LA. The law of adoption: Ancient and modern. *Vand Law Rev* 1956; 9:743,745.

6. Andrews LB. Surrogate motherhood: Should the adoption model apply? *Child Leg Rights J* 1986;7(fall):1,13; Aries P. *Centuries of Childhood: A Social History of Family Life,* 1962.

7. *In re* B.G.C., 496N.W. 2d 239(Iowa 1992); *In re* Baby Girl Clausen, 501N.W. 2d 193(Mich. App. 1993); *In re* Baby Girl Clausen, 502N.W. 2d 649(Mich. 1993); *DeBoer v. DeBoer,* 114S.Cct. 1 (1993).

8. Dean P. Disappearing acts. *Los Angeles Times,* September 19, 1989, sec. 5, 1.

9. Jalet M. Mysterious disappearance: The presumption of death and the administration of the estates of missing persons or absentees. *Iowa Law Rev* 1968; 54:177.

10. See, e.g., *Scott v. McNeal,* 154 U.S. 34, 14 S. Ct. 1108 (1894), *Martin v. Phillips,* 514 So. 2d 338 (Miss. 1987). The most notorious case, concerning an imposter who assumed the identity of a man absent for 8 years, until exposed by the absentee's return, occurred in sixteenth-century France and became the subject of the movie *The Return of Martin Guerre.* Davis NZ. *The Return of Martin Guerre.* Cambridge: Harvard University Press, 1983.

11. Dumas A, Pere. *Le Comte de Monte Cristo* (with A. Maquet), 1844, 45 (returning absent person assumes new identity, wreaks vengeance on those responsible for his disappearance); Tennyson EA. *Complete Poetical Works,* 1864, Cambridge ed. 1898 (returning formerly shipwrecked absent person does not reveal himself to remarried spouse); *My Favorite Wife,* dir. Garson Kanin (1940) (formerly shipwrecked absent person returns as husband is about to remarry); "The Search for Peter Kerry," *Murder, She Wrote* (CBS television broadcast, February 5, 1989) (returning amnesiac absent person is suspected of killing individual who induced him to return).

12. Uniform Simultaneous Death Act (1953); Uniform Simultaneous Death Act (1991), 8A U.L.A. 557 (Supp. 1992).

13. UPC @@ 2104, 2601 (pre-1990).

14. Carbon R. Female athletes: ABC of sports medicine. *Br Med J* 1994;309: 254.

15. Dingeon B, Amor Gueret M, Vercherat M, Schamasch P, Thome H. Development and proposition for a new method of gender verification for the next Olympic games. Presented at the Workshop on the Approved Method of Femhuty Verification, Monaco, November 10–11, 1990; Ljungqvist A, Simpson JL. Medical examination for health of all athletes replacing the need for gender verification in international sports: The International Amateur Athletic Federation plan. *JAMA* 1992;267:850–52; Yamagnchi A, Fukushi M, Fakuchi Y, Aparicio J, Wakisska A. A simple method for gender verification based on PCR detection of Y-chromosomal DNA and its application at the winter Uriversiade 1991 in Sapporo City, Japan. *Int J Sports Med* 1992;13:304–7; Thomson DM, Brown NN, Clagne AE. Routine use of hair root or buccal swab specimens for PCR analysis: Advantages over using blood. *Clin Chim Acta* 1992;207:169–74; Fergnson-Smith MA, Ferris EA. Gender verification in sport: The need for change? *Br J Sports Med* 1991;25: 17–19; Dingeon B, Hamon P, Robert M, et al. Sex testing in the Olympics. *Nature* 1992;358:447; de la Chapelle A. The use and misuse of sex chromatin screening for "gender verification" of female athletes. *JAMA* 1986;256:1920–23; Simpson JL. Disorders of gonads and internal reproductive ducts. In: Emery AEH, Kimoin DL, eds. *Principles and Practice of Medical Genetics.* 2d ed. Edinburgh: Churchill-Livingstone, 1990, 1593–1616.

16. What is a man, what has he got? *Irish Times,* October 13, 1994, 20.

17. Sports medicine experts address latest issues facing Atlanta '96. *Business Wire,* May 28, 1996.

18. Rask Pound. *Jurisprudence* 1959;4:384–94.

19. King PA. The juridical status of the fetus: A proposal for legal protection of the unborn. *Mich Law Rev* 1979;77:1647.

20. 65 F. Supp. 138 (D.D.C. 1946).

21. Roland F. Chase, Annotation, Liability for Prenatal Injuries, 40 A.L.R.3d 1222 (1971; Thomas M. Fleming, Annotation, Right of Child to Action against Mother for Infliction of Prenatal Injuries, 78 A.L.R.4th 1082 (1990); Sheldon R. Shapiro, Annotation, Right to Maintain Action or to Recover Damages for Death of Unborn Child, 84 A.L.R.3d 411 (1978)

22. *Roe v. Wade* U.S.113 (1973)

23. Condit C. *Decoding Abortion Rhetoric: The Communication of Social Change.* Champaign: University of Illinois Press, 1990.

24. Faux M. *Crusaders: Voices from the Abortion Front.* New York: Birch Lane Press, 1990.

17

The Role of the Public in Public Policy on the Definition of Death

Dan W. Brock, Ph.D.

WHAT SHOULD BE the role of the public in public policy regarding the definition of death? In this chapter I explore related issues raised by this question. How much of the complexity, uncertainty, ambiguity, and controversy about the definition and determination of death does, or should, the public want to understand? How much is the public able to understand? How important is it that the public understand a public policy like the definition of death and the basis for that policy? Is it better to cause public controversy and confusion up front in order to build a firmer foundation for public policy in the long run? Or is it instead better to hide or sidestep controversy and confusion in order to achieve important policy goals in the short run?

There are no interesting general answers to these questions that would be defensible for all policy questions in all circumstances. That is not to say, however, that there are not general considerations, relevant to other issues and other circumstances, that bear on these policy issues of the definition of death in the current circumstances of the United States. Even the correct characterization of the policy issue at stake here is more complex than the "definition of death" suggests. At least to the part of the public unfamiliar with this policy debate, the definition of death might seem to be simply a scientific question, more specifically a question for biology, the science of life, to settle for us, and not even properly considered an issue of public policy. Just as no one would take the definition of a *cell,* or of *metabolism,* to be a question for public policy, neither, it might seem, should be the definition of death, a biological concept that applies to all living things. At least two considerations explain its place in public policy—the first shows why it is in part an evaluative issue, not simply a scientific matter, and the second shows why it is an evaluative question properly settled by public policy, not individual choice. The definition of death is an issue of public policy in which the public has a significant stake, even if the biological meaning of the concept constrains the policy options for it.

The definition of death is in part an evaluative issue, not simply a scientific question, because in the case of humans it is controversial precisely to what kind of being the definition is supposed to apply—that it is to apply to us, and to beings like us, is not enough. Some would apply it to humans understood just as *biological organisms;* this application of the definition will conform most closely to its use with other organisms. Others, however, stress the application of the definition to *humans* and look to the death or destruction of what is distinctively human about us. Scientific investigation will tell us what features humans have and which of these differ from the features of other living organisms, but what is distinctively human is at least in part an evaluative question, not to be settled by science alone. Those who focus on what is *distinctively* human are typically interested in the features that they believe set us apart from other creatures in valuable ways and that give humans special moral or religious value or status. But these questions of moral or religious value or status are both notoriously controversial and plainly not scientific; what superficially appears to be a scientific question is in part an evaluative dispute about the kind of being whose death or ceasing to exist is in question. Closely related (but not the same, since some distinctive human traits may not be relevant to personhood) is the position that what we should be concerned with is the death of persons; the concept of a person is also a philosophical, and in part evaluative, concept, also not to be specified by biological science alone. The destruction or ceasing to exist of a person depends not only on the proper account of personhood, but as well on the conditions for the maintenance of personal identity over time, also a subject with an extensive and complex philosophical literature.

The second feature of the definition-of-death debate that makes it properly a public policy issue, not merely a question for biological science or an evaluative question for individual choice, is that every member of the public will at some point die, and the criteria for death that a society adopts will determine for each of us the medically, socially, and legally recognized point at which that happens. Nearly all of us also will be affected by the consequences that follow a determination of the death of others about whom we care. Both as a matter of social, historical, and cultural practice and as a matter of law, a variety of social and legal consequences are linked with an individual's death. Death signals the time for the removal of remaining medical treatments, the time at which organs can be taken for transplantation with the prior consent of the deceased or the family (or both), the time for disposition of the body by burial or cremation, the time for mourning, the time for the property of the deceased to pass to inheritors, and so forth.

For many of these consequences, having a predictable, socially agreed upon time at which they will occur—although we can question whether the time of death is the appropriate time—has important benefits. Different reasons will probably apply for linking each consequence with the time of death. However deeply connected with the time of death any of these medical, social, or legal consequences may in fact be, and however hard it might be to disentangle them in practice, none has any necessary connection to the time of death. But so long as they remain linked with the determination of death, they make the definition of death and the determination of the time of death important matters of public policy. The public is not only in fact, or even inevitably, but also quite appropriately involved in the issue.

It is important to be clear, however, that, to the extent that the public's stake in the definition of death depends on these consequences being linked to the time of death, that ground of the public stake could be at least in part removed. For example, Arnold and Youngner have argued that it is time to reexamine the so-called dead-donor rule, which requires that organs not be harvested for transplantation before the donor has died.[1] If the dead-donor rule is given up, then the public interest in transplantation programs would no longer ground a public interest in the definition of death.

Some of the other consequences of the determination of death, such as burial and mourning, would be more difficult, perhaps impossible, to detach from a determination of death, although the extent to which this is so for any particular consequence is an empirical question. But I believe there is no necessary connection between death, at least a medical or legal determination of death, and even such consequences as mourning. Since death can be applied to different kinds of subjects—for example, to human organisms, human beings, or persons, as distinguished above—it would be possible for the law to mark the death of the human organism or human being, while mourning followed the death of the person. That this is not merely possible but in fact occurs is seen when families of patients who enter a persistent vegetative state sometimes mourn the loss of their family member, the death of the *person* their family member was, even though that family member remains a live *human being* in the eyes of medicine and the law. But so long as these various social, legal, and medical consequences remain linked to the determination of death, they serve as important grounds for the public's stake in its definition. The issue of to what conditions these consequences of death will be linked should not be left solely to scientific and medical experts.

In the 1970s and early 1980s, the perceived need for change in the criteria for the determination of death, as well as the need many see today for additional changes, arose principally for two kinds of reasons. One was that the use of new technological capacities within medicine resulted in individuals whose entire brain had been destroyed, but who were still living because their respiratory and circulatory functions were being maintained by artificial means. This new phenomenon made untenable the traditional criteria for death of irreversible loss of respiratory and circulatory function, in significant part because of the linking of the determination of death with these various social, legal, and medical consequences. Despite the complete and irreversible loss of all brain function, treatment could not be removed without the family's consent, burial and mourning could not begin, organs could not be taken for transplantation, and so forth.

The second reason for the perceived need for change in the criteria for the determination of death, then as now, was the sense among professionals and the public alike that currently accepted standards do not correctly mark the point at which the patient has "really" died. Two decades ago, proponents of a whole-brain definition of death argued that patients who had permanently lost all brain function were "really dead," despite the artificial maintenance of their circulatory and respiratory function. Today, proponents of the so-called higher-brain definitions of death maintain that the persons that patients like Karen Quinlan and Nancy Cruzan once were, really died or ceased to exist at the point at which they permanently lost all capacity for conscious experience. In many cases, the families of such individuals also believe that their family member left them at that time, and only his or her body survives to be artificially maintained by medical technology. Part of the complexity of the policy issue arises from the need for the definition of death to respect both factors appropriately: first, the complex social, legal, and medical consequences that are linked to and follow death; second, the fact that the meaning, and in turn time, of death is not solely a matter of convention, nor a technical term or determination of science, medicine, or law, but instead is determined by a concept of death that is part of the everyday usage of ordinary persons.

Acknowledging a public stake in the definition of death, however, leaves open what aspects of its definition, and in particular what complexities, ambiguities, or controversies about the criteria or tests for death, the public does or should want to know about or understand. For example, some critics of whole-brain criteria have argued that accepted tests for determining when whole-brain criteria are satisfied are compatible with some continued brain activity at the cellular level and even with some continued functional activity of the brain at the cellular level.[2] Those who share the consensus on whole-brain criteria in effect agree to disregard this cellular activity or function, to understand it as activity but not function, or to consider it not a function relevant to the brain's integrative role in the functions of the organism as a whole which must be completely lost for brain death to be present. Would the public care about this complexity or ambiguity in whole-brain criteria for death if it knew or learned of it? Should it care about it? I believe that the answer to both questions is no, or at least not much, although that is not to say the matter should be hidden from the public. Let me explain.

It is very doubtful whether the existence or not of any continued cellular activity, in the brain or elsewhere in the organism, is part of the common public understanding of death. Ordinary people who can readily apply the concept of death to humans and other living things probably have little understanding even of what a cell is, much less of what kind of activity, functional or otherwise, it is capable of under various conditions. If that is correct, then it is doubtful that their conception of death includes any assumptions or beliefs about cellular activity or function in the brain, or lack thereof. Learning that there can be pockets of cellular activity or function remaining in the brain after death has been determined and declared, correctly according to currently accepted criteria and tests, would be unlikely to cause them to withdraw or question their belief that the individual is dead. If the public's conception or understanding of death would change if they learned of this cellular activity, then professionals might plausibly have an obligation to help inform and educate the public about it, but I doubt there would be any such change.

On the other hand, suppose the public were told that after death has been correctly declared, according to the standards and procedures of the Pittsburgh protocol, the individual's brain function often remains essentially intact and attempts to restore his or her cardiac and respiratory function might be successful.[3] Although no attempts will be made to resuscitate the individual, quite properly in light of his or her wishes, this news might well be disturbing because it is a part of the public, common-sense understanding of the nature of death that it is irreversible. Death as commonly conceived is the permanent loss of life of the individual, the permanent ceasing to exist of the individual. Some have argued that irreversibility is not part of the concept of death, but I believe such arguments are best understood as revisionist proposals to change the common understanding of death.[4] If the individual has truly died, then life cannot be restored to the bodily remains of the individual. But life could sometimes be restored to the individuals who satisfy the Pittsburgh protocol for death, and this implies, more accurately, that life has not yet been lost. Because cardiac and respiratory function could sometimes be restored with most brain function still intact, the individual has not died when he or she satisfies the Pittsburgh protocol for determining death.

It might be argued that the loss of cardiac and respiratory function is in fact irreversible when death is declared under the Pittsburgh protocol, because no medical attempt to restore it will be made.[5] It is not clear that even this claim is well established, at least at the high level of certainty typically thought appropriate for a determination of death. There are few firm data about spontaneous restoration of circulatory and respiratory function 2 minutes after they have ceased due to withdrawal of life support. The common sense understanding of the irreversibility of death is that it is not *possible* to restore the life or life functions of the individual, not that they will not in fact be restored only because no attempt will be made to do so.

What conditions make the loss of life functions irreversible is dependent upon the state of available medical technology and skill in restoring cardiac and respiratory function. This means that an individual who suffered cardiac or respiratory arrest at a time prior to development of the ability to resuscitate some such patients would have properly been declared dead, although he or she would not properly be considered dead today until resuscitation had failed or sufficient time had elapsed to make certain that any attempt would fail. Moreover, if an individual suffered cardiac or respiratory arrest in a location at which no means to attempt resuscitation existed, that patient would properly be considered dead once there was no meaningful chance of recovery of cardiac or respiratory function. There is relativity within the notion of the irreversibility of death, but it is relativity dependent on whether it is possible to restore life functions here and now, not on whether we choose to do so. If an individual's cardiac or respiratory arrest could likely be reversed by resuscitation, the individual is not correctly determined to be, and should not be pronounced, dead until sufficient time has passed to make any resuscitation attempt certain to fail.

Admittedly, physicians and others often speak of a patient who has just suffered cardiac arrest as having died but been brought back to life or saved by a successful resuscitation. Physicians also sometimes talk to patients in this way in the course of reaching a decision about the patient's code status—for example, "If you should die because your heart stops working, would you want us to try to save you by attempting to restart your heart?" But if the patient truly has died, and I am right that the conception of death is that it is irreversible, then no attempt to save him or her can possibly succeed. Physicians and others often talk about dying and death in confused and inconsistent ways, in both this and other contexts, but we should not infer from that talk that the conception of death does not include a condition of irreversibility.

My main purpose here, however, is not to elaborate or defend the proper interpretation of the condition of irreversibility that applies to death. One need only grant that the public's conception of death, rightly or wrongly, is that it is irreversible. If that is so, then the public should, and I believe would, want to understand the complexities, ambiguities, uncertainties, and controversies concerning the irreversibility of death under different criteria and tests for it. The more general point is that some of the complexity, ambiguity, uncertainty, and controversy about the definition and determination of death either directly concerns or bears indirectly on significant features of the public's conception of death, while others do not. It is reasonable to believe that at least some portions of the public would want to understand these complexities, ambiguities, uncertainties, and controversies with regard to irreversibility, but not with regard to pockets of brain activity or function at the cellular level. This is not to say, however, that professionals would be justified in deliberately withholding or distorting information on aspects of the debate in which the public may reasonably not have an interest when it is sought by or provided to members of the public. I will return to this issue later.

On other issues in the debate, it also seems reasonable to believe that the public would want to understand some aspects of the controversy, but not others. For example, in the controversy between proponents of whole-brain versus higher-brain criteria, it is not beyond the capacity of much of the public to understand what is probably the central point— whether the irreversible loss of all capacity for any form of conscious experience, a necessary condition for personhood on most views, is sufficient to establish death, or whether all functions of the brain, including functions of the brainstem, such as unassisted respiration or breathing, must be irreversibly lost as well before death has occurred.

In one interpretation, the essential difference between these two views is the nature of the entity whose death is in question—the person, for which consciousness is necessary, or the functionally integrated biological organism, for which other functions controlled by the brainstem, such as respiration, are also necessary. If we take as given the linking of death with the typical social, medical, and legal consequences that follow its pronouncement, members of the public are capable of considering and forming views on whether those consequences should follow from the death of the person or from the death of the human biological organism. They are capable of understanding many of the issues, both conceptual and pragmatic, in that debate, such as the greater difficulty at this point in time in achieving a level of certainty that higher-brain function, and so consciousness, has been permanently lost, comparable to the level of certainty that can be achieved that all significant brain function has been permanently lost.

Members of the public are capable as well of understanding and deciding about the acceptability for policy of many of the implications of the two definitions. For example, the higher-brain formulation seems to imply that still breathing, heart beating, and warm bodies are ready for burial or cremation, so long as death remains the triggering time for this consequence. We should operate with a strong presumption that an understanding of these points and others like them is within the grasp of much of the public and of concern to at least part of it.

Here, as elsewhere, if the public has a stake and interest in this or other aspects of the definition of death, that also extends to the fact that professional disagreement exists on these aspects of the issue. The nature and degree of professional disagreement is one factor, among others, bearing on what is appropriate pubic policy on the issue.

Consider another feature plausibly held to be a part of the common-sense conception of death held by ordinary persons—that life and death are a strict, nonoverlapping dichotomy, so that death must occur at a precise point in time, even if that point is sometimes difficult to determine. In this view, any individual is at any point in time either alive or dead; an individual cannot be both alive and dead, nor partially alive and partially dead, at the same time, even if controversy remains about the proper criterion for differentiating one state from the other. Linda Emanuel has recently argued that there are common cases in which this view is mistaken.[6] Dying is a process that takes place over time, an uncontroversial claim, but she argues also that death, understood as the culmination of the process of dying or the loss of life, cannot be assigned any distinct and unique point or time in this process. Let me quote one of Emanuel's examples:

> Tracking declining vital signs. Janet was dying of liver failure. Her liver failure led to a rapid decline in her kidney function. Despite appropriate therapies she was losing consciousness gradually and increasingly. Two days ago she recognized her husband and pressed his hand in response to his words. Yesterday she looked at him but without obvious response. Since this morning she no longer opened her eyes and responded only to deep pain. Tests indicated that she was getting enough oxygen, but her blood pressure was dropping. Between the toxic substances resulting from her liver and kidney failure and her low blood pressure her higher brain cells were probably beginning to lose their function. Her heartbeat was regular, as was her breathing until a few hours ago. Gradually her breathing began to be deep and sighing within longer and longer intervals. Next her heart rhythm became irregular and then extremely slow. Then her blood pressure became undetectable by a regular blood pressure cuff. Her breathing slowed to twice a minute or so, suggesting that her brain stem was also losing ground. She was still warm. Her pupils became wide and did not respond to light. Her heart was still going at about twenty a minute, but with increasing intervals. Then her breathing seemed to stop—she would breathe once and stop again. Her heart monitor began to show an almost flat line, with every so often an electrical complex. Then, seemingly from the middle of nowhere, a deep sigh. Her heart complexes carried on, just one every so often, until none was seen for so long that all stopped looking.

Emanuel seems correct that it is arbitrary to assume there must be a correct, precise time at which Janet died. Instead, the description we are given is of a progressive ebbing and loss of not just the signs of life, but of life itself. If we must, for some medical, social, or legal purposes, pick a precise time at which she died we could do so, but we would be aware of needing to pick a time for these further purposes, as opposed to identifying the precise time that marks a biological or ontological dichotomy between life and death. Suppose that Emanuel is correct that cases like this reveal a deep difficulty in our understanding of death and challenge a fundamental feature of the traditional Western view. Emanuel employs this case as part of an argument for recognizing a bounded zone within which individuals or their surrogates could pick the standard for determining when death occurs, but I do not wish to pursue her policy proposal here. Rather, I use it to show how a fundamental and complex difficulty for the conventional view can be understood by the public—Janet's husband and the hospital chaplain were present and had firsthand experience and understanding of the ambiguity in applying the traditional conception of death to Janet's death. The more general point again is that some aspects of the definition of death and of the complex medical and legal criteria and tests for it are part of the public's understanding of death's definition and determination, and others are not. We can expect the public to be able, and to have reason to want, to understand the former aspects, but not necessarily all of the latter.

I want to turn now to the question of how important it is that the public understand a public policy like the definition of death and the basis of it, on the assumption that much of the public is usually capable of understanding at least many of the issues concerning that policy. Editors of this volume posed to me the question of whether it is better to cause public controversy and confusion up front in order to build a firmer foundation for public policy in the long run, or instead better to hide or sidestep controversy and confusion in order to achieve important policy goals in the short run.

In an article some years ago I characterized this choice as between truth or consequences.[7] A too-easy answer to this question, one to which academics especially may be too readily prone, is to insist that in public policy, just as in research or scholarship, we should never deviate from a full and complete account of the truth as best we understand it, with all of its complexities, uncertainties, controversies, and ambiguities. But I argued in that earlier article that this seriously confuses two fundamentally different activities that quite properly have different goals. Let us grant that the goals of research and scholarship do and should center on an unqualified and unconstrained search for the truth, wherever it leads and without concern for the consequences of that search, though even there I believe some qualifications are necessary. But public policy, which by its very nature has important effects on the lives of large numbers of real people, is not and should not be understood as sharing truth seeking as its only or even most fundamental aim. Public policy should be guided by the aim of promoting the well-being and respecting the rights of the citizens subject to that policy. This means that on some occasions the likely effects on the well-being and rights of the public of exposing the full complexity, ambiguity, uncertainty, and controversy surrounding a particular public policy could be sufficiently adverse and serious to justify not exposing them and presenting the issue in misleading or oversimplified terms instead.

This is not to say, however, that hiding or sidestepping the complex and controversial full truth is always, or even usually, justified when public policy is at stake and the best policy consequences appear to be promoted by doing so. For many reasons, there should be a very strong presumption in a democracy in favor of seeking public understanding of any important public policy and the basis for that policy. First, and most obviously, there is the moral precept forbidding lying and requiring truthfulness in our relations with others; morality does not forbid lying and deception no matter what the consequences, but it does place a high presumption in favor of truthfulness. Second, from a political perspective, the core idea of democracy, self-rule by citizens, requires direct, or at least indirect, informed participation by the public in the formation of policy, which is not possible without public understanding of policy issues. Third, theoretical concerns based in democratic theory are strongly reinforced by pragmatic concerns about the likelihood of abuse of a self-bestowed authority to policymakers to mislead the public when they perceive the stakes in terms of policy outcomes to be high enough.

When policymakers believe the public does not, need not, and cannot understand the policies they institute and carry out, nor the reasons for those polices, an arrogant elitism is often produced or reinforced in the policymakers, together with a contempt for the supposedly ignorant public that is deeply corrosive of democratic ideals and institutions. It contributes to undemocratic beliefs on the part of policymakers that public policy should be determined by well-informed and expert policymakers (i.e., themselves) and need not be responsive to the desires, beliefs, and values of an uninformed public, at least to the extent that the public can be kept in the dark or successfully misled regarding policy. Attitudes on the part of policymakers that the public is to be manipulated in the service of desirable public policy, instead of brought into a common process of democratic deliberation, reinforce the worrisome cynicism of the public toward government and politicians that is so deep and pervasive in the United States today.

The complexity of truth-or-consequences choices is that, on the one hand, we cannot plausibly insist always on the full truth, with all its complexity, ambiguity, and controversy, come what may and at the expense of important policy consequences and goals, but, on the other hand, we have strong reasons based in morality, democratic theory, and pragmatic concerns about abuse in support of a very strong presumption in favor of truth even at significant cost to our policy goals. No general answer can be given to truth-or-consequences choices that will hold for all cases. In any particular instance of this choice, we must instead weigh the policy gains against the moral and political risks, and how that balances out will often be empirically uncertain and morally controversial.

I will give two examples from the definition-of-death debate of what I have called truth-or-consequences choices. Earlier I cited the following medical, social, and legal consequences tied to the definition and determination of death: death signals the time for the removal of any medical treatments the deceased is still receiving, the time at which organs can be taken for transplantation with the prior consent of the deceased or the consent of the family, the time for disposition of the body by burial or cremation, the time for mourning by those who knew and loved the deceased, and the time for the property of the deceased to pass to inheritors. It will be better policy consequences in terms of these policy outcomes, and no doubt others as well that I have not mentioned, that might justify hiding or sidestepping the complexities, ambiguities, uncertainties, and controversies in policy debates about the definition of death.

My first example of a truth-or-consequences choice is raised by Robert Burt in his summary essay for this volume (Chap. 20), where he argues that there are two incoherences identified in this book that are worth preserving: "The first is the proposition that death is a singular determinative event rather than a process that unfolds over time. The second is the proposition that the moment of death is an objective, technologically determinable issue for which human value choices are irrelevant." These propositions are not unrelated for, if the first is false, that suggests that we have a choice of times at which persons might be declared dead, to which social policy concerns might then be relevant. Burt argues that there are reasons for maintaining public confidence in these beliefs, despite his apparent agreement that they are intellectually indefensible. Regarding the first proposition, he argues from his own experience with a person close to him that, although a person may undergo "a kind of progressive brain death" in diseases like Alzheimer's dementia, the definitive, "at a moment" death that followed facilitated important individual and social processes such as grieving, a funeral, and burial. The intellectual incoherence was outweighed by the "emotional coherence" of death that occurs at a discrete moment in time.

My point is not whether Burt is correct or mistaken about the importance of the emotional and social roles played by the death at-a-moment fiction—as he himself notes, we lack the data to be confident about how widespread the phenomenon is to which he points us, and a full assessment of the fiction's other effects would be necessary. My more limited point is that he is correct to urge that the policy debate properly should consider not simply the intellectual defensibility or coherence of the death at-a-moment view, but the broader emotional and social roles played by that view. If the benefits from the emotional and social roles played by the death at-a-moment fiction are important enough for enough people, they could justify not trying to unmask and remove the fiction from public policy, but instead leaving it in place. The point on which I am in full agreement with Burt is that the policy issue cannot be properly settled simply by settling the intellectual issue of whether the death at-a-moment position is or is not a fiction.

My second example of a truth-or-consequences choice concerns the movement two decades ago to add the whole-brain concept of death to the traditional heart/lung concept, together with the contemporary debate now between proponents of whole-brain and higher-brain conceptions. In the earlier debate, it is widely believed that an important motivation for adding the concept of brain death to the traditional heart/lung conception was to increase the supply of organs for transplant. That is also one reason sometimes offered today for moving to a higher-brain conception, for example, to allow harvesting organs from anencephalic newborns. In the current debate, I share Burt's skepticism about whether moving to the higher-brain standard would significantly increase the supply of organs for transplant, but once again I agree with him that this consideration is relevant for the policy choice. But using a potential increase in organ supply as a reason for adopting a new definition of death threatens Burt's second useful fiction that the determination of death is an objective, scientific determination in which there is no role for values or policy consequences.

My guess is that the public for the most part believes this fiction and that it may be important in reassuring the public that medicine is not in the business of gerrymandering the determination of death even for worthwhile goals like increasing the supply of organs for transplant. Erasing that fiction has the potential to erode public confidence in the medical profession in general and in organ transplantation in particular, by playing into broader and increasing public concerns that physicians' commitments to their patients have weakened in the service of other goals, some worthy, like transplantation, and others less worthy, like maintaining their incomes within managed care settings. Even if a change to the higher-brain conception would increase the supply of organs for transplantation, if it erodes Burt's second useful fiction it might not be worth the risk to the fragile public confidence and trust in physicians' commitments to the interests of their patients.

By way of conclusion, let me emphasize that my purpose in discussing Burt's two useful fictions has not been to defend or reject his claims about their usefulness; my point is only that their usefulness or consequences, not just their truth, is relevant to whether we should attempt to preserve or undermine them. No general answer to all truth or consequences choices is defensible; they must be made on a case-by-case basis. I have argued that there is a strong presumption for involving the public in a public policy that affects them as profoundly as the definition and determination of death. But even when that presumption stands, there are aspects of that policy debate, including its complexities, ambiguities, and controversies, with which the public is and should be concerned, because they touch on the public's understanding of the definition and determination of death, and other aspects that do not do so and so need not be matters of public concern.

References

1. Arnold RM, Youngner SJ. The dead donor rule: Should we stretch it, bend it, or abandon it? *Kennedy Inst Ethics J* 1993;3(2):263–78.

2. Veatch RM. The impending collapse of the whole-brain definition of death. *Hastings Cent Rep* 1993;23(4):18–24.

3. University of Pittsburgh Medical Center Policy and Procedure Manual. *Kennedy Inst Ethics J* 1992;3(2):A-1—A-15.

4. Cole D. The reversibility of death. *J Med Ethics* 1992;18:26–30.

5. Tomlinson T. The irreversibility of death: Reply to Cole. *Kennedy Inst Ethics J* 1992;3(2):157–65.

6. Emanuel L. Reexamining death: The asymptotic model and a bounded zone definition. *Hastings Cent Rep* 1995;25(4):27–35.

7. Brock DW. Truth or consequences: The role of philosophers in policymaking. *Ethics* 1987;97(4):786–91.

VII

The Future of Death

IN THIS FINAL section, Steve Miles, H. Tristram Engelhardt, and Robert Burt each provide an overview of the current controversies in defining death with an eye toward the future. Miles welcomes the emerging controversy about death because it underscores the sociocultural dimension and frees our perspective from the "reductionistic scientific hegemony" of brain death. Echoing the proposals of Veatch, Fost, and Brody, he emphasizes two public policy alternatives. The first is to give individuals a choice from "a socially acceptable menu of definitions of death"; the second is to decouple death from various perimortal acts. He leans toward the latter alternative.

Engelhardt decries a "consensus that will not quite take place" in our postmodern world and pushes for what he sees as a preferable alternative: that the state stop "interfering with individuals who possess diverse moral visions in different moral communities when they peaceably pursue their own understandings of life and death." And what is the glue that could keep such a society from coming apart in conflict and intolerance? Engelhardt suggests it is the market. Individuals could realize their moral visions through tax surcharges or rebates, depending on the costs of their choices.

Although Robert Burt acknowledges that the traditional, simpler view of death is fraught with logical and technical inconsistencies, he is less sanguine than Miles and Engelhardt about relinquishing it. Concerned about fomenting anger among those with little tolerance for relativism and choice in the matter of when one is dead, his prognosis for the postmodern world is guarded. He suggests that, instead of tinkering with the definition of death, we allow individual choice in an arena where we have already gained a fair degree of social consensus: controlling when people die by the degree to which we limit life-sustaining treatment.

18

Death in a Technological and Pluralistic Culture

Steven Miles, M.D.

Death . . . can be demonstrated either on the traditional grounds of irreversible cessation of heart and lung function or on the basis of irreversible loss of all function of the entire brain.
—President's Commission, 1981[1]

The physician can only describe the physiological state which he observes; whether the patient meeting that description is alive or dead; whether the human organism in that physiological state is to be treated as a living person or as a corpse, is an ethical and legal question. The determination of the time of death . . . is essentially a theological and moral problem, not a medical or scientific one.
—Rabbi J. D. Bleich[2]

The irresistible utilitarian appeal of organ transplantation has us hell bent on increasing the donor pool . . . From fetal tissue transplants to non-heart-beating cadaver donors and beyond, these practices will inevitably pit our insatiable longing for better health and longer life against our deep seated notions of the sacred and profane.
—Arnold and Youngner[3]

IT IS IRONIC that so soon after the medical and legal legitimization of the concept of brain death, whole-brain criteria for death seem to be disintegrating—neurobiologically, clinically, and socially. This is due not to any single change in neuroscience, clinical practice, or social climate but to changes in all of these domains.

—Neuroscience is finding that consciousness is not, as had been thought, anatomically grounded exclusively in the neocortex. Consciousness requires neocortical activation by lower brain structures, although there is no clear understanding of the status of consciousness when the activation of the neocortex is destroyed but neocortical activity remains, as evidenced by neurophysiological studies. This finding challenges the simplistic distinction that had been made between whole-brain death and higher-brain death. It raises the possibility that the state of unconsciousness called persistent vegetative state is the highest form of locked-in state in which the cranial nerve communication that remains possible (e.g., as eye blinking) when the brainstem is intact is lost because the neocortex is completely isolated. In addition, the ability to detect cerebral metabolic activity raises (like an earlier debate about how high to amplify sensitivity to ascertain that an electroencephalogram is flat)[4] new controversies about the relevance and thresholds for determining loss of whole-brain function: Is it clinical loss, loss of brain-mediated electrical or neurohumoral feedback activity, or loss of detectable cellular metabolism?[5,6]

—Clinically, surgeons are taking organs from non-heart-beating donors whose cerebral or cardiac functions are not technically beyond resuscitation. If, as the surgeons claim, these are "dead" donors because there is no intent to resuscitate, the definition of death has been liberalized.[7,8]

—Socially, at the urging of minority religious groups initially, laws and hospitals are accommodating families who reject whole-brain criteria in favor of the traditional cardiac criteria and are continuing life support for the brain dead.[9]

To some, the deconstruction of whole-brain death is a worrisome regression. The use of non-heart-beating donors reflects a worrisome utilitarianism or even a profane cannibalism driven by undisciplined surgeons and the idolatry of money, which sacrifices humans for the rewards of organ transplants.[10,11] Families that insist on life support for brain-dead bodies reflect a lay culture that does not understand science or properly respect medical knowledge or the physician's authority to determine when death has occurred.

To others, and I am among them, the reopening of the debate about defining death and its consequences for perimortal care properly acknowledges the cultural basis for viewing the declaration of death as a threefold passage. Socially, a dying citizen goes from civic duties and protections to noncitizenship. Personally, death is the transition to ancestor or to soul. Biologically, an organism becomes disintegrating elements. By insisting that one scientific test or medical moment—particularly one drawn with the technological stylus of the Harvard criteria—is the one way to mark these three transitions, our society consolidates and impoverishes the most momentous passage in our personal and cultural life and closes the most heartfelt discussion in history.

Whole-brain death as death was an act of reductionistic scientific hegemony. No one should be surprised at—indeed, we should celebrate—the reopening of the discussion. In lay culture and in conversations between ICU workers and family, brain death is often seen as a sign of mortal illness, not a definition of death, as a vital organ failure, whose mortal consequence is confirmed by ensuing cardiac arrest.

The chapters in this book address diverse issues and present sometimes conflicting views. Even so, conflicting views about principles need not lead to irreconcilable differences in recommendations for public policy. This chapter considers where broadest support might be most readily found for new public policies about death and perimortal medical care.

Possible Consensus Points

Widespread agreement exists on several key points.

1. *Death occurs in the course of a continuous, individual, heterogeneous process of dying.* Neurobiology does not require the premise, or support a claim, that death is instantaneous and that a moment of death can be biologically determined. Biological processes and organ systems shut down over time in individualized sequences. There is no scientific or logical reason why the profound difference between the biological or social status of being alive or dead must, as Bernat maintains in Chapter 4, argue for biological dying as a universally identical, instantaneous event as opposed to a process. All definitions focused on the central nervous system will require arbitrary line drawing.[5]

2. *Different clinical and familial observers will view, detect, and interpret the clinical signs and advent of death in varying ways.* Aside from catastrophic

trauma, it will often be impossible to scientifically determine or reach universal agreement on a biological event or moment when the transition from life to death occurs, even if consensus can be reached about when death is confirmed as having taken place in the past. In the normal case of a slow death from a fatal disease, there is no reason to believe that family and medical observers, with their own values, psychological willingness, concepts, criteria, or tests for death, will simultaneously conclude when death occurs. Family may or not be persuaded by neurological or technological exams in confirming the fact or defining the time of death. Clinicians may not comprehend the "truth" in family statements that "grandma has died" when she is technically alive on multisystem life support. Grieving or mourning may precede brain death by hours or even months.

Human death is understood, defined, and declared in cultural frames with diverse understandings of the value and definition of persons, communities, and transcendent obligations. Cultures are inherently conservative in that they are transmitted; ours is also liberal in that the tradition that is passed along permits a range of reasonable or sensible choices. Several authors in this volume, including Campbell, Lynn and Cranford, and Englehardt, note how the value commitments and world views of patients, their loved ones, and their communities variously interpret the moment of death. Accordingly, a pluralistic culture that respects both enlightenment and religious traditions should accommodate various cultural views.

A precise moment or technological criteria may be needed or feasible only in some special forensic or organ donation circumstances; in most cases, they are unnecessary. Even when needed, the societal function—not the biological process of dying—should determine the relevant role of such criteria. In most cases, a uniform, precise technological moment or criteria for death are not necessary. Less time-critical public policies create more room for a lay-professional accommodation than does an imposed single biological moment of death.

The fact that people differ on whether a patient is dead and the fact that death occurs in the course of a very subtle process should not imply that dying persons pass through an intermediate state between being alive and being dead. It would be very difficult to define a new kind of personal existence and the rights of a person-corpse in this state. It would be easier to recognize a legitimately disputed territory during the course of dying for which public policy defines rules for assigning authority to engaged parties to assert the death status of a person. This could accommodate competing claims about dying and death. The permitted area of this disputed territory might range from a whole-brain-dead girl who "lives" at home on a respirator with her parents to a patient who has declined resuscitation and life support and who surgeons declare dead after 2 minutes of asystole (as in the Pittsburgh protocol), although many people argue that the patient is not dead.

Public Policy Perspectives

A public policy that offers only medical definitions of death or that only authorizes physicians to note that death has occurred will not easily accommodate the range of secular or religious definitions of death. Though American society is a liberal and pluralistic society, its public policy incorrectly presumes a cultural consensus about (1) the definition of death by its component cultures, (2) the authority of the medical profession in declaring death, and (3) the normative sequencing of perimortal rituals (e.g., mourning, organ donation, and ending filial obligations).

Instead, to reflect American pluralism, public policy should foster orderly tolerance of diverse definitions of death or diverse ways of relating perimortal medical treatment to organ donation or removal of life support. It must also decide the scope of accomodation for minorities that reject brain death in favor of a stringent cardiopulmonary definition of death (e.g., some Orthodox Jews), including policies toward health care and payment through public and private health insurance that is paid for largely by persons who do not share those views. Similarly, the scope of leeway for persons who might want to authorize organ donation by a family member who is in a PVS or demented or has anencephaly must also be determined.

A cultured understanding of death suggests that public policy for controversial choices in perimortal health care may take one of two broad approaches.

1. *It could explicitly offer individuals a choice from a menu of socially acceptable definitions of death,* as Veatch and Englehardt propose in this volume. For example, the value choice that a loved one is "dead" in the condition of PVS would permit that person to be an organ donor without the family regarding organ procurement as a form of killing. (There is

a fascinating problem of how to make people conscientiously declare their definition of death in advance and accommodate change while protecting against arbitrary changes in selection to secure permission for non-patient-centered actions—like a surviving widower who suddenly decides that PVS is death when a new marital prospect is available.)

This approach would require an immense and confusing redesign of public policy and public education about how to shift from a unitary concept of death. Experience with advance directives suggests that few people would undertake this task and that fewer would understand the implications of their choice. The proposal that people might be able to "buy" different definitions of death on their insurance would have powerful symbolic meaning and would probably be seen not as a choice but as an implicit threat. This option could be especially socially divisive in that it would impose secular liberalism on all cultural traditions, forcing people not merely to choose what is death but to embrace the idea that their choice about this ultimate profundity was just a choice. Finally, the radical step of creating a menu of death options is unnecessary to address the problems that the second option, decoupling, could handle equally well.

2. *It could decouple a variety of perimortal medical acts from a declaration of death.* This would take the socially controversial step of dropping the dead-donor rule, but would not make multiple definitions of death or create intermediate states between life and death. Decoupling declarations of death from various kinds of perimortal health care would not force moral communities to reconcile incompatible definitions of life and death, but would ask them to tolerate a broader variety of preferences by, or perhaps on behalf of, living persons. It would not require that new forms of perimortal care be preceded by declaring that the spiritual mystery of death itself was one choice among a legally codified and medically defined set.

Fundamentally, most social policies based on "decoupling" would attempt to use the highly regarded and broadly applicable principle of respect for autonomy in decisions to refuse life support by conscious persons or on behalf of decisionally impaired persons, or to donate organs, or perhaps to commit assisted suicide or voluntary euthanasia. Fost and Brody in their chapters in this volume support some variant of this position. Additional work is needed on the policy options for decoupling a variety of end-of-life health care practices from the definition of death.

An alternate policy option is to continue the current practice of using whole-brain death as a legal definition of death; it is a useful concept for resolving forensic problems and for permitting the discontinuation of life support and organ procurement. Exceptions can be made—such as the statutory provision in New Jersey—to accommodate those who do not accept brain death as death.

Redefining brain death to mean complete loss of all detectable cerebral metabolic function in light of recent evidence of some enduring brain activity would be expensive, impractical at many centers, and unnecessary, given that no survivors from more lax criteria are seen. Most clinicians recognize a spectrum of less than total, but still invariably lethal, losses of the brain's integrative functioning. A national consensus conference should consider the implication for brain death of recent findings in neuroscience that consciousness depends on cerebral activation by the brainstem. It should review whether it is possible or desirable to amend brain death to articulate clinically practical cost-effective neurological criteria of death with the same uses as the current ones. It should retain the concept of brain death rather than add a confusing new term, such as *brainstem death*. Even if brainstem-based definitions of central nervous system death can be developed, they will not, any more than whole-brain death, resolve the cultural debate about the role of brain criteria in defining death.

Return to a policy that recognizes that death has occurred only when there is irreversible asystole is not widely desired and would serve no useful purpose. Brain death has been useful. In the intensive care unit, it facilitated two goals: It provided legal permission for harvesting organs, and it helped some medical staff and family recognize death when a respirator prevented the use of cardiopulmonary criteria for declaring death. This neatly permitted the withdrawal of life support without that act constituting killing. The recent interest in new definitions of death is partly an effort to create a rationale so that new forms of perimortal medical care are not censured as killing.

References

1. President's Commission for the Study of Ethical Problems in Medicine and Biomedical and Behavioral Research. *Defining Death: A Report on the Medical, Legal and Ethical Issues in the Determination of Death.* Washington, DC: Government Printing Office, 1981.

2. Bleich JD. Establishing criteria of death. In: *Contemporary Halakhie Problems.* New York: Kiav & Yeshiva University Press, 1977, 372–93.

3. Arnold RM, Youngner SJ. The dead donor rule: Should we stretch it, bend it, or abandon it? *Kennedy Inst Ethics J* 1993;3(2):263–78.

4. Walker EA, and colleagues. An appraisal of the criteria of cerebral death: A summary statement. *JAMA* 1977;237:982–86.

5. Veatch RM. The impending collapse of whole-brain definition of death. *Hastings Cent Rep* 1993(August);4:18–24.

6. Halevy A, Brody B. Brain death: Reconciling definitions, criteria and tests. *Ann Intern Med* 1993;119:519–25.

7. Youngner SJ, Arnold RM. Ethical, psychosocial and public policy implications of procuring organs from non-heart-beating cadaver donors. *JAMA* 1993; 269;2769–74.

8. University of Pittsburgh Medical Center. Management of terminally ill patients who may become organ donors after death: The University of Pittsburgh Medical Center Policy and Procedure Manual. *Kennedy Inst Ethics J* 1993;3(2):A1-A15.

9. NJ Stat. Ann Sec 26 26:26A-5 (West supp. 1992)

10. Lynn J. Are the patients who become organ donors under the Pittsburgh protocol for non-heart-beating donors really dead? *Kennedy Inst Ethics J* 1993;3: 167–78.

11. Fox R. An ignoble form of cannibalism. *Kennedy Inst Ethics J* 1993;3:231–39.

19

Redefining Death

The Mirage of Consensus

H. Tristram Engelhardt Jr., Ph.D., M.D.

To APPRECIATE THE chapters included in this volume, one cannot simply attend to their arguments. One must place them within the framework of our controversies, with our failure to reach a consensus in this area. The cultural, religious, philosophical, and public policy controversies regarding our contemporary definitions of death run deep and suggest the need for a public policy open to a diversity of understandings and attitudes toward death. With respect to this diversity, I begin with a statement by Laura Siminoff and Alexia Bloch in Chapter 10). They note the often minority status of the dominant understanding that shapes high-technology medicine and that it is largely taken for granted by health professionals: "The subculture of biomedicine is not necessarily shared by lay people from the same society, although those belonging to the subculture of biomedicine (health care professionals) will share the broader 'webs of meaning' of American culture with a lay population." An implicit element of this criticism is that technology has for the most part functioned as a means for imposing a particular uniform understanding of the meaning of death and its appropriate determination.

I will conclude by developing Baruch Brody's and Robert Veatch's suggestions, which may allow technology to be harnessed in the service of recognizing and respecting the metaphysical and moral diversity that separates individuals and communities in disputes regarding the meaning of death and how it should be determined. In this chapter, I use the term *determination of death* to encompass the triad of (1) the definition or concept of death, (2) criteria for determining death, and (3) particular clinical tests for death, so as to underscore how tightly these three are bound together. Concepts or definitions of death involve a notion of both what it is to be alive and what it is to be embodied. Crucial to these disputes is the issue of whether the death that is to be determined is the death of a person or an organism, as well as what it means to be alive as a person or an organism. Identification of appropriate criteria for determining death can be made only against the background of a particular definition of death. Clinical tests simply specify the criteria in terms of particular operations of assessment.

These various issues have always been clearly distinguished, in that the most prominent proposal for a uniform determination of death, that of the President's commission, explicitly incorporated two different concepts of death, one focused on the irreversible cessation of all the functions of the whole brain and the other focused on the collapse of the organism as a whole. Two quite different understandings are fused in one recommendation. Such a heterogeneity of views is also reflected in this volume. The chapters show that determinations of death articulate complex interplays of metaphysical assumptions, guiding values, and available technologies. Moreover, this trinity is supported by particular communities, which often carry with them special commitments to particular tests, as may be the case within Orthodox Judaism. To understand the role of technology and our appreciation of the appropriate determination of death, we will need to attend to not only concepts, criteria, and tests, but also the sociology of the communities that make particular concepts, criteria, and tests seem plausible.

The Consensus That Will Not Quite Take Shape

Contemporary bioethics appears to be guided by a myth: rational consideration and discussion of what is at stake in defining death will lead reasonable persons to agreement regarding its definition. Modern secular societies in general and democratic polities in particular invoke consensus to legitimate the framing and imposition of policy. Unless one has a substantive and prescriptive definition of "reasonable person" so as, for example, to exclude traditional Japanese from being "reasonable persons" for not concurring with the generally accepted Western understanding of a whole-brain-oriented definition of death, such a consensus does not appear to obtain. Nor does it seem likely.

Consensus is often invoked in a secular context very much as religious conformity once was in the polities of medieval Western Europe. It sustains the illusion that all members of the polity are members of one society, which is one community united around a fundamental set of shared values. The more those values are recognized as disparate and the more the binding fabric of society is the outcome of a cluster of compromises among different communities, the more this myth is set in jeopardy.

The writers in this volume show that there is not one sense of the meaning of death or a consensus regarding how one should go about determining it. As a number of the writers underscore, real religious differences, significant philosophical disagreements, and substantial cultural differences lead to fundamentally divergent understandings of what is at stake in determining death. Technological advance and the secularization of the dominant culture have not suppressed these differences. Perhaps, if anything, they have led to a better appreciation of the gulf between different moral communities and their disparate understandings of what is at stake with a determination of death.

The differences among different understandings of death may not at first appear obvious. Somewhat like initial confusions between wolves and Tasmanian wolves, one might think that *death* has a univocal meaning in all discussions of death. Yet the first is an eutheria and the second is a marsupial, though similar ecological niches have driven an evolutionary convergence. Different body structures and ways of reproducing substantially distinguish the two animals. So, too, one might find that Hindus, Jews, and Roman Catholics all have priests. However, if a Roman Catholic is dying, it will not suffice to call a Hindu priest or a Kohen to give the last rites. Similar words identifying functions that have some family resemblances can be strategically deceptive. For some, death marks the cessation of particular duties to God; for others, death identifies the departure of the soul from the body; for others, death indicates a culturally acceptable point at which organs may be harvested; for still others, death marks the cessation of personhood; for others, death marks some combination of all of the above.

Determinations of death are lodged within webs of metaphysical commitments, moral understandings, and cultural as well as religious traditions and practices. The differences among these webs sustain different meanings of death and make plausible different ways of resolving controversies about an appropriate determination of death. Moreover, determinations of death have their significance within particular moral communities, with different moral and metaphysical commitments, and where different persons are in authority. The pope of Rome is in authority to resolve controversies regarding definitions of death for Roman Catholics, but not for Jews or Japanese Buddhists. Different persons are authorities regarding the different traditions, practices, moral commitments, and metaphysical assumptions that underlie the different understandings of death. Though people within different moral communities may seem at first blush to be involved in similar discussions about the meaning of death and its determination, those discussions, as the chapters in this volume show, often occur within different moral communities with different initial moral and metaphysical premises, moral and metaphysical rules of evidence, as well as traditions and practices that support different ways of proceeding to conclusions regarding what should count as an appropriate account of death and an acceptable mode of determining death. All of this is to say that divergent concerns regarding definitions of death occur within different communities of moral discourse and reflection.

A Diversity of Concerns: An Attempt to Give Some Order

The different levels of concerns about and sources of controversies regarding the definitions of death can be explored by placing them procrusteanly under five rubrics: metaphysical concerns, cultural concerns, secular philosophical accounts of the significance of death, conceptual or definitional concerns, and operational concerns.

Metaphysical Concerns

Concerns regarding the deep structure of reality and the transcendent significance of death fall under this rubric. The easiest examples here are religious concerns with death, such as those addressed in the chapters by Courtney Campbell, Margaret Lock, and Fred Rosner. However, a caveat is in order. What is advanced as a religious concern may often, under deeper exploration, prove to be a cultural one, at least insofar as one stipulates religions as communities with ultimate commitments to a transcendent God or gods. The point of drawing the distinction is that, though in some sense cultural and religious Roman Catholics, Protestants, and so forth, are all Roman Catholics, Protestants, and so forth, there are substantial and significant differences in the ways in which such individuals would accept particular approaches to the resolution of disputes concerning the determination of death. As Chapter 11 by Courtney Campbell intimates, this difference may lie at the root of some of the contrasts between fundamentalist Christians and the so-called mainline Christian religions. For a religious Roman Catholic, Protestant, or Orthodox Jew, transcendent issues of ultimate metaphysical importance are at stake in defining death and determining death. For individuals who are only culturally related to a religious body, quite different issues will be at stake, with different possibilities for resolving controversies and making compromises. Many of the issues bearing on religious interests in defining death reflect this confusion of cultural connections with a religious group and a full commitment to the metaphysics and transcendent concerns of that religion.

Cultural Concerns

Much of what is superficially understood as religious concerns regarding definitions of death may in fact prove to be cultural concerns, given the stipulative distinction just advanced between religious and cultural concerns. In this case, what is at stake may not involve transcendent metaphysical or moral commitments, but rather ways of life with their own ingredient and immanent moral practices and traditions. One finds ethics as mores, social customs. One confronts the question of whether the whole practice of tranplantation adversely influences the society's view of human beings, too. Schöne-Seifert reports that the theologian Grewel, in a widely published legal journal, states:

> By starting to legitimize organ transplantations via the concept of brain death, medicine . . . has subscribed to a system that, under the name of "bioethics," propagates a utilitarian view of man . . . Not every one with a human face is recognized and respected as a human any more, instead, respect for his human dignity and his right to life is tied to

the precondition, that he can prove certain minimum levels of functional ability and intactness, especially brain function (consciousness!), as an entrance ticket.

Schöne-Seifert seems to be reporting a reaction against some of what appear to be the cultural consequences of high medical technology, given the ways in which human life is appreciated and lived in such a context. In so doing, she also registers an interesting First World discontent with technology, a discontent that is often disconnected from traditional religious commitments and that reflects a cultural hunger for meaning now often expressed in a distrust of high technology.

Secular Philosophical Accounts of the Significance of Death

Here I wish to identify particular sets of arguments separated from a particular social community with intact practices and traditions. No doubt, all philosophies and schools of philosophy can in some thin sense be identified as carrying with them certain practices and traditions. However, here I wish to identify arguments that are regarded as understandable and exportable across cultural boundaries, as when one makes recommendations to the Japanese that they adopt a whole-brain-oriented definition of death on the basis of general secular rational considerations disembodied from any reference to a particular culture. At best, and that would be a great deal, secular philosophical arguments can provide a general way of resolving moral controversies within a secular space, which space does not exhaust or displace the moral spaces of the various moral communities and their own particular understandings of death and its appropriate determination.

Conceptual or Definitional Concerns

Defining death as the separation of the soul from the body, the cessation of the life of a person, the irrevocable cessation of consciousness, the end of organismic integration, and so forth, is an identification of what is at stake in identifying the occurrence of death. Such definitional concerns contrast with those regarding how one might best determine when the soul has left the body, when the life of a person has ended, or when there has been irrevocable loss of consciousness and spontaneous respiration. Definitions of death involve determining both what is important in death and what parts of the body are necessary for life. Thus, if one held that death is the cessation of the life of a person, one would also need to know what parts of the body are essential for the life of a person. One would need to know what it is to be a person (i.e., what minimal level of self-consciousness, sentience, etc., is required to be a person), and one would need to know something of the embodiment or incarnation of persons (i.e., whether the higher centers of the brain or of the liver are necessary for the life of a person).

The tripartite distinction among concept, criteria, and test may therefore not suffice for disentangling the controversies at hand. When addressing the issue of determining death, one might, in addition, underscore the difference between definitional concerns that encompass accounts of what it is to be alive and therefore of what it is to be dead, versus accounts of the necessary conditions for the embodiment of life and therefore for the determination of death. To give a coherent account of how one should determine death, one must know what it is no longer to be alive, both in terms of knowing what life is so that it can be gone, as well as where that life is necessarily embodied so that one can know what tests to cluster under what genre of general criteria. Thus, speaking of a whole-brain-oriented concept of death is not sufficient. One must know the account that makes the orientation to the whole brain significant. This has been the difficulty with the strategic ambiguity built into the understanding of the meaning of death forwarded by the President's commission,[1] which incorporated both a "primary organ view—[which] would be satisfied with a statute that contained only a single standard— the irreversible cessation of all functions of the entire brain" (37) and an "integrated functions view [that] would lead one to a definition of death recognizing that collapse of the organism as a whole can be diagnosed through the loss of brain functions as well as through loss of cardiopulmonary functions" (37).

These difficulties surface in the consideration of an autoresuscitation criterion (ARC) approach to determining death. As Joanne Lynn and Ronald Cranford recognize, this proposal from the so-called Pittsburgh protocol involves introducing a new concept of death under the guise of an extension of an old one. Lynn and Cranford acknowledge this as well in noting that an ARC does not tell us "what functions of the brain are irrelevant to the determination of death," yet this is what is necessary in understanding how to use criteria for death and in determining what tests to deploy.

Nor will the very interesting proposal by Halevy and Brody, further developed by Brody in Chapter 3, resolve the core difficulty, though it promises to be very heuristic within different moral communities for disclosing new approaches to end-of-life decisions. Their proposal is that one should disarticulate the question of when a person is dead into three questions:

1. When can care be unilaterally be withheld?
2. When can organs be harvested?
3. When can the undertaker begin his services?

They then offer the following answers to the three questions.

1. At irreversible cessation of conscious functioning
2. When current clinical tests for brain death are certified
3. At asystole

Halevy and Brody do not indicate what criteria should be used in determining death. In part, this is because how one should, indeed, answer these questions depends on the moral and metaphysical framework within which they are proposed. Not all Roman Catholics, for example, would hold that care may be unilaterally withheld when there is irreversible cessation of conscious function. Most significantly, how one answers these questions will depend on what one takes the determination of death to be about. In particular, one will need to be clear whether one is focusing on the death of the organism, as does Brody, or the death of the person. In either case, one will need to distinguish among different senses of organism and person.

Operational Concerns

Operational concerns focus on how one determines death, what criteria should be invoked, and what tests used, presuming one already knows what death is. Thus, if one held that death is the cessation of the life of a person as a moral agent, one might indeed theoretically be quite at peace with a higher-brain-center-oriented definition of death but still be afraid of an unacceptable level of false-positive determinations or other costs, should one attempt directly to focus simply on the destruction of higher-brain centers. Instead, one might make do with a whole-brain-oriented criterion for death. Schöne-Seifert appears to take this position with respect to a higher-brain-center-oriented definition of death. Finally, outside of the hospital, one might also focus on irreversible cessation of cardiorespiratory function as a reliable criterion for the destruction of the higher centers of the brain. This interplay of definition, criteria, tests, and background assumptions is complex, as Martin Pernick shows. His Chapter 1 contributes an interesting history of the various social, economic, and political costs that have influenced considerations or appropriate approaches to determining death. Understanding that history is further enriched if it is read against the counterfactual reading provided by Norman Fost (Chap. 9) of how brain-death law might have evolved through the courts absent what was in fact the significant reliance on legislation. Fost's concern should be regarded not just with what would be the most useful definitions, but with what would be the societally most useful way to have established policy.

Operational concerns, it should be noted, bring together both criteria for death and tests for death. Criteria for death function as chapter headings for tests, indicating what genre should be employed as dictated by a definition of death, which gives an account of what it is to be alive and to be embodied. As the disputes regarding the autoresuscitation criteria for death show, if one is not clear what definition of death is involved, one will not be able to judge whether a particular criterion and the particular tests it might involve should be acceptable. Chapter 2 by Plum illustrates this general point. The value of using a criterion of brainstem nonfunctioning as brain death depends in the end on background definitions of death, including what it is to be alive and for that life to be embodied. Indeed, his chapter shows the intimate interplay of criteria and tests and, by implication, their dependence on such background definitions. So, too, does the reaction of Bernat to Brody's criticism, where Bernat respecifies the appeal to "the permanent cessation of all functions of the whole brain" in terms of the "permanent cessation of the clinical functions of the entire brain." The criterion and the tests it brings with it reflect a particular background definition of death, which determines why such a criterion and the tests it entails should be relevant.

The foregoing five rubrics do not bring together issues all of the same level or kind. The first three identify framing constellations of assumptions and social structures, which sustain, to borrow a phrase from Ludwig Fleck, particular thought-communities with their thought-styles *cum* definitions of death and operations for its determination. The second two rubrics underscore the importance of distinguishing between a definition of death and an agreement regarding how one will determine that death has occurred, by invoking particular criteria and using particular tests. If one's definition of death is deeply rooted in metaphysical concerns, such as when the soul separates from the body, both the criteria and tests for determining death will probably follow rather closely from that account's definition of life and its understanding of embodiment. So, too, if one's definition of death is framed in terms of concerns to maximize the balance of benefits over harms, with special reference to transplant benefits and harms of excess treatment, one will look to finding tests that will allow one to recast criteria in the service of this background approach to the definition of death. Much of the debate about the so-called Pittsburgh protocol may reflect a suspicion that it involves in great measure considerations such as the latter.

Technology and the Reconsideration of Death

The chapters in this volume show the quite different ways in which technology has supported a reconsideration of the definition of death.

1. New opportunities and new costs have pressed for redefining death so as to reap particular benefits and to avoid particular harms. The advent of new technologies that can maintain biological functions past a point at which many individuals would hold those sustained to be dead has involved what they must regard as unjustified costs. The passion of judgments on this subject is well captured by Plum: "We view continued support of brain-dead bodies as a technological travesty against nature. The medical costs are huge, the experience drains the emotional reserves of families and care givers, and the longer cardiopulmonary support lasts, the greater becomes the threat that the body's visceral organs will not be suitable for safe and successful organ transplant." The ability mechanically to support ventilation and in critical care units to monitor and maintain bodily functions of those who are dead raises the question of when such treatment should cease because of the financial costs to society, the psychosocial and moral costs to the family, and the psychosocial and moral costs to the health professionals involved in providing care. Here Brody places one of his questions and one of his answers: the irreversible loss of consciousness.

The advent of organ transplantation has been a major motive in reconsidering the definition of death. If one can take essential, nonpaired organs only from dead people, then one must have a definition of death to harvest organs. The promise of organ transplantation thus invites liberalizing definitions of death and procedures for its determination. Here

Brody places the second of his questions and answers: the irreversible loss of whole-brain function.

As the history of the cultural reaction to the reconstruction of definitions of death provided by Martin Pernick shows, different costs and benefits have over time supported different determinations of death. The history also shows that the disputes have involved questions of who should be in power to make decisions, that is, who is an authority to authorize particular determinations of death. Here, too, he presents a good account of how framing considerations can make a particular determination of death look quite different. Should one redefine death so as better to protect the integrity of medicine and use medical resources appropriately? Or should one redefine death in order better to protect the public against the premature harvesting of their organs or against deformation of their culture? The second question is raised in recent German public policy debates, as recorded by Schöne-Seifert.

2. Technologies can provide operational definitions not previously available. They thus invite redefining procedures for determining death. In such cases, the conceptual definition of death is not challenged. Rather, technology allows one more reliably to determine death earlier or under circumstances not previously possible. Roman Catholics, for instance, came to accept a technologically supported determination of the separation of the soul from the body. A similar process may be taking place with regard to general secular moral concerns with death, which accord centrality to the death of persons, inviting a higher-brain-center-oriented definition of death, a point that emerges in some of the chapters. Technological advances also underlie an augmented ability to show complete cessation of not just consciousness but the ability to respire, as indicated in Chapter 12 by Fred Rosner. So, too, enhanced technology may render more precise the determination of the cessation of functions that have cultural importance for Japanese and Scandinavians, as is suggested by the chapters of Margaret Lock and Bo Andreassen Rix. Enhanced technology can as well be received as morally challenging, if not dangerous, as Schöne-Seifert's report regarding the German situation demonstrates.

3. Finally, technological changes have undoubtedly been heuristic for rethinking conceptual definitions of death, not to mention challenging well-entrenched operational definitions. Moreover, technological advances have evoked reactions against the ethos that comes with such technology, as is shown in Chapter 15 by Schöne-Seifert.

Coming to Terms with a Diversity of Understandings of Death

James Bernat criticizes Baruch Brody regarding one of the most important of his suggestions, namely, that individuals and groups should be at liberty to buy out of the general rule that treatment should be stopped when there is permanent loss of consciousness. What Brody recognizes is that, within a society composed of moral communities with diverse understandings of the nature and significance of death, different answers will be given, even when they are restated in terms of Brody's three questions. This point is endorsed by Robert Veatch in his affirmation of the New Jersey law, which allows a choice between a whole-body- and a whole-brain-oriented determination of death. Indeed, Veatch invites us to consider policy that would involve a larger menu of choices.

What is at issue is not merely a value pluralism, but a metaphysical pluralism supported within a diversity of moral communities. The dispute is not just about what one should value and how. It is also about what it is to be alive, what it is to be embodied, and what criteria and tests will both reliably and appropriately determine death. Were Veatch to be a bit bolder, he could integrate his important insights in a challenging proposal. One can imagine a world in which health care was provided, somewhat like spiritual care is in Germany. German citizens, by indicating that they are Roman Catholic or Evangelical Reform, commit themselves to paying a tax surcharge for a spiritual care system, which in being redistributive is a spiritual welfare system. *Mutatis mutandi,* to recognize the diversity of moral visions regarding abortion, third-party-assisted reproduction, physician-assisted suicide, euthanasia, the cessation of treatment for permanently unconscious humans, the harvesting of organs from bodies, as well as determining when bodies should be sent to undertakers, one could create both public and private policy options. Were there considerable savings of costs for some options, they could be passed back to those who participated. Were there significant additional costs, additional premiums could be required. Those who lived within moral communities sharing particular values could establish redistributive systems.

This diversity of moral understandings has significant public policy implications: one faces the challenge of taking account of the pluralism that characterizes even our high-technology, computer-driven societies. If one took this diversity seriously, individuals, through contract and within diverse moral communities, could pursue different understandings of the importance of birth, suffering, dying, the withholding of treatment, the harvesting of organs, and the determination of death. If postmodernity bodes the diversity that it likely indeed heralds and if, in our posttraditional society, we will share ever fewer common substantive moral understandings, we will need to devise ways in which society can avoid interfering with individuals who possess diverse moral visions in different moral communities when they peaceably pursue their own understandings of life and death.

Reference

1. President's Commission for the Study of Ethical Problems in Medicine and Biomedical and Behavioral Research. *Defining Death: Medical, Legal and Ethical Issues in the Determination of Death.* Washington, DC: Government Printing Office, 1981.

20

Where Do We Go from Here?

Robert A. Burt, J.D.

AT THE BEGINNING of each episode of an old television series (and recent movied) *Mission Impossible,* the protagonist entered a telephone booth, found a cassette player and switched on the waiting tape. (These were low-tech days.) The tape always began, "Your assignment, Mr. _____, should you choose to accept it, is to _____." The tape always self-destructed after 20 seconds, and the protagonist always accepted the daunting assignment; otherwise, since no instructions remained intact for another protagonist, there would have been no TV episode. So, too, though uncertain of its possible attainment, I feel obliged to accept the proferred assignment to summarize the various chapters in this book and to suggest directions for the future. I am somewhat reassured by the fact that this same task has been assigned to two others—to a philosopher and a physician, as well as to me, a lawyer. Thus, the three of us, with our presumably different professional perspectives, will converge on the same mission and, I hope, thereby enhance the likelihood of its success.

By my reading of these chapters, there is general consensus on the following propositions: (1) the existing brain-death criteria, as legislatively enacted throughout the country, are serviceable clinical guides; (2) if these criteria were applied in practice (which they frequently are not), it is likely that exceedingly few false positives—that is, an erroneous declaration of death for a rehabilitatable person—would be made; although (3) the empirically based research corroborating this second conclusion is not extensive. There is also wide, though not unanimous, agreement among the writers that the existing brain-death criteria are conceptually incoherent and that these criteria can in principle be made more coherent, with the result that more people will be declared dead more quickly (for all purposes or for some specific purpose, such as eligibility for organ donation) than the current brain-death criteria permit.

After this, the writers fractionate. Among those who want to adopt new criteria, there is disagreement about which revisions would be conceptually and practically preferable, and there are others who maintain that no revisions at all should be undertaken, notwithstanding the conceptual incoherences in the existing standards.

I count myself among this latter group. In my judgment the proponents for change in the existing brain-death criteria have not set out a persuasive case. These proponents advance both instrumental and deontological arguments for change, which I will briefly review in turn.

Three instrumental arguments are put forward. First, it is said that changed criteria would produce greater numbers of organs for transplantation. But I am persuaded by the views of other writers that this is not likely to occur. According to the best available empirical research, although physician behavior may bear some responsibility for the limited availability of transplantable organs, the principal obstacles arise from the persistent refusal of potential organ donors or the family of potentially eligible cadaver donors. State law reforms requiring physicians to request organ donations from patients or families have not produced increased yields, and there is no reason to think that speedier declarations of death by physicians will have any more significant impact.

There is even reason to believe that a backlash of diminished organ availability will result if the general public understands that state authorities and the medical profession are collaborating in expediting death declarations to obtain more organs. We already know the intense suspicions of many minority group members about the bona fides of physicians in pursuing organ availability. Misgivings among the general population about the beneficence of both the medical profession and the government has intensified since brain-death criteria were legislatively promulgated during the course of the past two decades. A new campaign for legislative changes in order to increase organ availability might well provoke greater public distrust.

A second instrumental argument for change is the claim that scarce medical resources are being wasted—in terms of high-technology interventions or simply of time spent in costly intensive care unit beds—on people who could and should be declared dead by more refined criteria. The magnitude of these misspent resources is, however, not at all clear. And if the change in criteria provokes intensified public resistance to organ donation—which seems plausible, if not likely—then this would be a substantial and, in my view, dispositive countervailing cost.

The third instrumental argument is that needless suffering is being inflicted on patients and their families through prolonged treatments on patients whose condition is truly hopeless but not certifiably so—that is, not officially eligible for death declarations—by existing criteria. But the existing legal regime can address this suffering without changing the current criteria for declaring death. Competent patients or the families of incompetent patients are now legally entitled in virtually every state to refuse life-prolonging medical treatment. Physicians who want to relieve the suffering of "hopeless" patients and their families do not need to declare death for this purpose but can, under the current legal regime, approach the family to suggest and obtain consent for the termination of treatment, which would lead to certifiable death. To be sure, some families may resist this suggestion, and physicians are most clearly entitled to ignore this resistance when they are authorized to declare death without prior patient or family concurrence. Where patients or their families are resistant, however, it is not obvious whose suffering the physicians are assuaging when they expedite the declaration of death.

Proponents for changed criteria also advance two deontological arguments. First, there is an intrinsic virtue in honesty, and the conceptual obfuscations in the existing death declaration standards violate this imperative. Second, because the determination of death—that is, within a broad range of possibilities, the specification of the exact moment at which life no longer exists—depends more fundamentally on values than on technological dictates, societal respect for pluralism requires a regime of patient and family choice among different possible determinative criteria.

I am not persuaded by these arguments. Though their proponents appear to view these two arguments as mutually reinforcing, I see a contradiction between them. It seems to me that the value of pluralism in our society is better served by continued adherence to the existing regime, not simply in spite of its obfuscating incoherences, but precisely because of those obfuscations.

Of the many conceptual incoherences that have been identified

throughout this book, there are two in particular that are worth preserving in the service of pluralism. The first is the proposition that death
is a singular determinative event rather than a process that unfolds over
time. The second is the proposition that the moment of death is an
objective, technologically determinable issue for which human value
choices are irrelevant.

Regarding the incoherence of the first proposition, several writers cite
the example of people whose cognitive capacities gradually fade away
through a kind of progressive "brain death," cell by cell as in Alzheimer's
disease or other dementias. It is certainly plausible to say of such people
that, although the body remains alive, the person inhabiting that body
dies. But as plausible as this may be and as much invoked in common
parlance, this claim for the coherence of the conception of death as a
process ignores an important aspect in the psychology of mourning.

On this matter, I can confidently speak only of my own experience. I
am not familiar with the full range of empirical research on mourning,
though I suspect that this question has not been exhaustively investigated
in this country or in other cultures. My claim about the values of pluralism adequately applies, however, even if my own experience is not
universally shared in this country or elsewhere—although my own un-
systematic observations of my family and friends persuade me that I am
not alone in holding to the conceptually incoherent proposition that
death is a definitive event rather than a process.

Two people very close to me recently died—one in 1991, the other
in 1993—after suffering progressive intellectual impairment during a
long preceding interval. I was sure about one and I was almost certain
about the other that, at some point in the progression of their illnesses,
neither person knew who I was. I could say, and I occasionally did say,
that both of these people had died though they were still alive. Many
others close to them and to me said this same thing, as they too experienced this same gradually progressive loss of the person whom we had
known and who had known us.

But a time finally did come when this progressive death was super-
ceded by a different kind of death, a definitive death. Funeral services
were held, the body was buried, mourning rituals were observed—and
this death was markedly different from the other. This death was true,
was final, was determinative. This death let loose feelings—of grief but
of relief, of loss but of rediscovered memories—that had been in suspension during the previous prolonged slipping away.

I can appreciate that, as an intellectual proposition, this definitive conception of death was incoherent. But as an emotional experience, it had a deeper coherence. Death conceived as a marked event permitted mourning.

Social meanings of death do of course change. And it is possible that the social validation of a process conception of death, such as the proponents of new medical criteria invoke, would lead to different mourning rituals and experiences. But if we value pluralism, we should not be too quick to disregard deeply held alternative viewpoints.

Some people might find an easy answer to this question through the invocation of autonomous individual choice, claiming that the values of cultural pluralism can be adequately respected by permitting me (for example) to opt for one conception of death while others with different attitudes toward biological meaning and psychological mourning could opt for another conception. But whatever its general virtues, in this context autonomous choice is an inadequate answer.

The reason for this inadequacy arises from another aspect of the psychology of dying—which brings me to the second obfuscation in the current criteria for determining death that is worth preserving in the service of pluralism. Like the comprehension of death as a determinative event rather than a process, which is conceptually incoherent but emotionally salient for some people, there are people who reject the idea that the definition of death is amenable to choice. There are people, that is, who passionately insist that the definition of death is a technical proposition, subject to unequivocal scientific determination that leaves no room for value choices by scientists or the laity. These people would be unhappy with most of the chapters in this book. They would certainly be unhappy with those here who insist on the absence of any singular, objective definition of death, but they would even be disturbed at those here who seem to agree in principle about the possibility of single-minded objectivity but disagree among themselves about the singular content of that objective definition of death.

I have no reliable empirical data about the number of such naifs in contemporary American society. There are surely some; even if their numbers are small, they too have a claim to recognition and respect in a culture that values pluralism. For many such people, moreover, it is no casual matter to insist that death is radically distinct from the realm of human choice. Choosing the moment of one's death would not only convey forbidden implications of suicide but, even more fundamentally, call into question God's independent, dispositive role in dispensing death.

Those who deny that the determination of death is intrinsically technical or univocally objective might try to invoke the standard rejoinder of pro-choice advocates in the abortion context—that is, "if you're opposed to abortion, then don't have one." But whatever force this rejoinder might have in the abortion debate, it has no logical application here because the opponents of choice don't simply contest those who exercise choice in dying; they deny the proposition that choice is epistemically relevant to the determination of death.

Accordingly, legislative enactments that give people a range of choices in determining death—that permit some to invoke brain death, or to hold out for cardiopulmonary failure, or to use brainstem or higher-brain criteria and so on—would not be an unequivocal victory for the principle of value pluralism. This regime would be a direct repudiation of those whose values dictate that there must be only one objective, technically dispositive definition of death. To use the currently fashionable vocabulary of public choice theory, we seem to be in a zero-sum conflict on this matter, where victory for one side constitutes total defeat for the other. In such conflicts, value pluralism cannot be vindicated. The values of some must necessarily be traversed in order to uphold the values of others.

There is, however, an aspect regarding the determination of death that—unlike the abortion dispute, for example—permits us not to resolve but to evade its zero-sum character. As the law has evolved during the past 20 years, we have constructed a two-track pathway toward the dispensation of death. One track is by the medical-scientific declaration of death based on criteria that have been the central focus of this book. The other track is through legislative and judicial recognition of patients' rights to refuse life-prolonging treatment. In exercising these rights, patients (or their proxies) do not "declare themselves dead," but they do exercise choice that directly affects the timing of that declaration. Through this second track, patients are authorized to assert control over medical-scientific claims to govern the administration of death—precisely the authority that proponents of choice would claim for patients in the death-declarative track.

The two tracks are not precisely interchangeable. The existing "right to choose" track is not formally effective for a patient who wishes to prolong medical treatment past the time when a physician is authorized to declare the patient dead under existing criteria. Nor does the right-to-choose track permit a patient to direct immediate surgical removal of his heart or other life-essential organs; the so-called dead-donor rule for organ donations is an independent restriction on patient choice in this matter. It is not clear, however, that these lacunae between the two tracks have much practical significance. Most hospitals are unwilling to disregard strong family protests to discontinue treatment modalities even if the patient meets formal criteria for a declaration of death. As to organ donations, I can see strong arguments both for and against abrogating the dead-donor rule. I will not try to resolve this question here. For present purposes, it is sufficient to observe that patients or their families truly intent on speedy organ donations can probably find medical personnel eager to declare their death at the earliest possible moment, if not immediately on demand.

The existence of these two tracks toward death thus permits, as a practical matter, a considerable accommodation of the wishes of those who want to assert choice in their dying and the wishes of those who want to deny that personal choice is relevant to their dying. This accommodation goes much further toward honoring the values of pluralism than a regime that, by providing choice for everyone regarding the criteria for death declarations, necessarily overrides the convictions of some that choice on this matter is disturbing and wrong. For these latter dissenters, the regime of "choice" is an oxymoron; it is a forced choice, a paternalistic imposition that they would choose to avoid.

Intellectual purists might respond with two propositions: first, that these dissenters are misguided, that their position is intellectually incoherent because the determination of death is value-laden and thus necessarily rests on choice; and second, that the virtue of honesty in public policy requires that this error be confronted as such. I am not persuaded by this position, for both instrumental and deontological reasons. Instrumentally, we can see the divisive social consequences of this insistence on clearly drawn ideological battlelines in our abortion dispute, the polarizing impact of which has spread far beyond this issue toward reshaping the role of religion in political life generally and, even more radically, toward transforming the very understanding of the meaning of politics in American life from a pursuit of an accommodationist "middle ground" to a quest for total victory over evil opponents. As a deontological proposition, I regard this Manichaean vision as antithetical to the ethos of democracy, whose underlying premise of equality demands mutual respect and constant effort to reach accommodation among people of fundamentally different views.

I consider us lucky, thus far, that the ideologically polarizing implications of the selection of criteria for determining death have not been widely appreciated in this country. The Japanese example indicates the potential for widespread, deeply divisive public obsession with this issue, as Margaret Lock's Chapter 14 vividly recounts. In my judgment, the United States needs another such divisive issue in our politics like we need a second visit from Hurricane Andrew.

What then follows from my position for the chapters in this book? The quickest implication might seem to be that the entire book should have been burnt in manuscript rather than published. I am unwilling, however, to carry my logic to this conclusion. I do believe in open deliberation in the academy and in the polis, and the chapters in this book are, it seems to me, a worthy contribution in both places. It is, of course, difficult to conduct an open inquiry, in the academy or in the polis, about whether belief should persist in an acknowledged falsehood—rather like a physician asking a patient whether he would like a placebo prescribed for his psychosomatic illness. So, too, it is difficult to imagine how public deliberation might proceed explicitly to consider whether to retain the incoherences and obfuscations in the current criteria for death determinations.

I suspect, however, that the publication of this book will not lead ineluctably to the launching of this widespread public debate—if for no other reason than the strength of the psychology of denial around the issue of death. In this context, at least, I hope that we can count on some such force to ensure that the book will sell a few thousand copies, almost all destined for library shelves, and then serenely sink from public view.

What is my answer to the question posed to me, "Where do we go from here?" If I had my wish, all of us would reconvene in 10 years to try to explain the persistence of the confusions we had identified in the publicly approved criteria for determining death.

Index

ADH, 86–88, 91

Advance directives, 116, 155, 173, 244, 316

African Americans, attitudes toward organ transplantation, 14–18, 29n. 38

AMA Council on Ethical and Judicial Affairs, position on anencephalics: Brody's critique of, 80–81; Veatch's interpretation of, 153

American Academy of Neurology, 85

American Bar Association (ABA), 21, 123, 127, 133

Anencephalic newborns, as organ sources, 90, 153, 159–160, 172, 178, 180, 191, 215, 281, 305, 315

Apnea test in death determination, 56–57 Table 2.9

Arnold, Robert: on dead-donor rule, 162, 295; on organ transplantation, 311. *See also* Youngner, Stuart

Arteriography, in determination of brain death, 46–48

Attitudes, U.S. public: toward brain death, 179–181, 183–188, 190–191; toward organ transplantation, 179–181, 188–191

Autoresuscitation criterion (ARC), 325, 327

Baby Doe rules, 169

Barnard, Christian, 259

Beecher, Henry, 1, 20, 22; attitude toward human experimentation, 28n. 24; on death decision by medical professional alone, 20; Harvard committee, 9–14, 16–17, 23, 27n. 20, 32n. 77, 33n. 90

Bernat, James: Brody's response to, 76–77; on death as loss of all brain functions, 67; on definition and criteria of death, 83–92, 134n. 4; on distinction between critical and clinical functions, 68, 75–76, 327; Miles's response to, 313. *See also* Culver, Charles; Gert, Bernard

Bifurcated standards, 112, 117–118, 120, 122

Böckle, Franz, 260–261

Brainstem auditory evoked potentials (BAEPs), as a test for brain death, 44–45, 73, 88, 97, 100

Brody, Baruch: Bernat's response to Brody and Halevy's criteria, 85–90, 330; Burt's response, 328–330; on criteria for declaring brain death, 71–82; on dead-donor rule, 224; on death as a process, 84; Fost's support of, 162; Pallis's response, 94–99; on retention of integrative functions in brain-dead patients, 68; on separation of decision to forgo treatment and pronouncement of death, 150. *See also* Halevy, Amir

Burt, Robert: Brock's response, 304–306; on effect of lack of consensus on public attitudes, 170–171; on need for individual choice in limiting treatment, 309–310

Library of Congress Cataloging-in-Publication Data

The definition of death : contemporary controversies / edited by
    Stuart J. Youngner, Robert M. Arnold, and Renie Schapiro.
        p.   cm.
    Includes bibliographical references and index.
    ISBN 0-8018-5985-9 (alk. paper)
        1. Death—Proof and certification.   2. Brain death.   I. Youngner,
Stuart J.   II. Arnold, Robert M., 1957–   .   III. Schapiro, Renie.
RA1063.D44   1999
614'.1—DC21   98-20216